CHRISTIANITY AND ISLAM: A MISSIOLOGICAL ENCOUNTER

CHRISTIANITY AND ISLAM:
A MISSIOLOGICAL ENCOUNTER

by
Glory E. Dharmaraj, Ph.D.
Jacob S. Dharmaraj, Ph.D.

ISPCK, DELHI
1999

Christianity and Islam: A Missiological Encounter—
Published by Rev. Ashish Amos by the Indian Society for
Promoting Christian Knowledge (ISPCK), Post Box 1585,
Kashmere Gate, Delhi-110006.

First Published 1998

Revised Edition 1999

© Glory E. Dharmaraj   1998
   Jacob S. Dharmaraj

Laser typeset and cover design by **ISPCK**, Post Box 1585,
1654, Madarsa Road, Kashmere Gate, Delhi-110006,
Tel.: 2966323, Fax: 011-2965490.

Printed at: Deluxe Universal Traders, Delhi

CONTENTS

viii

INTRODUCTION

Encounter with people of other faiths is no longer the privileged experience of tourists, scholars, missionaries, or travelling business people. The Western hemisphere which was traditionally considered Christian has changed in the past few decades because of immigration of ethnic groups from various religious, cultural, and national backgrounds. Global economy, vast world-wide communication technology, fast and efficient travel, and free exchange of ideas of people, cultures, and scientific discoveries have united the people and cultures in an unprecedented way.

The Christian Church which played a vital role in the human arena of politics, service, development, and transformation is increasingly becoming weak and vulnerable. The concept of mission, evangelism and ministry is constantly revised, redefined, and updated only to create more dissension and disagreement among Christian communities across the world.

Churches and their mission agencies are constantly challenged to rethink their position and role in a more and more pluralist society. In this book, the authors, like their fellow scholars in Christian mission, strive to find an adequate answer to some of the fundamental questions the messengers of the gospel wrestle with :

> Are people of other faiths being saved in their own religions? If yes, why did we send missionaries for hundreds of years to establish churches around the world? Were the missionaries sent only to export a certain form of civilization or culture or religion or God? If people of other faiths are not being saved in their own religions, what is the responsibility of the Church of Jesus Christ today? Furthermore, what is salvation today? How do we impart the biblical doctrine of salvation to people everywhere?

The collective notion among some scholars of religions is that all religions ultimately lead to God. Through one's own inherited or adopted religions, one can find hope, comfort, and salvation. However, this position fails to address whether all religions can simultaneously be true. If two religions, such as Christianity and Islam claim to have truth exclusively in their faiths, how can we interpret the diversity of these two religious faiths? If these two religions have a common origin which goes way back to ancient Judaism, Hebrew Scriptures, and Abrahamic religions, how are these two religions related to one another? Answers are hard to find.

In this book, the authors do not claim to have found an answer to the above questions; rather, they try to present the cases of Christianity and Islam, the two large world religions, in their historic and theological contexts to foster a better understanding between the adherents of these two monotheistic religions and attempt to create an atmosphere of mutual trust and respect in the current political and competitive climate.

The authors are greatly indebted to Laurie Zumwalt for her editorial work and invaluable comments.

Special thanks are due to Ashish Amos, General Secretary of ISPCK for his high professionalism and special abilities in getting this manuscript published in a book form and on time.

Glory E. Dharmaraj, Ph.D.
Jacob S. Dharmaraj, Ph.D.

ARABIA DURING MOHAMMED'S TIME

CHAPTER I
Life and Ministry of Prophet Mohammed

Mohammed was born in Mecca in the year 570 C.E. in the tribe of Banu Hashim, a lesser clan of the powerful tribe of Qurayish. Mohammed's father, Abdullah, died before Mohammed was born and his mother, Aminah, died when he was six, and then his grandfather, Abdul Mutalib, died when he was eight. Mohammed neither inherited wealth nor received any formal education from his family. Mohammed was raised by his uncle, Abu-Talib, a man with limited means. He could not afford to take care of the boy Mohammed at home for very long. Hence, Abu-Talib sent Mohammed to tend sheep and goats, and occasionally, he accompanied him on caravans.

From his childhood days, Mohammed was disturbed by the corrupt Meccan polytheistic society that worshipped 360 gods, one god for every day at the kaaba, a worship place at Mecca.[1] Mohammed's tribal people worshipped three major idols (Al-Uzza, Al-Manat, and Al-Lati) which were regarded as Allah's daughters. Opinions differ as to their definite forms and origin. Some say that Al-Uzza had her origin in a sacred tree and had her shrine in the city of Nakhlah. Al-Uzza was the most popular of the three shrines. Al-Manat had its origin in a white stone and her shrine was at Qudayd. Al-Lati was in human shape and its shrine was in the walled city of Taif. All three shrines represented God in female forms. Unlike the images and effigies of the Hindu puranas or the goddesses and consorts of the Graeco-Roman pantheon, the Arab gods did not have any mythology. They were simply worshipped as divine beings. The Arab gods were portrayed in their shrines by large standing stones like the fertility symbols used by the Canaanites during Biblical times or the Hindu Shivites of the modern times.

---

1. The Sumerian year consisted of 360 days and five additional days to perform special rituals or to undertake pilgrimage (hajj).

Kaaba of Mecca and Religious Pluralism

During Mohammed's time, Mecca and Medina were the two largest cities in Arabia. Mecca is about sixty miles from the Red Sea, almost midway between Aden on the Indian Ocean and Gaza on the Mediterranean sea. Mecca has also been called Bakkah (narrow), a description of the narrow locale between the mountains that surround the city and the valley of the sacred places. The Quran says, "The first sanctuary appointed for mankind was that at Bakkah, a blessed place, a guidance for the peoples" (Sura 3.96). Mecca, according to the Quran, is the "uncultivated" or "seedless" valley. Its residents have always depended upon commerce and trade for their livelihood because of the city's strategic location at the crossroads of Africa, the Mediterranean, and the East. Some of the major products exported from Arabia were myrrh and frankinscence which were produced from two kinds of trees which grew in Yemen. They were used for cosmetic purposes at religious ceremonies, and for embalming. The spicy materials were light to carry and valuable to sell. The spice trade made several Meccans wealthy and powerful.

Medina, originally called Yathrib, is about two hundred and fifty miles north of Mecca, and had a well organized Arabic Jewish community with rabbis and schools. Medina is situated in the midst of volcanic hills around a small plain called the Manakah, where camel caravans to the city would camp and rest. The trade route from Medina to Syria would have to pass through oases which contained Jewish communities. Arabia, during Mohammed's period, also had well-established Christian centres in certain southern cities and oases, as in the oasis of Najran, which is about five hundred miles northeast of Mecca.

Christian scholars believe that Mecca, at the time of Mohammed, might have had a mixed population of animist, Jewish, and Orthodox Christian communities. Orthodox Christianity was closely associated with Byzantium, a Christian imperial power, and hence Muslim historians give a scant reference to Christianity in Arabia, especially about Christians in and around Mecca and Medina. Christians living in Mecca might not have had an organized ecclesiastical hierarchy and their understanding of the principles of Christianity must have been very minimal as they were living far away from the religious and spiritual centres of Eastern Christianity. Moreover, the Bible had not been translated into Arabic or local dialects yet; therefore, the Christians' understanding of their creed must have been shallow. As for the political and economic situation in

Mecca, Inamullah Khan writes that the powerful and wealthy Qurayish in Mecca ruled the city and the neighbouring Bedouin tribal settlements, and took advantage of the shifting political and religious alliances of the day. Khan recapitulates the prevalent poiitical mood of pre-Islamic days in Arabia.

> There were at that time two world powers contending with each other, the Byzantines and the Persians. In the Arabian peninsula, Syria was a colony of the Byzantines, while Iraq and Yemen were under the tutelage of the Persian Empire. The desert tribes were sunk in illiteracy and ignorance and lived a primitive life, in which the priestly class of Quraish, as custodians of the 360 deities then worshipped by the different tribes, was exploiting the ignorant bedouins.[2]

The deities which the Bedouins worshipped were believed to be the protectors of individuals and tribes; and hence they venerated their gods with respect and fear. The bedouins associated the spirit of the gods with trees, stones, waterfronts, fire and air. Mecca housed a large number of deities in kaaba, its central shrine, which drew pilgrims from all over the region. Middle East historians say that a few other prominent cities in ancient Arabia (as many as five cities) had also housed deities similar to the kaaba in their temples. However, the kaaba of Mecca was the most important of all temples because of its strategic location and commercial connections. The business tribe, Qurayish, which managed the affairs of Mecca and kaaba made the city and the shrine not only popular but also safe and secure to do business and worship. The Qurayish had established a well organized administrative council called *dar an-Nidwah* and all important decisions were made by the council.

Kaaba is about seventy five feet high, thirty feet long and forty feet wide. A huge stone, an object of worship, is placed in the eastern corner of the kaaba, on the outside. The origin of the stone is obscure, although critics speculate that it was an asteroid. The building accommodated a pantheon of gods made in stone statues, painted pictures, and clay moulds. They were revered and worshipped with utter sincerity.

Islamic traditions say that the kaaba was originally founded by Adam. After his death, his son Seth, took care of it. After centuries of

---

2. Inamullah Khan, "Islam in the Contemporary World", in *God and Man in Contemporary Islamic Thought*, ed. Charles Malik (Beirut: American University, 1972), p.8.

neglect, Abraham and his son Ishmael rebuilt the kaaba and re-established the worship of One God, Allah. Abraham was commanded by Allah to go to mount Thabir and invite all people to make pilgrimage to the place of worship at kaaba.

E. Rabbath claims that the kaaba even housed a picture of Jesus and Mary in its pantheon. In support of his argument, Rabbath cites a pre-Islamic poem composed by Adi bin Zayd in which he makes an oath before the black stone, "In the name of the Lord of Mecca and of the Crucifix."[3] Rabbath's theory sounds logical as most of the pluralistic religious communities in Asia would not hesitate to add one or more new deities in their vast pantheon of gods as long as their collective presence brought blessings upon the community.[4] The gods in the kaaba were established in a hierarchical order. The supreme God in the pantheon was called the Sovereign God, whose name in Arabic was Allah.

Around the kaaba was a circular area where pilgrims gathered annually to perform the ceremony of *Tawwaf,* seven ritual circumambulations of the shrine following the direction of the sun. The shrine was surrounded by 360 gods. In and around the kaaba (twenty-mile radius from the shrine) violence, fighting, and sexual acts were absolutely forbidden. The land around kaaba was considered sacred and holy.

Mecca was the major religious, political, cultural and commercial centre in pre-Islamic Arabia. The presence of the kaaba brought pilgrims from all over the region. The safe atmosphere surrounding the kaaba provided by the Qurayish brought the Arabs across Arabia year after year not only to worship at the shrine but also to trade in the city. In her book *Muhammad,* Karen Armstrong narrates the strategic location of Mecca and its control of the caravan route between southern Arabia and Syria.

> Mecca was ideally situated for long-term business ventures. The prestige of the kaaba brought many Arabs on the *hajj* to the city each year and the Sanctuary created a climate that was favorable to trade. Mecca stood conveniently at the crossroads of the two major trade routes of Arabia : the Hijaz Road, which ran along

---

3. E. Rabbath, *L'Orient chretien a la veille de l'Islam* (Beirut: Librairie Orientale, 1980), p.174.

4. Even today, for instance, the religious Hindus would not hesitate to accept Jesus as a cosmic god. They would only disagree with Christianity's exclusive claim that Jesus Christ is the only God.

the eastern coast of the Red Sea and linked the Yemen with Syria, Palestine and the Transjordan, and the Najd Road, which linked the Yemen with Iraq. The Quraysh became highly successful. They ensured the security of the city of building alliances with the Bedouin in the area. The nomads were better soldiers than the Quraysh and, in return for military help, they had shares in the various Meccan companies. Cultivating a shrewd, calculating statesmanship, known as *hilm*, the Quraysh had become the greatest power in Arabia during the sixth century.[5]

Mecca often maintained trade relations with cities in the north and south. However, there was a steady stream of soldiers of fortune flowing through Mecca to cities in all four directions. The famous route that traversed Mecca was the famous "silk route" which stretched as far east as India. The caravan travellers and traders who passed through Mecca to North and South often came in contact with Christian monasteries and established Christian communities in cities like Syria and Najran situated enroute.

Call to Reform and the Origin of Revelation

From his early days, Mohammed became dissatisfied with the religious beliefs and moral character of his people in Mecca. Mohammed's first contact with Judaism and Christianity was on his caravan route to Syria and during enterprising days in Mecca. He heard about Jews and Christians and their worship of the One, Creator God.[6] Soon, Mohammed was impressed at the long, unbroken tradition of prophets Judaism had come to experience and the long, written history of sacred scriptures which Jews and Christians had come to share, love, and believe. Mohammed, then a young man, wondered why no prophet of God had ever arisen out of Arabia and why no holy scriptures had ever been given in the Arabic language.

Mohammed had earned a name in the Meccan community as a young, trusted person (Al-Amin). But he was disturbed by the ills of that society and often retreated to meditate in a cave in Mount al-Hira, a few miles outside Mecca. During the course of his meditation, Allah began

---

5. Karen Armstrong, *Muhammad: A Biography of the Prophet*, (New York: Harper, 1992), pp. 66-67.

6. W. Montgomery Watt, *Muhammad, Prophet and Statesman*, (London:Oxford University Press, 1961), p.41.

to reveal his will and teachings to Mohammed. Being uncertain about
the divine disclosure and having been overcome by the fear of being
misunderstood, Mohammed kept all the revelations to himself.

Soon Mohammed found a job under Khadijah bint Khuwaylida, a
wealthy widow and a caravan merchant, whom he later married. Khadijah
had been married twice before and came from the clan of Asad, which
was a more powerful tribe. When they were married, Mohammed was
twenty-five and Khadijah was forty and had a daughter and two sons by
previous marriage. Mohammed and Khadijah were married for twenty
five years, and had seven children, three sons who died in infancy and
four daughters. Mohammed's marriage to Khadijah gave him financial
security and a sedentary lifestyle. Mohammed was grateful for his life
of comfort and security. Later in his life, when Mohammed was given
revelations about his life of prosperity and comfort, he was commanded
to be more charitable and kind to the underprivileged by reflecting on
his former life as a poor orphan boy (Sura 93:6-7). The most famous of
the four surviving daughters was Fatimah, who would marry Ali, the first
legitimate successor and leader (Caliph) after the Prophet. Mohammed
attended to Khadijah's affairs in Southern Arabia and Syria, where, some
traditions say, he came in contact with a Christian monk named Bahira,
who taught Mohammed the fundamental doctrines of Christianity.

Mohammed was not the only one to be disturbed by the corrupt
polytheistic society and searching for the one living God. A group of
people, whom the Quran calls *Hanifs* (rightly inclined), were living in
Arabia during Mohammed's time and sought a deeper spiritual
experience. They did not succumb to paganism and polytheism. They
worshipped the One, Eternal God in purity and uprightness. They were
neither Jews nor Christians. The Muslims believe that the Hanifs were
the remnants of Abrahamic lineage who carried on the tradition of
worshipping the One Sovereign God in the midst of pagan and
polytheistic worship.

Mohammed, who had become acquainted with Christianity and
Judaism on his caravan journey along the spice route and later emigration
to Medina, was consumed with passion to preach on the judgment of
God and monotheism to his people. The society in which he was living
was going through major transformation from a nomadic life to sedentary
life, from communal living to independent living, from an agrarian cattle
trade to an urban commercial enterprise, from animistic, polytheistic
worship to a supreme, hierarchical monotheism. Neither displacing the

cultural milieu of the Arab society nor destroying the religious zeal of the eager worshippers, Mohammed took advantage of the presence of the one supreme hierarchical God, Allah, who had already been placed amongst the pantheon of gods in kaaba by the Meccan Arabs. The presence of the hanifs and their monotheistic worship gave an impetus to Mohammed's message. After all, he was not introducing an alien God or an adverse form of worship to an already cluttered pantheon of gods with crude ritualistic worship. Mohammed was only resurfacing the forgotten and hidden God.

The Jews, Christians, and Zoroastrians also practiced monotheism. But their political and religious sentiments were foreign to the nomadic, desert-dwelling Arabs. Mohammed, hence, yearned for a prophet of God to be raised from Arabia with a divine message in the Arabic language. Gerhard Endress observes :

> Even before Islam, Allah…was the name of God and the object of worship; individual men and women - they are called **hanif** in the Koran - had already taken the step towards monotheism. The shrine of the deities at Mecca, the Ka'ba, remained in a shrine and became the spiritual centre of monotheistic Islam, and even the rituals of the old faith were incorporated into the Islamic pilgrimage…But what has previously become an empty shell, and of primary importance because of the markets, the holy months and the truce which was linked with them, now received new meaning: founded by Abraham, the ka'ba became the cornerstone of sacred history, the symbol of the true religion which had been established earlier and was now renewed and completed in the Arabic Koran.[7]

The Quran says Abraham was the one who founded the kaaba and established early, original monotheism in Arabia. Unfortunately, Abrahamic religion gradually degenerated into polytheism and idol worship by his successors and had reached its worst during Mohammed's time. The hanifs were the only remnants who kept the monotheistic tradition alive in Arabia. Some Muslim scholars say that Mohammed was one of those hanifs who worshipped the One God.

Even after his marriage, Mohammed often went to the nearby hills by himself to meditate. One night, in the month of Ramadhan, when he

---

7. Gerhard Endress, *An Introduction to Islam*, trans. Carole Hillenbrand, (New York: Columbia University Press, 1988), p.26.

was about forty years old, Mohammed received a special revelation from Allah through the mediation of angel Jibril (Gabriel). The angel addressed Mohammed the "Messenger of God" *(Rasul Allah)* and commanded him:

> Recite thou in the name of thy Lord who created man out of a germ-cell. Recite for your Lord the Most Generous One who has taught by the pen, taught man what he did not know! Mohammed protested and refused to recite as he was not one of the prophets of God. Then the angel embraced him until Mohammed had reached the limits of his endurance. At that point, the divinely inspired words spontaneously poured from his mouth.[8]

Islamic traditions say that Mohammed received revelation by means of *Wahy*, a form of divine inspiration, which he recited to his listeners until his death. All his recitations were later put together as a book, which is called the Quran.

The night on which Mohammed received his call to be a Messenger of God and to recite the divine revelation was named *Laylat-al-Qadr* (the Night of Power). Mohammed shared the visions and revelations with his wife Khadijah, members of their family and their friends who believed and became the first Muslims. Mohammed's wife, Khadijah, being a woman of wealth and high status, must have influenced several people in town and some members of the Qurayish tribe so that they might believe in Mohammed's teachings.[9] Mohammed had a small band of followers who believed in his message and encouraged him to teach them more about the ways of God.

Some Islamic traditions say that the Prophet was confused and frightened by the revelation he received from Angel Gabriel, and in trepidation the Prophet resolved to kill himself. When he was contemplating suicide, a voice said to him :

---

8. See Martin Lings, *Muhammad: His Life Based on the Earliest Sources*, (London: Inner Traditions International, 1983), pp. 43ff.

9. Some of the early converts to Islam were Ali, his cousin and son-in-law and Abu Bakr, his future father-in-law and the first Caliph. Mohammed's converts contained several women whose tribes were in opposition to his teachings. One of Mohammed's converts was Umm Habiba, daughter of Abu Sufyan, Mohammed's arch rival. When Mohammed and his followers were persecuted in Mecca, women converts and their families with children emigrated to Abyssinia.

"O Mohammed! You are the messenger of God and I am
Gabriel" and encouraged him to serve as the messenger of
Allah. Mohammed was also assured by his wife that he was not
hearing a Jinn's or a devil's voice. She said to him, "No, you
have nothing to fear. God will never let you down; you are kind
to your relatives, you are astute and patient, you give to the
needy, you are generous to guests, and never fail to relieve
people from distress."[10]

Then Khadijah took Mohammed to her Christian cousin, Waraqa Ibn
Qusayy, who assured Mohammed that he had been called to be a prophet
and said to him, the angel who had come to Moses had come to
Mohammed also. Just like the Hebrew prophets, he would also be called
a liar and treated contemptuously. The Hadith accounts for this meeting
with Waraqa :

Narrated Aisha: Khadija then accompanied (Mohammed) to her
cousin Waraqa who, during the Pre-Islamic Period became a
Christian and used to write with Hebrew letters. He would write
from the gospel in Hebrew as much as Allah wished him to
write. He was an old man and had lost his eyesight. Khadija
said to Waraqa, "Listen to the story of your nephew, O my
cousin!" Waraqa asked, "O my nephew! what have you
seen?"Allah's Apostle described whatever he had seen. Waraqa
said, "This is the same one who keeps the secrets (angel Gabriel)
whom Allah had sent to Moses. I wish I were young and could
live to the time when your people would turn you out." Allah's
Apostle asked, "Will they drive me out?" Waraqa replied in the
affirmative and said, "Anyone who came with something similar
to what you have brought was treated with hostility; and I
should remain alive till the day when you will be turned out
then I would support you strongly." But after a few days Waraqa
died and the Divine Inspiration was also paused for a while (1:4;
1.1.3).

Mohammed was sent by Allah to warn people in Mecca and to
reform the existing idolatrous religious practices of the people. He
was commanded to preach the oneness of God and instruct his people
to abandon their idol worship. Allah said to Mohammed, "O thou

10. Abd Al-Rahman Azzam, *Batal al-Abtal Muhammad*, 2nd Ed., (Cairo: The House
of Arabic Books, 1954), p.16.

enveloped in thy cloak, arise and warn! Thy Lord magnify, thy raiment purify, pollution shun! And show not favour, seeking worldly gain! (Sura74.1-7). Mohammed went straight to the kaaba of Mecca itself and preached to the idolaters and polytheists about the unity of Allah. He denounced the polytheistic worship practiced by the Meccans, vehemently. He invited his audience to return to worship the One, Eternal, Sovereign God who revealed himself to Abraham, Moses, Jesus, and several other prophets whose performances have been recorded in the Bible. He summoned the Meccans to submit themselves to God's will by abandoning the pantheon of gods clustered in the shrine.

During the early part of his ministry, Mohammed was convinced that he was the messenger of God who was sent only to the Arabs, just as Moses had been sent to Pharaoh and Jesus had been sent to the Jews (Sura 73:15). Through further revelation, the Prophet was assured that he was called to preach the message of Allah to people everywhere (Sura 49.13). The Quran says : "Thus We send thee [O Mohammed] unto a nation before whom other nations have passed away, that thou mayst recite unto them that which We have inspired in thee (Sura 13;30, 37)."

Mohammed claimed that he was only a prophet of God, like Abraham or Moses of the Hebrew Scriptures. Yet, unlike the prophets of old, he professed to have brought the final revelation to the world. He insisted that there was nothing in himself distinctive. He maintained that he was a mere human being who was commissioned by Allah to receive His inspired message and recite it to people all over the earth so that they might learn of God's ways. Those who would pay attention to his message, he claimed, would be amply rewarded by Allah.

Mohammed "The Seal of the Prophets"

Mohammed validated his message through the Quranic saying, "O men! I am (sent) to you only to give a clear warning. Those who believe and work righteousness, for them is forgiveness and a sustenance most generous. But those who strive against our signs, to frustrate them, - they will be companions of the fire." (Sura 22:49-51). The Prophet admonished his listeners regarding the impending dangers of God's judgment upon the evil ones and the punishment that would come upon the disobedient. He invited the idolaters to repent and obey Allah. In order to give credence to his message, he claimed to stand on the prophetic tradition of Jeremiah, Amos, John the Baptist, and several other prophets who were either persecuted or killed.

Mohammed never preached that he was going to found a new religion. His message was plain and simple : Allah is the One, true God; He is the Most Great God (Allahu Akbar) and all of humanity must worship and submit to him. Mohammed insisted that his message from God was the most recent and the ultimate of all revelations. The earlier revelations given to the Jews and Christians were distorted by the Jewish rabbis and Christian priests. But once again, in his abundant mercy, God had raised a prophet to reveal his will in complete form one final time.

The Prophet of Islam found some disturbing inconsistencies in Judaism and Christianity. He was convinced that God had called him to purify those ancient monotheistic religions which were corrupted by their religious and political leaders. He often wondered why the people who worshipped the One Eternal God practiced rituals and ceremonies. He could not comprehend why the Christians who worshipped the God of Abraham, Isaac, and Jacob offered prayers to saints who were mere human beings. The prophet could not deduce why the Christians who claimed to have the knowledge of the revealed God claimed God was three (Sura 5:16).

Apparently, critics contend, Mohammed misunderstood the Christian concept of the Trinity and thought of it as the worship of three gods : God, Jesus and Mary. He mistook Mary as God's consort, and Jesus as God's own son who was born after God's physical union with Mary. Consequently, Mohammed denounced the Christians of dividing the Godhead, attributing anthropomorphic characteristics to God, and making Jesus, a mere human being into "Son of God" or "one of three Gods." Mohammed believed that the prophets of God had successively renewed the religions of the world with a divine message since Adam, whom the Quran calls the first prophet of God. Whenever the faith of a people was in decline, God sent His prophets and messengers to warn and remind them about the One, Eternal God. Judaism and Christianity had their prophets. However, the followers of those religions had failed not only to practice the teachings of the prophets, but had also corrupted the revealed and written message of God. Therefore, God had to send yet another prophet with an untainted message. All the earlier revelations given to the ancient prophets were recorded in the form of Holy Books. Nevertheless, the Books had been so corrupted by their religious and political leaders that one could no longer identify which was God's pristine truth and which was erroneous human interpolation.

However, Mohammed affirmed, God had not given up on humanity. God had called Mohammed as the last and final prophet before the end of time. God also had decisively and conclusively revealed himself to the Prophet. Mohammed's message abrogated all the earlier revelations as he was "the Seal of the Prophets" *(Khatam an-nubuwwah and Khatam al-anbiyah)*. After Mohammed, no revealed message will be given by God to any other human being.

The way the Prophet received the divine inspiration is elaborately narrated in the Quran. The Quran says, Mohammed was aided by the angel Gabriel in reading the tablets of heaven (the original Quran), which contained the message of God so that Mohammed might memorize and recite it to the people. The contents of the tablets were revealed only through angelic mediation or, at times, by direct inspiration of the prophet. Unlike the experience of the Biblical prophets, God had never spoken to Mohammed at any time during revelation. According to the Quran, "God speaks to no human except through revelation *(Wahy)*...He sends a messenger (angel) and reveals whatever He wills...(which is) a straight path, the path of God' (Sura 42:51-53). The God of the Quran is Real. He is a transcendent and Sovereign God who does not directly involve himself with the affairs of humanity. He exhibits his qualities in the cosmos and reveals His message through the prophets, thereby making himself known to the created beings. All the creatures in the world convey the magnificence and sovereignty of God and summon people to submit to his awesome Being.

Mohammed's preaching against idolatry in the kaaba was opposed by the powerful Qurayish tribe who worshipped the idols in the kaaba and administered the shrine. Mohammed's message about the unity of God was perceived as an economic and religious threat to the Meccan Qurayish. Kaaba, which united the Arab people for centuries religiously and economically, was challenged by a man of no extraordinary background, who claimed to be sharing and standing on the long tradition of prophets which Judaism and Christianity had come to know. Mohammed resolutely challenged the Meccans who questioned his authority as a prophet by saying, "If thou were in doubt as to what We have revealed unto thee, then ask those who have been reading the Book from before thee : the Truth hath indeed come to thee from thy Lord : so be in no wise of those in doubt" (10.94). When opposition mounted up against him, Mohammed quoted from history and said that all of Allah's prophets had been mocked and derided in the past since they brought message from Allah himself. Any resistance to Mohammed's message, wherefore, was a resistance to Allah's message. Mohammed affirmed that he had been sent as *Al-Nbi Al-Ummi*, meaning "the uneducated prophet" to the people everywhere. *Al-Nabi Al-Ummi* has also been loosely translated as prophet of the nations or prophet of the Gentiles. In the Quran, the Prophet states :

> Say : 'O men! I am sent unto you all, as the Apostle of Allah, to whom belongeth the dominion of the heavens and the earth: there is no god but He: it is He that giveth both life and death. So believe in Allah and his Apostle, the unlettered Prophet, who believeth in Allah and His words : follow him so that ye may be guided' (Sura 7.158).

Mohammed contended that Moses brought the divine message from Mount Sinai about the oneness of God, but his commandments were corrupted by the Jews. Jesus proclaimed about the oneness of God in the Gospel, but the Christians have abandoned this by making Jesus God and inventing a new concept of the Trinity. Mohammed hoped, sooner or later, the followers of Judaism and Christianity would acknowledge his prophetic ministry and come to embrace his message.

The Jews and Christians refused to accept Mohammed as a Prophet. Some of his opponents called him "possessed". Mohammed was disappointed with the response of the Jews and Christians and severed all religious and social ties with them. When Mohammed was accused of being "possessed," he responded to them that his calling as a prophet of Allah follows practically the same course as that of the earlier prophets of Judaism and Christianity who were also mocked, insulted, and persecuted (Sura 15.38, 37.36, 44.14, 68.5). He told them that he would be vindicated, eventually.

Mohammed avowed that he was living proof that God cared about the Arabs and raised him as a prophet to restore the primordial, monotheistic religion of Abraham who was not Jewish (21:53-58). The Quran says :

> O People of the Book [Jews and Christians], why will ye argue about Abraham, when the Torah and the Gospel were not revealed till after him?...Abraham was not a Jew, nor yet a Christian; but he was an upright man who had surrendered [*Muslim* i.e., to God], and he was not of idolaters. Lo! Those

of mankind who have the best claim to Abraham are those who followed him, and this Prophet and those who believe [with him] (Sura 3:65, 67, 68).

The Arabs who inherited the monotheistic worship from Abraham practiced monotheism only for awhile. Soon they abandoned monotheism for polytheism and forgot the Creator God. Despite God's repeated attempts through his messengers and prophets to bring the Arabs back to monotheistic worship, they never did turn back to the One Sovereign God of Abraham. Nevertheless, the deep longings and earnest prayers of the descendants of Abraham and Ishmael were answered when the spring of revelation flowed again through Mohammed. He was raised as a sign to the Arabs that God still cared about them. Mohammed was sent as a messenger first to the Arabs, then to the rest of the world. In order to establish a long lasting monotheistic worship and a permanent channel to God, the Quran was given to the people.

Muslim scholars trace Mohammed's and Arab Muslim's genealogy back to Haggar, the bondwoman spouse of Abraham. According to the Book of Genesis, Abraham slept with Hagar by the request of his first wife Sarah. Hagar gave a son, Ishmael (the name means, God hears), to Abraham. Sarah, the mother of Isaac, consumed by jealousy persuaded her husband to banish the bondwoman and her son into the desert. Confused, lost, and driven by hunger and thirst, Hagar gave up any hope of surviving in the desert left her child under a shrub to die. But God heard the cry of the mother and the child, and made the spring of Zamzam to provide water to save them.

The Bible says :

> What trouble you, Hagar? Fear not; for God has heard the voice of the lad where he is. Arise, lift up the lad, and hold him fast with your hand; for I will make him a great nation. Then God opened her eyes, and she saw a well of water; and she went, and filled the skin with water, and gave the lad a drink. And God was with the lad, and he grew up; he lived in the wilderness, and became an expert with the bow (Gen. 21:17-20).

The Muslims concede that Jews, Christians, and Muslims have the same spiritual father Abraham (*Ibrahim* in Arabic); therefore, all these three religions are interconnected. However, the Muslims are quick to add, Islam alone has received the complete and final revelation, so it abrogates all the earlier revelations.

Pledge of Al-'Aqaba and the Hijrah

When persecution mounted against Mohammed and his followers, several of them left Mecca and migrated to Abyssinia (Ethiopia), a monophysite Christian kingdom where they were given protection by the emperor Negus. The Muslims who migrated to Abyssinia were the first ones in Islamic history to take part in *Hijrah*, emigration. The Meccan Qurayish, who opposed Mohammed and his teachings, went after the followers of Mohammed who emigrated to Abyssinia in order to subdue them and bring them back to Mecca. But the Christian king refused to turn them over to the Meccans.

Mohammed continued to stay in Mecca and tried to establish his base. While he was not able to make inroads in Mecca and the opposition was growing violently against him day by day, Mohammed contacted the leaders of the nearby town of Taif, which was situated fifty miles southeast of Mecca. Taif was the seat of the much revered idol Of Hubal. Mohammed assumed the Taifans would be glad to receive him, as they were not in good neighbourly relationship with the Meccan Qurayish. Mohammed and his companion Zayd walked up the rugged terrain to Taif to negotiate with the tribal leaders and to seek help. Contrary to the Prophet's expectation, he was humiliated and driven out of the city by senseless people and undisciplined children.

During that time of loneliness and disappointment, a delegation from the tribe of Khazraj from the oasis town of Yathrib (later to be known as Medina), which was situated about three hundred miles north of Mecca, came to meet with the Prophet at a secret location. Yathrib was open to Mohammed's teachings right from the beginning. Some of his followers were already living in the town. The delegation extended an invitation to him and his followers to migrate to Yathrib. They promised to support Mohammed as a prophet and leader of the tribal group in Yathrib. The town contained two strong but divided Arab tribes, the Aws and Khazraj, who were open to Mohammed's teachings, and a strong Jewish community. After two years of intense negotiation, six Yathrib men of the tribe of Khazraj pledged to support Mohammed in a meeting held at 'Aqaba. This pledge is known as Pledge of al-'Aqaba (*Bay'at al-'Aqaba*). The men from Yathrib promised that they would not associate anything with Allah and would accept Mohammed as Allah's prophet and obey him. Mohammed seized the opportunity to migrate to Yathrib to serve as their leader, judge, and prophet.

Mohammed's migration to Yathrib was not without resistance from the Meccan Qurayish. According to a Muslim legend, Mohammed and Abu Bakr (a confidant and a follower of the Prophet) did not travel to Yathrib with the large band of Muslim followers. Instead, they left for Yathrib on camels by a different route and hid themselves in a cave in Mount Thawr. They had suspicion that the Meccans would attempt to capture and kill them. So they travelled to Mount Thawr under the cover of the night and asked Abd Allah, Abu Bakr's son, to take the camels back to the migrants, which he did.

When the enemies of the Prophet came from Mecca at night to the main camp looking for Mohammed and Abu Bakr, they were nowhere to be found. They saw Ali, Mohammed's son-in-law, occupying Mohammed's bed. The Meccans ordered a thorough search of the camp and the neighbouring areas the next morning. When the enemy soldiers were searching the neighbouring hill area, an Acacia tree began to grow rapidly and almost blocked the entrance to the cave in which Mohammed and Abu Bakr were hiding. A dove flew from nowhere into the opening of the cave, hurriedly built a nest and laid an egg. A large spider appeared from the darkness and wove a net across the entrance. When the search party arrived at the cave and saw the entrance blocked by a tree, an undisturbed dove nest, and a spider web, they assumed the cave had been unoccupied. After the enemies had left, Mohammed and his friend took a different route to Yathrib.

Mohammed and his seventy followers were received with much enthusiasm and warmth. Soon many more joined them. Those who followed Mohammed to Yathrib were called *Muhajirun* (emigrants). The town of Yathrib was soon known as *Medinat al-nabi*, the city of the Prophet. The shortened form of the name of the city is Medina. Mohammed's flight to Medina, historically called *Hijrah*, took place in the year 622 CE., at the end of September, probably on the 17th. That journey marks the beginning of the Muslim calendar, as designated by Caliph Umar in 638 CE. Of this flight from Mecca to Medina, the Quran says, "And when those who disbelieve plot against thee (Mohammed) to wound thee fatally, or to kill thee or to drive thee forth; they plot, but Allah (too) plotteth; and Allah is the best of plotters" (Sura 8:30). The flight to Medina was a turning point in Mohammed's prophetic career. The number of his followers began to increase dramatically. Mohammed negotiated with the inhabitants of Medina and established a strong Muslim community, which eventually took on a political form and changed the course of Arab history forever.

Life at the newly formed community was not for Mohammed's followers from Mecca. They found it difficult to settle at Medina because of its different social conventions and local customs. The Meccan Muslim background was trade, travel, and urban; whereas, the Medinans' was sedentary, agricultural, and rural. Mohammed realized that his main job was to integrate all the unassimilated and divided communities into one unified population under God. Hence, he combined both the secular and sacred offices of leadership with no essential differences, and became their sole chief administrator.

Mohammed appreciated the Medinans who helped him and his followers in their mission to serve God. The Quran calls those who helped Mohammed as *Ansar* (helpers) and those who followed the Prophet from Mecca as *Muhajirun* (faithful followers). The Prophet asked the *Muhajirun* to serve as soldiers and defenders of his mission in Mecca. Soon Mohammed began to raid Mecca bound caravans and sought to disrupt the commercial establishment of Mecca. Further, he was trying to find new ways to support the newly established Muslim community.

The Conquest of Mecca and the Establishment of Islam in Arabia

The aggravated Meccans waged a war against Mohammed and his followers. The worst battle between the Meccans and Mohammed took place in 624 CE., at the wells of Badr, near Medina, where Mohammed challenged the 950 well-armed Meccan soldiers with 300 ill-trained Muslim soldiers. The Muslims were able to rout the Meccan soldiers and establish a name among the local communities. The victory over the strong, organized Meccan army was attributed to God's favour upon the Muslims and his vindication of Mohammed's role as his messenger.

However, the victory celebration was short-lived. In the following year, in the Battle of Uhud in 625 CE., the Muslim army was defeated, and Mohammed himself was injured. The Meccans wanted to put an end to Mohammed and his army once and for all, and so they set out to invade Medina. Historically, the invasion was known as "the Battle of the Ditch." It is so named because it originated from the trench the Muslims dug to thwart the Meccan cavalry. The strong resistance given by the Muslims forced the Meccan Qurayish to withdraw. After that, the Muslim army was strengthened, consolidated, and more organized. Mohammed's reputation as a strategist and an army general was acclaimed by nearby tribal groups. Several tribes began to seek after Mohammed for protection. In time, the balance of power shifted in favour of Mohammed, and the Meccans were forced to acknowledge him as a leader of Central Arabia.

In 628 C.E., Mohammed established a treaty with the Qurayish Meccans at Hudaybiyah to let his followers go to worship at the kaaba. In the following year, Mohammed took control over the Hijaz and led the Muslims on a pilgrimage. On Wednesday, the tenth of Ramadan in 630 CE., accusing the Meccans of breaking the treaty, Mohammed entered Mecca with a vast army of 10,000 soldiers and captured the city without any bloodshed. He destroyed the idols and statues in the kaaba and cleaned up the worship place as a sanctuary for monotheistic worship. Mohammed did not take vengeance upon his former enemies in Mecca. He forgave them and asked them to embrace Islam. As a sign of surrender and an acknowledgment of the Prophet's leadership, the Meccans converted to Islam. The following two years, Mohammed continued to expand his authority over Arabia by defeating the surrounding, pagan Bedouin tribes and incorporated them into the Islamic community. Several small tribal communities sent delegations to Mohammed to establish peace treaties. Within a short period of time, every one of the surrounding communities embraced Islam and accepted Mohammed as leader and Prophet. Mohammed sent Muslim leaders to all of his conquered territories to teach the Quran and the ways of Allah.

However, the inhabitants of Taif refused to join Mohammed, as he was considered the enemy of their god, Hubal. They organized the Hawazir confederacy of tribal clans against Mohammed and fought the Muslim army. After an intense battle in which Mohammed himself was injured, the Taifan army was subdued. The town was captured and annexed to Muslim territory. Having captured all the local Arab lands, Mohammed set his eyes upon the Roman and Persian empires.[11]

In the year 632 CE., Mohammed himself led the Muslims on a pilgrimage to Mecca and preached his farewell speech at Mina to the assembly of 40,000 believers.[12] He admonished them and said :

> Know ye that every Moslem is a brother unto every other Moslem, and that ye are now one brotherhood. It is not legitimate for any one of you, therefore, to appropriate unto himself anything that belongs to his brother unless it is willingly given him by that brother.[13]

---

11. When death cut his mission short four years later, his followers carried out his ambition and conquered the east Roman and Persian empires.

12. Islamic tradition says Mina as the site where Abraham sacrificed the ram in the place of his son Ishmael. It is an important pilgrim centre for Muslims who go to Mecca.

13. Quoted in Philip K. Hitti, *History of the Arabs*, 9th edition, (New York: St. Martin's Press, 1966), p.120.

Mohammed confessed his fears that the believers might go astray and return to their former jahiliyya ways of life. He exhorted the Muslims to be faithful to his message and uttered at the end of his speech "Allah, you are my witness," and then recited, "This day have I [Allah] perfected your religion for you and completed My favour unto you, and have chosen for you as religion Al-Islam" (Sura 5:3). The large crowd of believers who had gathered to listen to the Prophet began to weep aloud for the end of God's revelation had come to a close and the time for the Prophet to depart had finally arrived.

CHAPTER II
Mohammed : Prophet and Messenger of Arabia

Mohammed and his followers were convinced that Allah had indeed raised a prophet from among the people of Arabia and given the final revelation in the Holy Quran. Since God had helped all of His messengers in the past and vindicated them in the end, Mohammed hoped that he would also be absolved on the last day. Often, the Prophet preached about God's sovereignty, His unlimited mercy, and the impending Day of Judgment in which God's people will be vindicated and others punished. The Quran enumerates a long list of Allah's prophets who were saved by the power of God and vindicated at the end of their ministries : For example, Noah was saved from the flood. "We helped him against people who rejected Our signs, truly they were a people given to evil, so We drowned them (in the flood) all together" (Sura 21.77). Likewise, Abraham was rescued from the fire. "They said, 'Burn him and protect your gods, if ye do' (anything at all). We said, 'O fire! be thou cool, and (a means of) safety for Abraham!" (Sura 21.68,69, 15:17). Also, Moses was delivered from the hands of the Pharaoh as Allah had bestowed a special favour upon His messenger (Sura 2.50). And again, Aaron and others were freed from great misfortunes. "We bestowed our favour on Moses and Aaron, and We delivered them and their people from their great calamity; and We helped them so they overcame (their troubles.) And We gave them the Book...We guided them...Peace and salutation to Moses and Aaron!" (Sura 37.114-120). Even, Jesus was delivered from the hands of the Jews. Thus, Mohammed assured his listeners that he would also be saved from all sarcasm, insults and mockery of his enemies, and his message would ultimately triumph.

Mohammed's fight against idolatry involved both a fight against both polytheism and tribal solidarity. Mecca, the location of kaaba, brought the Arab tribes together for worship and commerce. Anyone who disrupted the tribal solidarity, founded on the dual purpose of religion and trade, was exiled from the community. Without the help of fellow tribal members, a nomadic individual or family could become vulnerable and defenseless in the cruel desert. This commonality in religion provided not only communal solidarity but also physical security which was what the powerful Qurayish tribe in Mecca insured and offered to all under them.

Being convinced of his divine message, Mohammed was willing to risk it all. Perhaps he had heard about the Biblical account of Moses mobilizing an army of Levites and ordering them to slay all those who made and worshipped a golden calf in the Sinai desert as narrated in Exodus 32:27-29. The Quran repeats the same story in Sura 2:54. When Mohammed began to gain a larger following, he commanded the Muslims to resist the rebllious idolaters and fight anyone who opposed his message.

Converts to Islam came from all the neighbouring communities. Mohammed provided them with both spiritual and political support. The new converts abandoned their local tribal solidarity in favour of a larger, deeper commitment to the community of the faithful which Mohammed called the Umma.

Messenger Vs. Prophet

The Quran calls Mohammed the *Ummi* Prophet, the uneducated prophet. Arabs who listened to Mohammed delivering the message were surprised at his linguistic style and were convinced that his source of message was Allah himself. Mohammed's delivery gave authenticity to his message. Whenever the Prophet recited the message, his listeners memorized and wrote down the words on stone tablets, bones of dead animals, dry parchments, papyrus and walls. The totality of all his utterances comprises the Quran. When his opponents challenged him to prove the authenticity of his prophethood and mission, the Prophet and his followers responded that he had brought the Quran from heaven for all of humanity and that was the only sign he could provide. His followers challenged the critics that even if his opponents could recruit angels they would not be able to produce another Quran like the one Mohammed had brought for them. Mohammed never performed any miracle and he never claimed personal infallibility. He said he was only Allah's messenger who brought the ultimate revelation.

The Quran attributes two honouric titles to Mohammed : messenger *(rasul)* and prophet *(nabi)*. A messenger, according to the Quran, is the one who is called of God for a specific mission and to a particular group of people.[1] A messenger brings major new revelation. The Quran lists a number of special messengers who were sent with major divine revelation. They are : Adam, Seth, Noah, Abraham, Ishmael, Moses, Lot, Salih, Hud, Jesus, and Mohammed. However, Mohammed was the only one who was given a universal message and commissioned to spread the message to the whole of humanity until the end of time. Only Mohammed was an exception to the role of a messenger as he was also the "Seal of the Prophets."

According to the teachings of the Quran, a messenger not only receives special revelations from God, but also records them as a book for the guidance of the present and future generation. Essentially, all messengers brought the same message, as its origin was God. When the messengers were sent out by God, he assured them of success and guaranteed that those who would oppose them would face death and annihilation. Islamic history says Salih, one of God's messengers, admonished the Thamud people to honour the conventions about a sacred camel by providing it with drinking water during drought. When the people refused to listen to Salih, God destroyed them. The Quran declares God's wrath fell upon those who refused to obey Noah, Abraham, Moses, and several others also.

Contrary to the role of a messenger, a prophet merely proclaims the message received from God and works with the framework of his or her religion. A prophet is also called *Bashir*, the "one who brings good news," and *Nadhir*, "the one who warns."

The term "prophet" in the Quran is a very inclusive word.[2] God had sent thousands of prophets before Mohammed, but only a few messengers (Adam, Noah, Abraham, Moses, and Jesus) had come with a special

---

1. The word messenger also means envoy. The Quran frequently refers to "those who are sent".

2. In the Bible, the prophets of the Old Testament talked about a God who was redemptively involved in human history. YHWH was known by what he did to His chosen people, and he asked his community to respond to His love and redemptive acts. And hence the Bible documents the history of divine-human encounter, and people's response to God. The prophets served as the source and interpreter of divine revelation in human history. They made the divine message known to the people by their preaching and writing. The prophets of the Bible belonged to the inner circle of God, and; therefore they "saw" and "heard" the revealed Word of the Lord (Isaiah 1:1, Obadiah 1:1, Micah 1:1, Habakuk 1:1).

message from God.[3] Although the Quran mentions the names of only twenty eight prophets, the Hadith (a book of Islamic tradition) says that Allah has sent 124,000 prophets so far to guide from time to time. Of the twenty eight prophets named in the Quran, eighteen of them are found in the Hebrew Scriptures and three of them (Jesus, John the Baptist, and his father Zechariah) are found in the Christian Scriptures.

Muslims believe in non-canonized prophets whose names have not been mentioned in their scripture by supporting their argument based on the following Quranic reference. "Allah says : of some apostles We have already told thee the story; of others we have not ..." (Sura : 4 :164). The names of the prophets mentioned in the Quran represent diverse backgrounds and different ages : "Say ye (Muslims) : We believe in Allah and the revelation given to us, and to Abraham, and Ismail, Isaac, and Jacob, and the tribes, and that given to Moses and Jesus received, and that given to (all) Prophets received from their Lord : We make no difference between one and another of them : and we bow to God (in Islam)" (Sura 2:136). Those prophets were sent to several nations and various peoples. Unfortunately, many of them persecuted the prophets and rejected their message.

The Quran refers to four prophets (some traditions say they were all Arabs) who were sent specifically to the Arabs. Those prophets were: Salih, Hud, Shuab, and Mohammed. However, Mohammed was the only one to be elevated in the tradition of Abraham. Human history has seen several messengers and prophets who have come and gone, yet Mohammed was the only one to be made the Vice-regent and Supreme Ruler on earth.

The prophets of God were sinless and infallible, excellent in character and honest in speech. After all, God cannot reveal his Holy Book to an unrighteous person. A special grace of God ('isma) protected them from committing any immoral act. The Quran attests that all the prophets, right from Adam, form a common fraternity. "O you Apostles! enjoy all things good and pure, and work righteousness; For I am well-acquainted with all that you do. And verily this brotherhood of yours is a single brotherhood, and I am your Lord and Cherisher : therefore fear

---

3. The Quran adds some unknown messengers whose names were not mentioned in the Bible, eg., Salih, who was given a mission among the Thamudians, an Arab community. Hud was sent to the people of Ad in South Arabia. Shuayb was sent to the Midianites who were living east of the gulf of Aqaba. The names of some prophets are not easily identified. For example, Idris (19:56,57) has been translated as either Esdras or Enoch. Such confusions occur on other names as well.

Me (and none other)" (Sura (23:51-52). In his book, *Islamic Way of Life*, Abul A'la Maududi elaborates the Quranic theme of commissioning the prophets and establishes that all the prophets appointed by God had the same mission and proclaimed the same message.

> These prophets were raised in all epochs, in all lands and in all nations. Their number exceeds many thousands. All of them brought the same message, all advocated the same way of life, i.e., the way which was revealed to man on the first day of his existence. All of them followed the same guidance : the guidance which was prescribed by the Lord for man at the outset of his career on earth. All of them stood for the same mission: they called men to the religion of Islam, asked those who accepted the Divine guidance to live in accordance with that and organized them into a movement for the establishment for the Divine Law, and for putting an end to all deviations from the Right Path. Every prophet tried to fulfill this mission in the best possible way. But quite a number of people never accepted their guidance and many of those who accepted it, gradually drifted astray and after a lapse of time, lost the guidance or distorted it through innovations and perversions.[4]

Although the Quran does not attribute any miraculous qualities to Mohammed, after his death, his followers transmitted stories of the miracles that surrounded the birth, life and ministry of the Prophet. Many Muslims believed Mohammed had power over Satan. When Mohammed was born, the Emperor of Persia was distressed and the light that emanated from the Prophet's mother's womb brightened castles in Syria. Mohammed was believed to have been endowed with special spiritual gifts and God always watched over him from being harmed by his enemies. It was also believed that he was born without foreskin and thus he was never circumcised with human hands. Some Muslims believe God has given Mohammed a special place of honour after his death and on the Day of Judgment the Prophet will serve as a Mediator for the faithful.

The Muslims compare the grandeur of the kaaba with the greatness of the *Shekinah* of the Hebrew Scriptures. In the Hebrew Scriptures, God made a covenant with Abraham that he would multiply his seed like the stars of the sky and abide with them for ever. The Presence of God was revealed in Shekinah and hovered upon the Ark of the Covenant during

---

4. Abul A'la Maududi, *Islamic Way of Life*, (Kuwait: ILFSO, 1977), p.6.

the wandering years of Israelites, until Solomon built the Temple in Jerusalem and moved the Ark into the Holy of Holies area of the Temple. The Holy of Holies area was separated from the people and priests with a curtain.

The Gospels document, when Jesus died on the cross and gave up his spirit, the curtain in the Temple was torn into two from top to bottom. By doing so, the Epistle to the Hebrews says, God abolished all blood sacrifices and removed all barriers that separated the roles between laity and priests. Every one was given direct access to the spiritual presence of God and priestly mediation was invalidated.

Muslims assert that the splendour and magnificence of kaaba combines both the Ark and Holy of Holies. Nevertheless, the kaaba does not enclose the Divine Presence, but, rather, as the designated place of gathering for worship it has a unique sanctity and spiritual holiness. Muslim traditions say that Abraham, the first monotheistic worshipper, prayed incessantly that God would feed the people at Mecca and raise a prophet from among the Arabs. Islam denies that God chose one group of people over the others to give a favourite status. God sent messengers to people everywhere, but only a few listened. It is inconceivable for the Muslim mind to accept the doctrine of the Incarnation. The Creator God of utter peerlessness cannot beget a son and allow him to share His sovereignty which belongs only to the Almighty God. Any religion or scripture which fosters such a doctrine of God is an undeveloped religion. Such a religion is a product of human imagination, not a result of divine revelation. Islam teaches that the message the prophets received from God is much more important than what the prophets talk about themselves. History, narrations, commentaries, and rituals have no room in God's sacred scripture.

The Allah who revealed his will to Prophet Abraham spoke directly to Prophet Moses also and gave the Law. But the people who listened to Prophet Moses limited his teaching to themselves and added too many rituals. Moses was the first prophet to combine both the spiritual and political aspects of a messenger. He was the prototype of Mohammed who combined both politics and religion in Arabia.

The Quran teaches that just as Abraham and Moses preached the unity of God, so did Jesus. Prophet Jesus *(Isa)* received Allah's revelation which came to be known as the Gospel *(Injil)*. However, after Jesus' death the Christians corrupted and compromised his teachings by giving a cohort (Mary) to Allah and by elevating Jesus as God. The Christians invented the Trinitarian nature of Allah and divided the unity and Oneness of Godhead. Because all the teachings of the earlier prophets were either diluted or compromised by the Jewish and Christian religious leaders, Allah had to send yet another prophet, Mohammed, six hundred years after Jesus with the final message. The Quran affirms Mohammed's uncompromising message of strict monotheism and infallible tradition of prophetic ministry in clear terms: "This day have I perfected your religion for you, completed My favour upon you, and have chosen for you *Al-Islam* as your religion" (Sura 5:4).

Jews and Christians : The People of the Book

Mohammed was disappointed when the Jews and Christians, whom he called *Dhimmis* (People of the Book), refused to acknowledge him as a prophet. When Mohammed and his followers became a politically powerful force to rule Medina, he levied a poll-tax upon the Jews and Christians and cautioned his followers :

> Fight those who believe not in Allah nor the Last Day, nor hold that forbidden which hath been forbidden by Allah and His Apostle, nor acknowledge the Religion of Truth (even if they are) of the people of the Book, until they pay the *jizya* with willing submission, and feel themselves subdued. The Jews call Ezra a son of God, and the Christians call Christ the Son of God. That is a saying from their mouth; (in this) they but imitate what the unbelievers of old used to say. Allah's curse be on them : how they are deluded away from the Truth (Sura 9:29-30).

In order to live in harmony with people outside the Islamic community, Mohammed prepared and publicized a charter which came to be known as the Constitution of Medina. The charter spelled out the relationship between the Muslims and non-Muslims and the rights and duties of all Medinans. "This document," according to Gerhard Endress, "promulgated soon after Hijra, regulated the relationship of the tribes, the Meccan 'Emigrants' and the Medinan 'Helpers' and bound together in a new, larger community, called *umma*, which was not based on blood relationship but on religion. From then onwards, there stood above the tribes of the umma, the community of believers under the authority and protection of God and under the leadership of Mohammed."[5] The

---

5. Gerhard Endress, *An Introduction to Islam*, trans., by Carole Hillenbrand, (New York: Columbia University Press, 1988), p.31.

charter recognized Jews and Christians as individual communities which were allied to the umma. However, the Jews and Christians were forbidden to convert any Muslim nor proselytize any other people.

The religious charisma and the political strategy of Mohammed enabled him to become a sole ruler in Arabia before he died in 632. The defeats of the Qurayish tribe, the Christian, and the Persian Empires by the newly risen Muslim power earned respect and prestige from the surrounding Arab tribes. They began to flock into the Muslim umma. The Muslim umma grew rapidly. And although the Jews and Christians were given religious and cultural autonomy, the Muslim umma was given a more privileged status.

The Christians and Jews did not complain openly about the newly introduced Islamic charter. After enduring centuries of oppression from the hands of the Persians, Greeks, and Romans, dominion under fellow Arabs appeared to be much more tolerable for both the Jews and Christians.

One other reason Islam was able to establish deep roots among the Arabs was the low spiritual condition in which the Jews and Christians were living in pre-Islamic days. Judaism, which opposed Mohammed's teachings, was existing in the enclaves of Arabia and was confined to small commercial centres in fear of Byzantium. Many Jewish communities were living in isolation without rabbis or synagogues. Similarly, Christianity, which forsook idolatry and challenged Mohammed's prophethood was not living up to the teachings of Christ. The Church during the seventh century, according to Henry H. Halen, "had become paganized with the worship of Images, Relics, Martyrs, Mary and the Saints."[6] As a result, Christianity in Arabia became weak and vulnerable. Mohammed's message of an Undivided God took the Christians by surprise.

In his book *The Call of the Minaret*, Kenneth Cragg shares Halen's observation and succinctly presents the prevailing mood of Christianity and the cause for the rapid expansion of Islam :

> Among the factors contributing to the rise of Islam was the Christian failure of the Church. It was a failure in love, in purity, in fervour, and a failure of the spirit. Truth, as often before and

---

6. Henry H. Halen, *Halley's Bible Hand Book*, 24th Edition (Grand Rapids: Zondervan Publishing House, 1965), p.765.

after, was involved to its hurt in the spiritual fault of its trustees. Islam developed in an environment of imperfect Christianity and later by its own inner force gathered such strength as to become, and remain, essentially at odds with the pure faith beyond the imperfection.[7]

Moreover, several forms of Christianity were in existence during Mohammed's time. The deserts were the habitation for all itinerant and non-conformist preachers, philosophers, and spiritual leaders who ran afoul of Byzantine. They and their adherents brought their own doctrinal forms and spiritual wares of Christianity to Arabia.

Christianity in Arabia had no organized power. The Bible had not yet been translated into Arabic. Syriac (a foreign language), not Arabic (the local language), was the language of worship in the established churches. The stories of the Christian and Hebrew Scriptures were transmitted orally among the Christians which gave rise to distorted understanding of the Christian faith. The fundamental doctrine of Christianity was constantly debated. The itinerant preachers who gave their own garbled, slanted interpretations of the Christian faith which confused the desert-dwelling, isolated Christian communities. Lack of spiritual leadership, inadequate understanding of Christian creed, and virtual isolation from fellow Christians which had already eroded the foundation of the Christian community in Arabia paved way for Islam when it came with a plain and simple message about One God. When Islam appeared with a claim to have brought a message from the very presence of God, Christians were not able to counter the new religious force with informed Biblical knowledge.

The Islamic Umma and Muslim Mission
The Muslim umma is essential for the very existence of Islam and the protection of its adherents. The communal living enables the leaders of the faith to make decision when war, infidelity, or heresy threaten the faith community. The umma, by virtue of the solidarity it offers to its members, provides physical security and political unity, spiritual integrity and religious stability. The Sunni Muslims take this solidarity seriously by calling themselves *Ahl Al-Jama* (the people of the Community). In times of crisis, such communal unity helps the Sunnis seek the unanimous

---

7. Kenneth Cragg, *The Call of the Minaret*, (New York : Oxford University Press, 1956), p.245.

consent of the community. The umma, since Mohammed's time, has grown so rapidly and established its roots all over the world. Hence the opinion and decision of the members of the umma in one part of the world is given validation and approval by the umma in another part of the world. Especially, when Islamic faith is threatened in one part of the world, the umma from all around the world would join together to lend their support to the endangered Muslim community. A religious and spiritual decision made by a Muslim community in one part of the world is generally honoured by the religious community everywhere.[8]

Badru D. Kateregga aptly summarizes the transforming and all-embracing effects of the Islamic umma, the material community.

> As Islam spread, the Ummah, which was essentially based on Islamic law, was quickly transformed from an Arab Ummah into a universal Muslim Ummah. It is not surprising that the Ummah extended very quickly, after the Prophet's death, far beyond the confines of the Arabian Peninsula. In the process, it brought together, peoples of different cultures, races, and nations to form one great Ummah.[9]

During his pilgrimage to Mecca, Malcom X, an African-American Muslim convert, was profoundly touched by the spirit of unity and equality among Muslims of different races, colours, and nationalities that transformed him from a black nationalist to a black human rights advocate. Later, he wrote, to the American audience:

> America needs to understand Islam, because this is the one religion that erases from its society the race problem. Throughout my travels in the Muslim world, I have met, talked to, and even eaten with people who in America would have been considered "white" - but the "white" attitude was removed from their minds by the religion of Islam. I have never before seen *sincere* and *true* brotherhood practiced by all colors together, irrespective of their color.[10]

---

8. For example, Ayatollah Khomeini's call to punish Salman Rushdie has been accepted by the Muslim community everywhere.

9. Badru D. Kateregga and David W. Shenk, *Islam and Christianity: A Muslim and a Christian Dialogue*, (Grand Rapids: Eerdmans, 1980), p.52.

10. Quoted in Alex Haley, *The Autobiography of Malcom X*, (New York: Ballantine Books, 1965), p.340.

Each Muslim is nurtured to believe that he or she is a missionary of Allah. Islam must always forge forward. Muslims must go out and liberate people who serve false gods, and bring the world under the One True God. Allah told Mohammed, "(The Quran,) a Scripture which we have revealed unto thee (O Mohammed) that whereby thou mayst bring forth mankind from darkness unto light" (Sura 14:1). What was revealed to Mohammed by God has been now passed on to the believers. As the Prophet Mohammed carried the message of Allah to the unbelievers, so should all the Muslims until the whole world comes to know Allah.

As a result, the Quranic message is being propagated by both rich and poor, men and women, laity and clergy everywhere. Inamullah Khan testifies how Islam has stretched itself around the world and how the Muslims find spiritual comfort in the umma :

> East to West from Indonesia to Morocco, and South to North from Tanzania to Turkey, there lies across globe the Muslim belt consisting today of 38 independent countries. Apart from the sovereign Muslim States, there are Muslim minorities in other countries of the world, some big...others small and varying sizes. During the nearly fourteen centuries since its inception the ideology of Islam has spread to all corners of the world. Today there is no country in the world where there does not exist a community of Muslims, big or small, with its mosques from where the Mu'addhin proclaims *Allahu Akbar* (God is Great) day in and day out.[11]

Although Islam has not had a religious hierarchy or an ordained priesthood since its inception, it continues to function as a missionary religion. Individual Institutions and private organizations like Al Azhar University in Cairo and World Muslim League in Saudi Arabia provide intellectual and monetary support for Islam's missionary cause around the world. One of the strong yet fundamental beliefs of the Muslim community is that the umma will be established among people everywhere, and then Jesus, the Messiah, will come to judge the world.

---

11. Inamullah Khan, "Islam in the Contemporary World", p.1.

The Islamic Jihad

In the event Muslims face resistance or persecution in propagating their faith, they should resist and resort to jihad. The word *jihad* refers to the spiritual obligations of all Muslims to strive or struggle in the path of Allah through teaching, preaching, and, if necessary, armed struggle. Jihad means a call for opposition to injustice and oppression. It is also an invitation to fight for the complete success of Allah's cause. If the need arises, all adult males are called to fight the enemies of Allah with all their possessions. All aggressions against Islamic faith must be resisted and checked. The Quran mandates :

> Fight them (the oppressors) on until there is no more tumult or oppression, and there prevail justice and faith in God; but if they cease, let there be no hostility except to those who practice oppression (Sura 2:193).

Jihad must be undertaken only when there is a reasonable prospect of success assured. Muslims are commanded in the Quran to defend the cause of Allah and fight against unbelief and infidelity even to the point of sacrificing one's own life.

> So let them fight in the way of God who sell the present life for the world to come; and whosoever fights in the way of God and is slain, or conquers, we shall bring him a mighty wage. (Sura 4.74).

Those who offer their lives for Allah's sake will be amply rewarded for they are the martyrs *(Shuhuda)* and they will go to paradise directly where they will enjoy all the heavenly privileges.[12] The martyrs will be given special honour by Allah himself. The Quran promises, "God has preferred in rank those who struggle with their possessions and their selves over the ones who sit at home" (Sura 4:95). When the umma is persecuted, God himself sanctions war.

> To those against whom war is made, permission is given (to fight), because they are wronged; and verily, God is More Powerful for their aid; (They are) those who have been expelled from their homes in defiance of right, (for no cause) except that they say, "Our Lord is God." Did not God check one set of people by means of another, there would surely have been

---

12. Ignaz Goldziher, *Muslim Studies*, Vol.2, ed., S.M. Stern (London: George Allen & Urwin, 1971), p.354.

pulled down monasteries, churches, synagogues, and mosques, in which the name of God is commemorated in abundant measure. God will certainly aid those who aid His (cause); for verily God is full of strength, exalted in might, (able to enforce his will) (22:39-40).

Those who offer their lives for Allah's sake will be given special honour by Allah himself. "God has preferred in rank those who struggle with their possessions and their selves over the ones who sit at home" (Sura 4.95). However, jihad is a complex and broad concept. It means both an inner spiritual renewal of a believer and an outer defense of Islamic umma. In the West, it is often interpreted as "Holy War." During the colonial period, Muslims associated jihad with liberating Muslims from oppressive power and unjust rule. Abu al-'Ata Mawdudi defended and supported such a religio-political stand in two of his works :

> The real objective of Islam is to remove the lordship of man over man and to establish the kingdom of God on earth. To stake one's life and everything else to achieve this purpose is called *Jihad.*[13]

> A man who exerts himself physically or mentally or spends his wealth in the way of Allah is indeed engaged in *Jihad*. But in the language of the Shariah this word is used particularly for a war that is waged solely in the name of Allah against those who practice oppression as enemies of Allah.[14]

Mawdudi's militant approach has been shared by Sayyid Qutab, the deceased leader of Muslim Brotherhood in Egypt. Qutab believed that the challenges of political power and oppression of infidel nations cannot be counter-matched with mere preaching. Physical force must be met with physical force, and Islam has its answer in jihad.[15] Qutab maintained Mohammed himself had taught about jihad.

> Central to (Sayyid Qutab's writing is the concept of jihad… The Prophet Muhammad taught that jihad is engaged at four levels: in their heart, as the place of spiritual striving; by the

---

13. Abu al-'Ata Mawdudi, *Khutubat* (An English Version), 2nd ed. (Chicago: Kazi, 1977), p.243.

14. Abu al-'Ata Mawdudi, *Towards Understanding Islam*, 6th ed. (Salimiah, Kuwait: International Islamic Federation of Student Organization, 1982), p.142.

15. See Sayyid Qutab, *Milestones*, rev.ed. (Cedar Rapids, Iowa: Unity Publishing, n.d.), pp.55, 57.

tongue, as the means of preaching and teaching the message of Islam; by the hand, as the means of its social application; and finally by the sword, as the implement of its defense and confrontation against ungodly forces. This last meaning of militant struggle was exemplified in the Prophet Muhammed's strategy against pagan forces of Mecca from his home base in Medina.[16]

However, the interpretation of jihad and its imposition varies from group to group within the Islamic community. There are a lot of unanswered questions which surround the declaration of jihad. Some of the major questions that do not have definite answers are : Who has the power and authority to declare jihad? When is the right time to enforce it? For what cause? Against whom? For how long?

The Quran asserts, jihad should not be undertaken for territorial expansion or destruction of properties or the advancement of one's own whims and fancies. Azzam writes,

The aims of [jihad] are circumscribed. Contrary to the aims of all the imperialist states, they do not include territorial expansion or the incapacitation and paralysis of other nations; they do not envision the destruction of their capacity to compete in life by their exclusion from markets and fields of trade, or the monopolizing of sources of wealth, the treasures of the world, and the raw materials essential for industry, or any other action designed to enhance the power of one nation. Nor do those aims advocate the supremacy and self-magnification of any nation in this world so that it becomes more populous and "racially" superior to other. Instead, the aims of war have a defined and limited purpose : to establish freedom of worship of God, give the poor their due, enjoin kindness, and forbid iniquity.[17]

Modern history, nonetheless, shows the declaration of jihad was used primarily for political and territorial expansion. The Quranic affirmation that jihad should be undertaken only when the umma or the faith of Islam is under severe threat has been largely ignored. However, as the concept

---

16. David Kerr, "The Challenge of Islamic Fundamentalism for Christians", *International Bulletin of Missionary Research,* October 1993, p.171.

17. Abd Al-Rahman Azzam, *The Eternal Message of Muhammad* (Oxford: The Aldon Press, 1993), p.130.

of umma or the meaning of Islamic faith could be defined in broad neutral political and territorial terms, jihad has been used, at times, in questionable ways and to spread Islam by force.

Is Conversion Through Jihad Justified?

The Quran uses the word jihad only for spiritual struggle. It is also referred to self-defense and restoration of peace and order. The Quran uses a distinct word for military activities. That word is : *Qital*, not *Jihad*. Although religious history proves that the umma has extended its territory through war and conquest, the Quran does not condone it. Incursion of any kind is discouraged in the Quran.

People of the world can neither be coerced to submit to Allah's will nor thrust into the sphere of peace *(Dar Al-Islamai)* and compelled to join the umma. The Quran clearly legislates, "There is no compulsion in religion, The right direction is henceforth distinct from error" (Sura 2:256). Any form of resistance is justified only to ward off evil. "Fight in the way of Allah (only) against those who fight against you, ...And fight them until persecution is no more, and religion is for Allah. But if they desist, then let there be no hostility except against wrongdoers" (Sura 2:190-193). Some enthusiastic followers interpret the above suras loosely. Any threat (political, economic, social, cultural and religious) is perceived as a "discord on earth" and arouse the members of the Islamic community to take up arms and defend the cause of the Allah and His messenger (Sura 9:33-34).

Amir 'Ali, at the end of nineteenth century wrote:

> By the laws of Islam, liberty of conscience and freedom of worship were allowed and guaranteed to the followers of every other creed under Moslem dominion. The passage in the Koran, "Let there be no compulsion in religion," testifies to the principles of toleration and charity inculcated by Islam. "If the Lord had pleased, verily all who are in the world would have believed together." "Wilt thou then force men to believe when belief can come only from God."[18]

Abdulaziz A. Sachedina says sectarian groups within Islam continue to debate over the issue of forceful conversion and the freedom of conscience. The Mutazites believe Islam and its teachings cannot be

---

18. Amir 'Ali, *The Spirit of Islam*, (London: Methuen, 1967), p.212.

forcefully thrust upon unbelievers as Allah is the One who "grants or withholds the gift of faith, who either makes the heart receptive to warnings or hardens it upon unsatisfactory actions or attitudes on the part of an individual." In contrast, the Ash'arites insist Allah's will is revealed only through the Quranic teachings. Only the People of the Book were permitted to practice their religions and all the idol worshippers and infidels must be forcefully converted.[19]

Islamic history shows converts were brought into Islam not only through genuine religious conversion but also by force and material incentives.

> Caliph al-Ma'mun, who declared in a public meeting in A.D. 830 that although many under his rule had converted to Islam for purely religious reasons, many others had done so from less honorable motives. They belong to a class who embrace Islam, not from any love for this our religion, but thinking thereby to gain access to my Court, and share in the honour, wealth, and power of the Realm; they have no inward persuasion of that which they outwardly profess.[20]

Caliph al-Hakim, in the eleventh century, forcefully converted Christians living in his territories. Those who refused to embrace Islam were persecuted. Church properties were seized and converted as mosques by simply building domes on the roofs of the churches. Christian religious symbols were burned and forbidden to be placed for public display. The Church of the Holy Sepulchre in Jerusalem, a sacred site for Christians, was destroyed. Christian leaders, pastors and bishops were incarcerated. Muslims were ordered not to maintain any social relationship nor to practice any commercial alliance with the Christians. Searle Bates chronicles that nearly a century before the Crusader's arrival in the Middle East, between 1012 and 1014, about thirty thousand Christian churches were damaged or destroyed in Egypt and Syria alone.[21]

---

19. Abdulaziz A. Sachedina, "Freedom of Conscience and Religion in the Quran", in *Human Rights and the Conflicts of Cultures: Western and Islamic Perspectives on Religious Liberty*, (Columbia, S.C.: University of South Carolina Press, 1988), pp.67 ff.

20. Kerr, *International Bulletin of Missionary Research*, October 1993, p.166.

21. Searle Bates, "Islam and Religious Liberty", *The Muslim World*, Vol.36, (January 1946), p.59.

Jihad could be interpreted as an order to bring Islam into everyday life. Some religious leaders teach jihad as the sixth Pillar of Islam and present it as a form of worship and service offered to Allah and His cause. Allah is the Commander-in-Chief of Jihad. He will help the holy Muslim warriors in their struggle against oppression as he did it at the Battle of Badre, where, according to the Quran, an unseen army of angels fought alongside the Muslims to victory. The Quran pledges, the warriors of Allah will be blessed with both victory and spoils of war in this life.

On the other hand, failure to defend the Prophet and Islamic order in the event of danger and invasion would also be guilty and blameworthy. The logical conclusion, therefore, is to resort to jihad and mobilize the entire Muslim community to take arms against the threat. The participation of the entire community will protect everyone from the danger of apostasy and desertion.

Islam is both a religion of the individual and the community. An individual believer and the collective members of the umma are responsible to fellow believers, state, and Allah. As Allah and the umma are closely bound together, any threat against the one is considered a threat against the other. Such a concept brings religion and politics as one constitutive unit. As establishing one universal community of believers is the ultimate goal of Islam, any force or power which impedes the above mentioned progress must be faced with consequences. Ibn Taymiyya, a medieval Muslim theologian, says religious expansion and territorial conquest go side by side, politics and religion must join hand in glove.

To govern the affairs of men is one of the most important requirements of religion, nay, without it religion cannot endure…The duty of commanding the good and forbidding the evil cannot be completely discharged without power and authority. The same applies to all religious duties (holy war, pilgrimage, prayer, fast, almsgiving), to helping those who are wronged, and to meting out punishment in accordance with the legal penalties…The purpose of public office is to further the religion and the worldly affairs of men…when the pastor exerts himself in proportion to his ability to further both, he is one of the most excellent fighters on the path of God…The exercise of authority is a religious function and a good work which brings near to God, and drawing near to God means obeying God and His Prophet.[22]

22. Kerr, International Bulletin of Missionary Research, October 1993, pp. 165-166.

Taymiyya's views are espoused by many twentieth-century Muslims as well. Several Islamic nations consider the separation of religion and state a Western policy which should be rejected. As the union of religion and state was practiced by the Prophet himself, all Islamic nations should follow such convention. Separating the two, according to the late Ayatollah Khomeini of Iran, was like cutting off Islam's head and giving the rest to the people. Sadiq al-Mahdi, a political leader of Sudan, vehemently condemned the Muslim political leaders who supported the secular national state and said :

> The concepts of secularism, humanism, nationalism, materialism and rationalism, which are all based on partial truths, became deities in their own right : one-eyed super beings. They are responsible for the present Euro-American spiritual crisis. The partial truths in all these powerful ideas can be satisified by Islam.[23]

This new and forceful politicization of Islam, according to Kenneth Cragg, has become a major religious phenomenon in the twentieth century.[24]

The proponents of such an ideology find support from the Quran and justify the use of force against the enemies of Islam. During the time of Mohammed, the enemies of the Prophet broke their pledges and attacked him and his followers. His enemies raided Medina in 622 A.D., and tried to plunder the city of all its riches and wealth. Mohammed used force against his enemies to subdue them. He also warned his followers:

> Will ye not fight a folk who broke their solemn pledges, and purposed to drive out the Messenger and did attack you first? (Sura 9:13).

> If they withdraw not from you, and offer you not peace, and refrain not their hand, take them, and slay them wherever you come to them; against them We have given you a clear authority (Sura 4:91 93).

---

23. Quoted in *International Bulletin of Missionary Research*, October 1993, p.165.
24. Ibid.,

Although, at the early part of the Quran, Jihad is justified to defend rebellion against the established Islamic moral order, Muslims were called to fight and bring people of all nations under Islam and to work toward eliminating corruption on earth by all means possible. The Quran says:

> And fight them on until there is no more tumult or oppression, and there prevail justice and faith in God altogether and everywhere; but if they cease, verily God doth see all that they do (Sura 8:39).

> And fight them on until there is not more tumult or oppression, and there prevail justice and faith in God; but if they cease, let there be no hostility except to those who practice oppression (Sura 2:193).

However, one needs to bear in mind that the concept of jihad in Islamic faith is a complex issue. It blends religion, politics, culture, and the daily affairs of the entire society. A simplisitic answer to a much complex concept of Islam would only betray one's religious ignorance of an organized religion. The call for jihad has to be taken in its context and understood in its national and religious background. Abdulaziz A.Sachedina, in his article "The Development of Jihad in Islamic Revelation and History" aptly summarizes the ambiguous and complex interpretation surrounding the doctrine of jihad:

> The issue is not a simple one, especially since the verse in question (8:39) also occurs at 2:193. On the one hand, if the verse is interpreted in the context provided by the general Qur'anic justification for engaging in Jihad (response to aggression or moral wrong), it can be construed in terms of a moral requirement to fight "persecution" *(Fitna)* which, according to 2:191 "is worse than slaughter." On the other hand, if the verse is interpreted in terms of the development of Muslim political power, then it may be said to provide a warrant for wars of expansion. Undoubtedly, the Sunni jurists regarded the conquests up to the end of the 2nd/8th century as the outcome of a legitimate jihad. However, these conquests were undertaken with the explicit aim of expanding Islamic hegemony, not with

the goal, as stated in the Qur'an, of ensuring that "the religion is entirely God's." Moreover, offensive jihad against "those who do not believe in God and the Last Day and do not forbid what God and His messenger have forbidden and do not practice the religion of truth, from among those who have been given the Book {i.e., the Jews and the Christians}, until they pay jizya {poll-tax}" (9:29) points more to the complex relationship and interdependence of religious and moral considerations in the treatment of the "People of the Book" than to their conversion to "God's religion," Islam.[25]

---

25. James Turner Johnson and John Kelsay, Eds. *Cross, Crescent and Sword*, Abdulaziz A. Sachedina, *The Development of Jihad in Islamic Revelation and History*, (New York: Greenwood Press, 1976), pp.39-40.

CHAPTER III
The Origin of the Islamic Umma

While he was in Medina, Mohammed continued to receive divine revelation and spoke to the people about Allah. He organized his followers into a community that worshipped Allah, and he gave them instructions for conducting Arabia's political, moral, and religious life. Mohammed's followers began to recite and relay his teachings to the local citizens. His followers, who came from Mecca to escape persecution, and those who listened and believed in him in Medina formed a strong and unique heterogeneous Islamic community. Rather than tribal kinship, this community was based on religious beliefs with an ardent desire in practicing what Mohammed had preached. That first heterogeneous community was come to be known as the umma, a community of Allah and a community of peace. The Quran says of the community :

> Let there arise out of you a band of people inviting to all that is good, enjoining what is right and forbidding what is wrong : They are the ones to attain felicity (Sura 3:104).

> Ye are the best of Peoples, evolved for mankind, enjoining what is, forbidding what is wrong, and believing in Allah (Sura 3:110).

> Thus have We made of you an Ummat justly balanced that you might be witnesses over the nations and the Apostle a witness over yourselves. (Sura 2:143).

The Quran instructed the Muslims to give up any tribal allegiance before they became members of the umma. The solidarity of the umma was to indicate the divine unity the believers were required to practice. The Quran praised the believers who forsook their homes in Mecca and undertook a voluntary exile with Mohammed to Medina. The Quran commended the believers in Medina who gave asylum and relief to the Muslims who migrated from Mecca. By doing so, all of them had become like a large family of Allah.

Those who believed, and adopted exile, and fought for the Faith, with their property, and their persons, in the cause of Allah, as well as those who gave (them) asylum and aid, -these are (all) friends and protectors, one of another. As to those who believed but came not into exile, ye owe no duty of protection to them until they come into exile; but if they seek your aid in religion, it is your duty to help them, except against a people with whom ye have a treaty of mutual alliance. And remember God seeth all ye do. Those who believe, and adopt exile, and fight for the Faith, in the cause of Allah, as well as those who give (them) asylum and aid, -these are (all) in very truth the Believers; for them is the forgiveness of sins and a provision most generous (Sura 8.73-74).

In Medina, Mohammed became the uncontested leader and commander of the faithful. He taught the newly formed umma the fundamental principles of Islam and the ordinances of a newly established society, which were readily applicable for worship and communal living. His regulations were deeply rooted in justice, mercy, and camaraderie (Sura 16:90, 4:58, 135, 5:8, 6:153).

Mohammed preached that Islam was a way of life and asked his followers to observe the teachings of God as revealed in the Quran and witness the reality of God as expressed in the Shahada, "There is no god but God" (La Illaha Illa Allah) (Sura 3:64, 42:13, 2:136). Consequently, Mohammed's teaching was not only culturally appealing, socially uniting, communally binding, but also spiritually eclectic and religiously intrinsic. Ignaz Goldziher writes:

Mohammed did not proclaim new ideas. He did not enrich earlier conceptions of man's relation to the transcendental and infinite... In an historical evaluation of Mohammed's work the issue is not whether the contents of his revelation were completely original, absolutely trail-blazing creation of his soul. The Arab Prophet's message was an eclectic composite of religious ideas and regulations. The ideas were suggested to him by contacts, which had stirred him deeply, with Jewish, Christian and other elements, and they seemed to him suited to awaken an earnest religious mood among his fellow Arabs. The regulations too were derived from foreign sources; he recognized them as needed to institute life according to the will of God.[1]

1.Ignaz Goldziher, *Introduction to Islamic Theology and Law*, trans. Andras and Ruth Hamori (Princeton, N.J. : Princeton University Press, 1981), p.5

Steadily, converts began to pour into umma and soon Muslims made up a majority population in Medina. Of the rapid growth and transformation of Medinan society, Inamullah Khan writes:

> Within a span of two decades the Holy Prophet created a veritable revolution in Arabia. All people had become one nation, loyal to the one God, and believing in the brotherhood of man and enjoying social justice of the highest order.[2]

In order to instruct his followers of the true path of Allah and worship him in a proper way, Mohammed built a *Masjid* (mosque, a place of prostration) at Quba, Medina adjacent to the place of his dwelling.[3] It was the first mosque ever to be built in the history of Islam.

By establishing the umma in Medina, Mohammed brought a solidarity among the Muslim community. He taught that each individual believer in the umma was responsible for the other believers. Then again, the entire community was collectively responsible for summoning the wayward humanity back to God. Mohammed also instituted a charter for the community social order. In the charter, he decreed that all disputes would be referred to the Prophet, and he would serve as the head and judge of the umma. The charter said, "Whenever a dispute or controversy likely to cause trouble arises among the people of this document, it shall be referred to God and to Mohammed, the apostle of God. God is the guarantor of the pious observance of what is in the document."[4] Mohammed thus became the undisputed leader of Medina both in religious and political matters.

As a prophet of Allah, Mohammed was given an esteemed honour as a Muslim ruler, a commander, a judge, an arbiter, a reformer and a living Quran. By becoming the head of umma, Mohammed had far exceeded the temporal power of all previous prophets. He had also proven himself to be different from the founders of some of the earlier monotheistic religions. Commenting on the material success of Mohammed, Bernard Lewis writes:

---

2. Inamullah Khan, "Islam in Contemporary World", in *God and Man in Contemporary Islamic Thought*, p.68

3. During pre-Islamic days, the area around the kaaba was called the masjid.

4. Andrew Rippin, *Muslims : Their Religious Beliefs and Practices*, Vol.1 : The Formative Period, (London and New York : Routledge, 1990), p.33.

Moses died before he entered the promised land; Christ died on the cross. Mohammed attained not martyrdom but power. During his lifetime he became a head of state, commanding armies, collecting taxes, administering justice, and promulgating laws. The resulting interpretation of faith and power of religion and authority, has remained characteristic of Islam throughout most of its history.[5]

Sunnah and Hadith

After Mohammed died, the Muslims were advised that they must emulate the life of Prophet Mohammed as instructed in the Quran. The Quran says, "Ye have indeed in the Apostle of God a beautiful pattern (of conduct) for any one whose hope is in Allah and the Final Day, and who engages much in the praise of Allah" (33:21). Mohammed's companions and his followers collected, compiled and recorded all the revelations given to the Prophet after his death. The collection of the revelation was called the Quran. However, the standard edition of the Quran was published only long after Mohammed had died, by Uthman, the third Caliph. Minor improvements in orthography were made in the Quran in ensuing years. The Muslims still proclaim the splendour of the Quran because of its unique linguistic style and the aesthetic sense it provides to the listeners. The Quran's poetic content articulated by a man with no formal education is often cited as the valid evidence to Mohammed's message and frequently quoted as a strong testimony of the miraculous process of revelation even after nearly 1400 years.

The Muslims also collected and collated the sayings and deeds of the Prophet which came to be known as the Sunnah (meaning custom, usage). The Sunnah includes the prophet's opinion about good and evil practices. The Sunnah contains customs and conventions the Prophet practiced in his life which the Muslims are encouraged to adopt. The Sunnah is given much reverence by the Muslims in their everyday living, as it serves as the commentary and interpretation of the Quran. The Sunnah gives guidance to the Muslims in the areas of social, ethical, economic, political, cultural, legal, and international affairs. It supplies instructions in matters like worship, liturgy, faith and obedience, marriage, divorce, intoxicants, gambling, murder, theft, and adultery as the Quran is not explicit in certain issues. At times, the Sunnah's

---

5. Bernard Lewis, *The Jews of Islam*, (Princeton, N.J. : Princeton University Press, 1984), p.5.

expectation of a believer exceeds the Quranic expectations. For example, the Quran refers to only three daily prayers, but the Sunnah sets five (Sura 24:58, 11:116). Even the Salat (canonical prayer) is based almost totally on the Sunnah. As the founder of the religion, the prophet's words and practices were important to emulate. The Sunnah is categorized under two major subgroups as "confirmed" and "supplementary". Certain rituals the Prophet did everyday or repeatedly became obligatory and legal practice for all Muslims, and they were called *al-muakkadah* (that which is confirmed). Certain things he did in his lifetime which were not repeated in the everyday life of the Prophet (such as marrying many wives) were called *As-Sunnah Al Za'idah*, that which is optional.

The Sunnah guides the believers and the community including what to believe and how to exercise their faith which resulted in the distinctness and uniformity of the umma around the world. While the Quran has enabled the Muslim community to believe in One God, modelling the life of Mohammed equipped the believers to set a standard and sameness in their worship and communal living.

The reports about Mohammed's life practices and utterances were later collected and compiled as traditions *(Hadith)* and passed on in oral and written form to succeeding generations. If the Quran does not contain guidance for an individual or a community in their decision-making, the Hadith is usually consulted. Although the followers of Mohammed have been warned that Mohammed was only Allah's messenger, his life and teachings were given special veneration at the ordinary level. Soon, the Hadith stood alongside the Quran in interpreting, explaining, and commenting on its verses and guiding the umma in matters encompassing their daily living.

Mohammed is considered the final and ultimate realization of the ideal. Since he was the recipient of God's revelation, he is esteemed as the authentic messenger of God to interpret and expound the revelation given in the Quran. Four major Muslim historians wrote, praising Mohammed's life in the classic Islamic period : Muhammad ibn Ishaq (767), Muhammad ibn Sa'd (845), Abu Jafar at-Tabari (923) and Muhammad ibn Umar al-Waqidi (820). These and a few other historians give important details about the life of Mohammed and the social and cultural history of Arabia.

The Hadith is divided into two major sections. The first section contains the long list of transmitters that goes way back to the eyewitness of Mohammed's teaching and lifestyle. The section also contains a narration which God himself gives through the prophet as a complementary revelation. Such revelation is called the "Sacred Hadith." The second section contains the actual narration of events and reports containing the acts the prophet performed and utterances the prophet said. The traditions, the sayings, and the practices of the Prophet were carefully examined; the authenticity of the transmitters was meticulously analyzed before the Hadith was put together. The Hadith plays an important role in the formation of *Sharia*, the Islamic law, second only to Quran.

Of the six collections of the Hadith, two of them are considered Sahih, authentic and high standard. They were compiled by Mohammed Ibn Ismail al-Bukhari (870 CE) and Abul Husayn Muslim ibn al-Hajjaj (875 CE). The other four books were collected and put together by Abu Dawud (875 CE), At-Tirmith (892 CE), An-Nassan (915 CE) and Ibn Maja (886 CE). Two other books which are accorded special respect are the Muwatta of Malik ibn Anas (which is the first oral tradition to be reduced to written form) and the *Mushnad* of Ibn Hanbal.

In the process of putting the Hadith together, Al-Bukhari alone collected over 600,000 hadiths, many of which, of course, were the same reports from different sources. However, he concentrated on the reports and the chain of transmission *(Isnad)* that were traced back to the Prophet. Al-Bukhari eliminated all the unauthentic or fabricated stories and traditions, and managed to include only about 2,600 different reports. Al-Hajjaj managed to trace about 3,000 reports and included them in the hadith.

The Shiites include stories and narration that trace the *Isnad* back to Ali and the Imams of Shiism. Hence they call their hadith as *Khabar* (news). The Shiites' version of hadith was collected at a significantly later period (932-1062) which contain allusions to Imams not mentioned in Sunni version. Hence Shiite collections of hadith are much larger than Sunni collection. The hadith became the basis for the formation of Islamic jurisprudence and development of harmonious umma.

The Mission of Mohammed

The mission of Mohammed was not only to bring the whole of humanity to submit to Allah's will, but also to establish a new world order as revealed in the Quran : "We sent aforetime our apostles with clear signs and sent down with them the Book and the Balance (of right and wrong), that men may stand forth in justice" (Sura 57:25). Sayyed Qutab, a late Egyptian conservative Muslim leader, declared the task of Mohammed was to fight polytheism and stand against tyranny.

> The mission of Mohammed was a revolution against the tyranny of shirk (polytheism). In this sphere of doctrine it perceived God as Perfect, beyond similarity and above partnership. The tyranny of polytheism is one that has deep roots in the human spirit. Despite the many Prophets, the messages and the works of the scholars expounding monotheism, humanity still suffers from polytheism. The mission of Muhammad was also a revolution against the tyranny of fanaticism:fananticism in all its manifestations, above all religious fanaticism. The mission of Muhammad was a revolution against the tyranny of race prejudice and color prejudice.[6]

Mohammed preached that life in the umma should be governed by the Law of Allah - the *Sharia*. All members of the umma were equal in status. Exploitation of any kind was violently condemned. "Those who unjustly eat up the orphans, eat up a fire into their own bodies: they will soon be enduring a blazing fire!" (Sura 4:10). The Prophet preached that everything in the umma belonged to God. The members of the umma were only the trustees (khalifah) of God. They had a God-given responsibility to govern the world.

Maududi writes that God has placed human beings in this world with a dual purpose: for total allegiance to God and for unequivocal commitment to his creation.

> God has put us to serious trial on two counts : (a) He has left man free but even after giving him that freedom He wishes to see whether or not man realizes his true position; whether he remains honest and steadfast and maintains loyalty and allegiance to the Lord, or loses his head and revolts against his own Creator; whether he behaves like a noble soul, or tramples underfoot all values of decency and starts playing such fantastic tricks as make the angels weep; (b) He wants to see whether man is prepared to have such confidence in God as to offer his life and wealth in return for what is a promise, that is to

---

6. Sayyed Qutab, *The Mission of Muhammad*, (Karachi : Islamic Foundation, n.d.), p. 8.

materialize in the next world—and whether he is prepared to surrender his autonomy and all the charms that go with it, in exchange for a promise about the future.[7]

Life in the umma made no distinction between sacred and secular. The criminals, unjust and wicked human beings were severely reproached. Initially, the Jews and Christians were given rights to practice their religion. However, over times, when the umma became a socio-religious and political unit, the rights of the People of the Book were checked and curtailed.

When the umma grew larger, Mohammed gave them instructions on social, political, and legislative matters. Executing justice for humanity and proclaiming witness to Allah, the One, Eternal God, occupied the central purpose of the existence of the umma. The Quran admonishes:

O ye who believe! Stand out firmly for justice, as witnesses to Allah, even as against yourselves, or your parents, or your kin, and whether it be (against) rich or poor : For God can best protect both. Follow not the lusts (of your hearts), lest ye swerve, and if ye distort (justice) or decline to do justice, verily Allah is well-acquainted with all that ye do (Sura 4:135).

Mohammed saw his people inside and outside the umma were spiritually thirsty and socially ripe for transformation. Consumed with zeal for his God, he set out to accomplish his mission as a prophet with intensity. Endress summarizes the mission of the Prophet in clear words:

Mohammed gave a disintegrating society both a diagnosis of its malaise and a therapy for it; he was able to answer the fundamental social, economic, and ethical questions of the world around him because he saw them as religious and answered them in that way. He was able to create an Arab nation because he brought the Arabs, in the language of the Revelation, a language of communication and literature; because he—the Seal of the Prophets—gave to the Arabs as recipients of the final truth a place in sacred history, because he made a tribal society which was out of joint, into a community of believers under his own guidance, as the messenger of God.[8]

---

7. Maududi, *Islamic Way of Life*, pp. 10-11.

8. Endress, *An Introduction to Islam*, p.34.

Mohammed's Conquest of Mecca

After imposing poll-tax upon the Jews and Christians who refused to accept him as a prophet, Mohammed turned his attention back to Mecca. He was determined to disrupt the economic and political stability of Mecca by raiding the camel caravans and blocking the trade route going in and out of Mecca. After several battles (battle of Badr, battle at Uhud, battle of the Trench), a treaty called *Treaty of Hudaybiya* was established with the Meccans, which gave freedom for Medinans to go to kaaba to worship. When Meccans failed to keep the Treaty, Mecca was invaded by Mohammed and his followers and the kaaba was captured without bloodshed.

Nearly ten years after his flight from Mecca to Medina, Mohammed returned with 14,000 Muslim soldiers to his birthplace, Mecca, and destroyed all the idols in the city. He conquered the powerful Qurayish tribe which opposed him, and made the kaaba the vehicle for propagating his message of the unity of Allah. By making kaaba as the centre of worship, Mohammed restored the ancient Arabian monotheism of Abraham and added a few more legal and liturgical aspects suitable to the Arabian populace. He made Mecca, especially the kaaba, a place of pilgrimage *(Haji)* to Muslims everywhere.

In the year 620, Khadijah, Mohammed's wife, died and soon after that his uncle, Abu Talib, also died. His uncle, who never became a Muslim, was a strong supporter of Mohammed. The death of those two close members of Mohammed's family devastated him. Mohammed himself said when they died he "went down into the pit" with them. Khadijah was buried in her tomb in the Hajun, a hill near Mecca where her family and tribes were buried.

During that period of aloneness and being in an alien place where his cousin Umm Hani was living, Mohammed was transported at night from Mecca by an animal *(al-Buraq)* to Jerusalem from where he ascended *(Miraj)* to heaven. In narrating Mohammed's experience with heavenly angels and earlier prophets, Islam introduces multiple heavens. Mohammed was given a tour in heaven, and shown the glory of heaven and earth. He also met the prophets who were sent by Allah to the earth earlier and led them in prayer. The Quran says of this journey: "Glory to [God] who did take his servant for a journey by night from the sacred mosque to the farthest mosque, whose precincts We did bless, - in order that We might show him some of Our signs: for he is the one who heareth and seeth (all things)" (Sura 17:1). The farthest mosque referred to here is the site of the Temple of Solomon in Jerusalem on the hill of Moriah at which stands the Dome of the Rock.

Islamic tradition says Prophet Mohammed was awakened from sleep one night by angel Gabriel and was carried on the back of the winged horse, al-Buraq, to Jerusalem to al-masjid al-aqsa (the farthest mosque) where Mohammed was greeted by Abraham, Moses, Jesus, and several other prophets. They prayed together on the mount. After the prayer, Mohammed was offered three goblets which contained water, milk, and wine. Mohammed chose to drink milk as middle course of his belief and teachings that he tried to avoid the extreme asceticism and radical hedonism. Soon after he finished drinking milk, he ascended into the first heaven through a ladder Gabriel brought. Mohammed continued his ascent to the presence of the very throne of God at the seventh heaven. As he progressed, at each heaven he met different prophets. In the first heaven, Mohammed met Adam, who showed a vision of hell. In the second heaven, he saw John the Baptist, in the third he saw Joseph, in the fourth Enoch, in the fifth Aaron, and in the sixth Moses, and in the seventh, at the presence of God, Abraham.

When Mohammed was ushered into the presence of God, he was given the command of fifty prayers a day for his followers. With the encouragement of Moses, (a narrative similar to the prayer offered by Abraham for Sodom and Gomorrah as documented in Genesis 18), Mohammed pleaded with God to reduce the number of prayers. God finally gave in because of the Prophet's importune prayer and reduced it to five prayers a day.

When Mohammed returned to his followers and related his experience with the prophets of old and the Sovereign God, some sceptics refused to believe in him and asked for proof. As one of his proofs, Mohammed said, he had passed a certain caravan in a certain valley. One of the camels saw the al-Buraq, got scared and ran away. Mohammed helped the owners find the lost animal. The Prophet said:

> I showed them where it was while on my way to al-Shams. I carried on until I reached Dajana where I passed by another caravan. The people were sleeping; they had a jar of water which was covered with something. I uncovered it, drank some water and replaced the cover as I had found it. The evidence of this is that their caravan is now approaching from Al-Bayda at

the pass of al-Tan'im; it is led by a dark-coloured camel with two sacks on it, one black, the other multi-coloured. The poeple hurried to the pass and it was as Muhammad had described.[9]

Then the Prophet's listeners believed in his message and became his followers. To date, Muslims regard Jerusalem as the third holiest city and make pilgrimage to the site within the Old City where the Byzantine church from which Mohammed ascended stood. King Sultan built a mosque on that site in Jerusalem in the 12th century, it is now well-known as the Mosque of Omar or Dome of the Rock.

Mohammed's Marriages

In the year 620 CE, Mohammed went through a severe social and spiritual turmoil. That was the year, his wife Khadijah and uncle Abu Talib died. In the place of Abu Talib, another uncle, Abu Lahab, became the head of the clan. He was not an enthusiastic supporter of Mohammed's beliefs and teachings. In fact, he joined his wife, Umm Jamil, sister of Abu Surfyan, Mohammed's arch rival, and opposed the Prophet's spiritual mission.

After losing support from his own clan, Mohammed sought help from his followers in Yathrib who had converted to Islam. After two years of negotiation, in 622 they pledged to support Mohammed in a secret meeting held at 'Aqaba. They pledged to support Mohammed as a prophet and leader of the tribal group in Yathrib which later came to be known as Medina. During the course of his negotiation and his intention to move to Medina, Mohammed's aunt Khawla encouraged him to remarry. When he asked Khawla whom she would suggest, she replied, "Aisha, a virgin or Sawda, a non-virgin." Mohammed asked Khawla to speak with both of them.[10] Mohammed took both of them as his wives. Mohammed's marriage with Sawda took place soon after Khadijah's death. Aisha's marriage took place later, as she was only six years old at that time. Aisha's father, Abu Bakr, was a staunch supporter of Mohammed. Aisha was betrothed to a non-Muslim when her parents were approached by Khawla. When Aisha's mother and father went to the betrothed boy's parents to release Aisha from the contract, they did it gladly. The boy's parents were afraid that by marrying Aisha, he might

---

9. Rippin, *Muslims: The Religious Beliefs and Practices*, Vol. 1, p.42.

10. Having more than one wife was not uncommon during pre-Islamic days.

also become a Muslim. Some scholars argue, when Mohammed was married to Khadijah, he must have made a contract with her that he would not take another wife while she was living.[11]

When Mohammed moved to Medina with his wife and family, he did not have a permanent dwelling place. After being in somebody else's house for awhile, a home for Mohammed and his family, and a mosque with a large courtyard to conduct community affairs were built. Mohammed took in a few more wives who were mostly war widows. Several small houses around the mosque were built for Mohammed's wives. Mohammed took turns sleeping in the houses of his wives.

When Aisha was about ten years old, Abu Bakr wanted to strengthen the ties with Mohammed. Hence, he asked Mohammed why he had not consummated his marriage with Aisha yet. Mohammed told Abu Bakr that he had not been able to come up with money to pay for the marriage.[12] Abu Bakr contributed money from out of his personal funds and made clear the way for Mohammed to consummate his marriage with Aisha in Abu Bakr's house. Musnad 6:211 documents Aisha's recollection of her marriage to Mohammed when she was ten years old.

> My mother came to me and I was swinging on a swing...She brought me down from the swing, and I had some friends there and she sent them away, and she wiped my face with a little water, and led me till we stopped by the door, and I was breathless (from being on the swing) and we waited till I regained my breath. Then she took me in, and the Prophet was sitting on a bed in our house with men and women of the Ansar (Medinians) and she set me on his lap, and said, "These are your people. God bless you in them and they in you." And the men and women immediately arose and went out, and the Prophet consummated the marriage in our house.[13]

---

11. See Nabia Abbatt, *Aisha, the Beloved of Mohammed*, (Chicago: University of Chicago Press, 1942), p.3. Maxine Rodinson, *Mohammed*, trans. Ann Carter, (New York: Penguin Books, 1971), p.55.

12. It was customary during pre-Islamic days for the groom to pay "dowry" to the parents of the bride.

13. Quote taken from Leila Ahmed, *Women and Gender in Islam*, (New Haven; Yale University Press, 1992), p.51.

Aisha moved into Mohammed's house where Sawda had already been living. They were joined by several other wives and Mohammed's daughters who were born to Khadijah.

Polygamy was widely practiced in the Middle East during Pre-Islamic days. What Mohammed did was not something uncommon to the culture and the time in which he lived. Some of Mohammed's wives were daughters of his staunch supporters. Parents gave their daughters to Mohammed to establish a strong bond between the Prophet of God and them. It was during this time the Sura which supports polygamy was revealed. Mohammed said to his followers:

> Marry women of your choice, two or three, or four; but if ye hear that ye shall not be able to do justly (with them), then only one, or (a captive) that your right hands possess. That will be more suitable to prevent you from doing injustice (4:3).

Many of the widows had come from Mecca with their husbands to Medina following Mohammed. When their husbands were killed at the battle of Uhud, Mohammed took in more wives and encouraged Muslim men also to take in more wives and support them and their children.

In the early days, however, Muslim men who came from Mecca seldom married Medinan women. The Medinan women were more self-assured. They considered themselves on par with men by working side by side with their husbands in the fields and at home.[14] The Meccan women, being urban in background, were not used to being around with their husbands' businesses. The cultural and family practices among Medinan women also alienated Meccan men from entering into marital relationship. The Meccan women inherited half of their husband's or father's property as most of the asset was in cash or in business. Conversely, Medinan women were not used to such inheritance as their men's holdings were in landed property. Their land investments were passed on from father to son and then on to his male heirs. Such sole male propriety and ownership put the Meccan men in a disadvantaged position as they stood to lose so much by marrying a Medinan woman who would bring no immediate monetary gain into the family. Consequently, there existed a cultural and social hesitancy among Meccan men to marry Medinan women, and vice versa.

---

14. W. Montgomery Watt, *Muhammad at Medina*, p.381.

CHAPTER IV
Islam and Its Mission

Mohammed taught his followers to witness the *Shahada* and the oneness of God to people everywhere. In his farewell speech to his followers at Mina, the Prophet said that they should live together in unity and be obedient to Allah's commandments. They should never waver in their commitment to God and they must not wander away from the umma, the Islamic community. The Prophet reiterated in his message that they are Muslims and God had given them a new teaching in al-Islam which no other people have been fortunate to receive. After Mohammed's death, his followers were determined to emulate his lifestyle and adhere to his teachings. Leaders of the umma constantly reminded the Muslims of their mission in this world. The religious leaders of the community took every effort to further the message of the Quran through the collective endeavour of the umma.

The Quran teaches that the Muslims must establish the umma everywhere they go, make the nations aware of proper worship of god and bring the people of the whole world in the understanding of Allah's ways which were revealed through the teachings and life of the Prophet Mohammed. These goals can be achieved only through preaching, witnessing, and worshipping the One, Compassionate, and Merciful God.

The mission of the Muslims is built on the themes of *Dawa* and *Jihad*. *Dawa* means calling of the followers of Allah to witness and inviting of the non-believers to accept the path of Allah. *Jihad* means personal striving to be virtuous and absolute willingness to lay one's life on the line to defend Islam.

The Muslims are taught to emulate the life and example of Mohammed. The believers have been instructed that if they follow the path of Allah they will be rewarded with success in this life and endowed with pleasures to enjoy in the life to come. They are instructed to be spiritually watchful and religiously alert in order to maintain the purity of the revealed message. They are nurtured to believe that any threat to the Islamic umma or Muslim way of life must be taken seriously and strictly resisted.

The Islamic umma crosses national, cultural, and linguistic boundaries and fosters a deep sense of kinship among its believers. The Quran calls for its community to treat its fellow Muslims in love and care, and warns that "no one is a true believer who does not desire for his brother that which he desires for himself." The fellow Muslims are "naught else than brothers" (49:10). The Quran reminds the believers that all of them have a common experience of having been delivered from eternal damnation and having been brought together as one family by the grace of God. Mohammed admonished the believers in his farewell speech not to forget who they were before they became believers in Allah and how miraculously they were delivered by him before they were brought to a place of peace and prosperity : "Remember with gratitude Allah's favour on you; for you were enemies and He joined your hearts in love, so that by His grace, ye become brethren; and ye were on the brink of the pit of fire, and He saved you from it. Thus doth God make His signs clear to you: that ye may be guided" (Sura 3:103). Commenting on this parting words of Mohammed, Philip K. Hitti observes:

> By one stroke the most vital bond of Arab relationship, that of tribal kinship, was replaced by a new bond, that of faith. Herein lies one of the chief claims of Muhammed to originality. A sort of *Pax Islamica* was instituted for Arabia. The new community was to have no priesthood, no hierarchy, no central see.[1]

The umma does not allow its members to stray outside the fold of Muslim community nor does it permit anyone to embrace the teachings of other faiths. The umma strictly guards its doctrinal territory by protecting its scared creed from alien religious influence. It shields its divine worship from pagan influence and guards its members from renouncing Islam. Hence, Islam is branded by the critics as a one way religion. Muslims often hold that, "A Muslim who abandons Islam, whether or not he or she subsequently embraces another faith, is guilty of the crime of apostasy, which is punishable by death under Sharia law."[2] The Quran teaches that its message is for all - for those who are

---

1. Philip K. Hitti, *The Arabs: A Short History* (Chicago: Henry Regenry, 1943), p.40.

2. Abdulaziz A. Sachedina, "Freedom of Conscience and Religion in the Quran," in *Human Rights and the Conflict of Cultures: Western and Islamic Perspectives on Religious Liberty*, (Columbia, S.C.: University of South Carolina Press, 1988), p.67.

within and without the confines of the umma-, therefore, every Muslim
must strive to witness the path of Allah wherever he or she lives. In short,
Islam affirms that every Muslim is Allah's missionary.

Those who are converted to Islam must not live in isolation. They
should live together in harmony as one family, regardless of national or
racial differences. The Quran upholds this in saying :

> And verily this brotherhood of yours is a single brotherhood,
> and I am your Lord and Cherisher : therefore fear Me (and no
> other). But people have cut off their affair (of unity), between
> them, into sects : each party rejoices in that which is with itself
> (Sura 23: 52-53).

Whenever Muslims get together, the Quran exhorts, they must
worship Allah, for Allah himself has said, "I created the Jinn and
humankind only that they might worship Me" (Sura 51:56). Worshipping
Allah as a community is an essential ritual and an imperative command.
Mohammed witnessed in the Quran, "Lo! my worship and my sacrifice
and my living and my dying are for Allah, Lord of the Worlds. He hath
no partner. This am I commanded, and I am first of those who surrender
(unto Allah)" (Sura 6:163-164). The Quran commands that the family
of Allah must constantly expand in concentric circles until the whole
world is encompassed as the Islamic umma. Bernard Lewis comments
that the guidance given to Muslims to live in equality has been taken
seriously by the Muslim community. They practice the directions of the
Quran wherever they go or live. Lewis writes, "...the phrase ascribed to
the Prophet, 'I was sent to the red and the black' [is] an expression taken
to embrace the whole of [humanity]" and they follow it with utter
sincerity.

The Islamic umma is a combination of the "House of Islam" *(Dar
Al-Islam)*, which serves as the house of justice and peace, and a
"community of conscience" (Dar Al-Adl-Islam), which cares for the
needs of Allah's servants. Outside the umma is "the house of war" *(Dar
Al-Harb)*, which is inhabited and dominated by non-Muslims who are
considered infidels and enemies of Allah. Consequently, Islam exists in
a state of perpetual tension until the whole of humanity is brought to
submission to Allah's will. The striving to maintain its own identity as
umma and its struggle to witness the name of Allah has kept the Islamic
community in ceaseless spiritual jihad from the beginning of time.

---

3. Bernard Lewis, *Race and Color in Islam* (New York: Harper and Row, 1971), p.19.

Islam presents itself as the true religion. All other religions have been accused of having been broken into sects and divisions, and they are denounced as having lost the revelation given to them. Islam is exalted as a faith that restores the unbroken, primordial relationship which existed between God and his creation at the garden of Eden.

Islam discredits the Judeo-Christian concept of sin. Islam teaches that human beings are not inherently sinful. Consequently, Islam undermines the need for Christ's incarnation and his atoning death on the cross. Salvation can be experienced neither by confession of sin nor by the shedding of blood by substitutionary sacrifice, but only by the confession of Shahada and by submission to Quranic teachings. Salvation comes not by memorizing a set of creeds nor by trusting in a catalogue of rules, but by the obedience of God's commandments as revealed through the Prophet.

The call to absolute obedience and toal submission begins with proper worship. Islam alone offers the correct form of worship, which is called *Ibadah*. It demands that Muslims trust Allah, take refuge in Him (Sura 114:1-2), offer prayers for others (Sura 1:1-4), and feel sorry for their sins of disobedience (Sura 39:54). Belief in Allah demands that a Muslim make a public and oral confession. God's favour cannot be obtained through rituals or sacrifices. Allah is Compassionate and Merciful, and he will bestow his mercies upon any one who submits and turns to him in worship.

The members of the umma are expected to practice communal and corporate worship on Fridays in a mosque led by the Imam (the leader in worship). It is obligatory for every Muslim to attend. On other days, the Muslims can pray from anywhere facing toward Kaaba in Mecca five times a day as stipulated in the Hadith.

The Divided Umma : Shiites and Sunnis

The successors of Mohammed called themselves *Khalifat Rasul Allah* (in English it is called Caliphate, successor to the Messenger of Allah), who combined both the political and religious offices of the umma as their predecessor Mohammed did. They organized themselves into a religio-political state with an ideology of their own, under the rubrics of Islam. Within a few decades after the death of Mohammed, Arab Muslim warriors invaded the neighbouring states, which had been highly advanced in cultural and social aspects, and subdued them. In the East, the Muslim troops challenged the Sassanian Empire from Iraq as far as eastern Iran and brought it to an end. In the West, the troops challenged by Byzantium provinces of the Near East, conquered a vast area of that territory. The newly found religious fervour, combined with the ancient enmity against the imperial powers, enabled the Muslim warriors both to control the neighbouring states and deplete their riches. Under the Caliphs of the Umayyad dynasty, the army reached as far as the Atlantic and the Indus valley by 711 CE.

As the Muslims were enlarging their territories through invasion, the umma was divided into two major groups. The division occurred not over theological or paradigmatic issues but over the question of succession after Mohammed and the issue of leadership over the umma. A few years after the death of Mohammed, the umma split into two major groups : Shiite Muslims and Sunni Muslims.

One group of Muslims, who later called themselves Shiites (derived from an Arabic word meaning "partisans"), insisted that the head (Caliph) of the umma should be a descendant of Prophet Mohammed. They called themselves conservative and devout Muslims. They wanted Ali ibn abi-talib, Mohammed's son-in-law, to be the successor and leader of the umma.[4] Ali was married to Fatimah, Mohammed's youngest and favourite daughter, born to Khadijah. Ali was also Mohammed's first cousin. Shiites contended that Ali had acquired Mohammed's charisma and charm, which he would be able to transmit to his descendants if he would become the next Caliph after Mohammed. They asserted Mohammed himself chose Ali to be his successor "through designation (Nass) and personal legacy (Wasiyya) as the spiritual leader (imam) and head of theocracy. The 'light' of divine inspiration passed from Mohammed to him and then to his corporeal and spiritual successor."[5] But others, who called themselves Sunnis and orthodox in conviction made Abu Bakr, a close companion of Mohammed, as the immediate successor to Mohammed.

Abu Bakr led the umma for two years and then he died (632-634 CE). During his reign, Abu Bakr expanded the umma by invading the city of Iraq (Hira), Syria and the neighbouring countries and looting them

---

4. The Shiites maintain a long succession of religious heritage and close solidarity beginning with Ali to the modern day Imams. They preserve the official list of those who should lead the Muslim community and instruct the believers in spiritual and secular matters.

5. Endress, An Introduction to Islam, p. 36

in 633 CE). He brought the spoils to the umma and distributed them among the believers.

Abu Bakr was followed by Umar ibn al-Khattab (634-644 CE), who completed the conquest of Syria in the battle of Yarmuk in 636 CE after crushing the Byzantine army. By 638 CE., Umar was able to expand the Muslim territory to Damascus, Antioch, Jerusalem, and the whole of Syria. Then he challenged the Persians at the battle of Niharand and defeated them. After subduing the Persians, Umar turned his attention on Egypt in 639 CE and conquered it in 642 CE. Umar was the first Caliph to expand the Islamic umma far and well beyond the confines of Arabia. Lewis aptly captures and presents the political mood of the mid-seventh century Arabia.

> The Arab conquests and the creation of the Islamic caliphate brought together the eastern and western halves of the Middle East for the first time since the death of Alexander the Great. The Persian Empire was overthrown and its territories absorbed in their entirety. The Byzantine Empire remained standing, but was reduced to Anatolia and southeastern Europe. Syria, Palestine, Egypt, and North Africa were conquered, and their Jewish communities, now joined to those of Iraq and Iran, formed the overwhelming majority and also the most advanced and active part of the Jewish people.[6]

However, Umar's reign over the umma was not peaceful and chaos-free. He introduced a new and controversial edict which produced a new social class among the Arab Muslims. The edict gave privilege and entitlement to the early converts, the Muslim migrants from Mecca to Medina, and all those who had close association with Mohammed. The edict not only divided the community but also caused dissension among the Muslims.

Umar sanctioned state pensions for the wives of Mohammed, who were called "the Mothers of the Faithful." Aisha, the youngest and the favourite wife of Mohammed, was given the highest pension. Aisah was regarded as the fountain of resource to the Muslim community who shared with them about Mohammed's character, teachings, and practices which were all later collected and included in the Sunna.

---

6. Lewis, *The Jews of Islam*, pp. 75-76.

Umar introduced another controversial law by preventing women from going to the mosque, which, he later compromised by creating a separation for women to worship in the mosque and by appointing women imams to minister to women. A few women who served as imams in early Muslim history were : Umm Waraka, Aisha and Salama. After their death, women imams disappeared.

During Uthman ibn 'Affan's reign (644-656), the army moved westward to challenge and defeat the tough Roman army. Some of the islands in the Mediterranean were captured by Uthman's soldiers. In 649 CE Cyprus was taken, followed by Rhodes and Crete. He restored women's freedom and abolished all the restrictions imposed by his predecessors.

Uthman was a member of the Banu Umayya clan of Mecca and the only one to have converted to Islam during the turbulent Meccan years. He was known as a pious man and he was attributed with the title "the rightly guided one." Nevertheless, Uthman was not able to command the respect of the umma for too long. His caliphate was surrounded by controversy and nepotism. The major achievement of his reign was the establishment of a committee of scholars to collect all the available copies and variants of the Quran, and to produce a standard text which is still used to date. Uthman's reign was short lived as he was murdered at his residence in Medina in 656 CE. When he was assassinated, Aisha went to the mosque, veiled, and gave a rousing speech and declared Uthman's murder would certainly be avenged.

Ali ibn abi Talib, Mohammed's son-in-law, was selected as the fourth Caliph and successor of Uthman in 656 CE. Ali was falsely accused of having a part in the murder plot of Uthman. However, he successfully managed to control all the opposition and effectively brought the umma under his rule. Ali moved the capital from Medina to Kufa, a new military settlement at the desert's edge near the Euphrates river in Iraq. His leadership was surrounded with uncertainty, confusion, riot, and turmoil right from the beginning. Ali's caliphate was challenged by Aisha, Talha, al-Zubayr, and several others who were closely associated with Mohammed and his successors. Aisha planned and led an army of soldiers to fight Ali in 656 CE. In order to challenge Ali, Aisha herself went to the battle field and gave instructions to the soldiers while sitting on a camel. Despite her efforts, Aisha's soldiers were routed by Ali's army. Talha and al-Zubayr were killed. Ali cut off the hoofs of the camel on which Aisha was observing and directing the battle.

Ali's power as a single, strong Caliph was only short lived. Muawiya, a nephew of Uthman and the governor of Damascus (Syria), rebelled against Ali and challenged him at the Battle of Siffin on the upper Euphrates in 657 CE. Muawiya challenged Ali's political and military might. After fruitless negotiations and a long battle, Ali's enemies, with the encouragement of Amr ib al-'As (the ruler of Egypt) raised the pages of the Quran on their spears and called for arbitration "according to the will of God." Ali, despite opposition from his supporters, agreed to arbitration. The experts on both sides negotiated and Ali was not satisfied with the outcome. Amr, who argued in favour of Muawiya, forced Ali to adhere to the arbitration which both parties had agreed upon. As a result, Ali was bound to rule a tumultuously weakened umma which was chaotically divided by the Umayyads and Shiites. Shortly, thereafter, the leaders of Kuta rebelled and said they would not accept Ali or Muawiya as their Caliph. A few months later, in 661 A.D. Ali was assassinated by a rebellious member of the newly formed Kharijites.

Before Ali died, he named his eldest son, Hassan, to be his successor. Hassan could not stand the forces of Muawiya and moved to Medina on a state pension where he was poisoned to death. Hassan named his brother Hussein as his successor before he moved to Medina. Hussein, nonetheless, was murdered shortly after assuming the leadership of the umma.

In the place of Ali and his sons, Muawiya emerged as the unopposed ruler of the umma. The Kharijites declared they would not accept any human agent or mortal government to direct them in spiritual or political matters, be it Ali or Muawiya. They claimed human conscience alone should guide the believers and common tradition alone should serve as the bench mark of the community. They fostered the idea that anyone who disrupts the umma should be removed or killed without any retribution from the believing community.

A group of Muslims who had seen the illegitimate ascension of Muawiya and the violent massacre of Ali's sons opposed the chaos, bloodshed, and irregularity, which surrounded the umma and drifted from the main stream Islamic community. The Kharijites strengthened their own umma and paid no attention to the orthodox Caliph nor the sunna, which the Sunni Muslims revered. The Kharijites strictly followed the Shariah mysticism which anthropomorphized God. They had their own religious slogan : there is no judgment except that of Allah (La Hukum

Illa Li-Allah). The Kharijites gave prominence only to the Quran and its teachings and hence they were also called the Scripturist Party.

As soon as Ali was murdered, Muawiya took control of his home province of Syria and became its leader. Then he invaded Kufa in Iraq, the cardiovascular power centre of Ali, and emerged as the sole leader. He consolidated his power base by putting down or deporting the rebel leaders, and established a strong Umayyad dynasty which lasted until 750 CE. Muawiya ruled and controlled the political and economic affairs of the umma, first as governor of Syria, and then as Caliph for the next forty years. Muawiya was the first to become the Caliph of the Umayyad dynasty and the first to establish the capital in Damascus, Syria. The Umayyad dynasty ruled for ninety years. History had thus come full circle. The old Meccan Qurayish nobility finally came back in power and took control of the Islamic umma once again.

Shiite Doctrine of Twelve Imams and the Mahds

After Ali's death, his followers elected his oldest son Hassan as Caliph but he was poisoned by his opponents at Medina shortly after. Then his younger brother, Hussein, counting on the help and support of the people of Kufa rebelled against Muawiya and attempted to become the Caliph. The Kufites abandoned Hussein and his supporters at the last minute, and refused to fight against Muawiya. Without the help of the people of Kufa, Hussein could not withstand the powerful onslaught of Muawiya's Syrian army led by Yazid, Muawiya's son. Hussein and his soldiers lost the battle. Hussein was eventually murdered at Karbala in 681 CE. Thus, Ali's family lost both of his sons born to Fatimah.

The Shiites commemorate the death of Hussein as a passion play called "Consolation" *(Tazia)* on the tenth day of the first month of the year in Iraq, Iran, Lebanon, East Africa, Pakistan, and India. The entire commemoration is observed in the Muslim calendar as Muharram. The Muslims' abandonment of Hussein's army in its effort to fight the enemy forces has been considered the great betrayal in Islamic history. The Muslims consider the duplicity tantamount to Judas' betrayal of Jesus at the Garden of Gethsemane. Hussein is considered a great martyr for the Muslims' cause. In order to vindicate their ancestors' act of betrayal and abandonment of Mohammed's own grandson Hussein, during Muharram, some Shiites scourge themselves publicly.

Shiites have made the Karbala, the tomb of Hussein, and Mashdad in Iran where Ali Rida, the eighth Imam, was buried as sacred spots and pilgrim centres apart from Mecca, Medina, and Jerusalem. Of all the Muslim martyrs, Hussein has been esteemed the most high and considered the paradigm of the affliction of the virtuous. Frederick M. Denny writes :

> [Hussein became] the prototype of the suffering righteous person, whose wounds would be used by God to redeem the Shiites if they sustained their faith and dedication to what they consider to be true Islam. The martyrdom of [Hussein] and ritual repetitions of it by means of the taziya sacred drama are finally not tragic at all; rather, they are a persistent showing forth of victorious faith in God's ultimate vindication similar to the expression of the battered and humiliated Old Testament figure Job, who declared as his lowest point, 'I know that my Redeemer lives, and that on the latter day he will stand upon the earth.'[7]

Ali's followers regrouped themselves and formed Shiat Ali (the party of Ali) to avenge the death of Ali and his sons. The party of Ali came to be known as the Shiites. The Shiites refused to accept the leadership of Muawiya and maintained a separate lineage of spiritual authority and political direction starting from Ali and his martyred sons. The orthodox Sunni Muslims denied the Shiite derivation of authority by making Muawiya as the legitimate successor of Ali, the Caliph and the fifth Imam of the umma. The disagreement between the Shiites and the Sunnis over the issue of leadership resulted in a major divergence of theological and ideological conviction within the Muslim community.

One of the important doctrinal beliefs of the Shiites is twelve Imams have watched over the destiny and welfare of the Islamic umma since the death of Ali. The twelfth Imam disappeared into the mosques of Samara (Iraq) in 878 CE., and is believed to be still alive. From his hiding, the Imam guides the believers in the path of al-Islam.[8] He will

---

7. Frederick M. Denny, *Islam and the Muslim Community,* (San Francisco: Harper, 1987), p.97.

8. There are some Shiites who believe only in seven imams and they are called seveners or Ismailis. The name "Ismailis" was given to the seveners as there were some who supported Ismail's son Mohammed as the seventh imam instead of Musa al-Kazin. Both seveners and twelfers wait for the last imam to reappear. However, those who believe in seven imams are small in number.

return during the "end of days" to escort the faithful to the Paradise. The Shiites who believe in the twelfth imam to be the last are called *Ithra Asharis* (the Arabic word for twelve). The Shiites have developed their own tradition, theology, imamology, and chronology which reached the zenith by the development of philosophical theology and Nasir al-Din Tusi (1273 CE). Shiite traditions say the twelfth Imam was Mohammed al-Mutaza, who was known as the "hidden" Imam and al-Mahdi. The hidden Imam is ageless and sin-free. The Shiites are eagerly waiting for his return. The list of twelve Imams is as follows:

1. 'Ali ibn abi Talib (661 CE) buried in Najaf, Iraq.

2. Hassan ibn 'Ali (669 CE) buried in Medina.

3. Hussein ibn 'Ali (680) (Ali's second son) buried in Karbala, Iraq. The most important shrine of all.

4. 'Ali Zayn al-'Abidin (Hussein's son, 712 CE) buried in Medina.

5. Muhammad al-Baqir (Zayn's son, 731 CE) buried in Medina.

6. Jafar as-Sadiq (Muhammad's son 765 CE) buried in Medina.

7. Musa al-Kazim (Jafar's son, 799 CE) buried in Kazimayn in Baghdad.

8. 'Ali al-Rida (Musa's son, 818 CE) buried in Mashhad, Iran.

9. Muhammad al-Taqi al-Jawad ('Ali's son, 835 CE) buried in Kazimayn, Baghdad.

10. 'Ali al-Hadi (Muhammad's son, 868 CE) buried in Samarra', Iraq.

11. Hasan al-'Askari ('Ali's son, 873 CE) buried in Samarra', Iraq.

12. Muhammad al-Mahdi al-Muntazar, Hasan's son, born in 868 CE but disappeared from the world when his father was killed in 873 CE., and is expected to return at the end of time as Mahdi ("the awaited one"). He is considered al-Qa'im, the permanent imam until the end of time.

When the hidden Imam comes back, the world and its inhabitants would be prepared for the day of judgment. Shiites believe, the Imam would reappear in the role of the messianic Mahadi (the divinely guided one), "to restore true Islam, to lead the righteous into battle against the evil ones, and to conquer the whole world to usher in a short millennium before the end of all things."[9] The good will triumph over evil and the Imam will be able to rule over the world in peace and truth.

At last, the Imam will be able to guide the whole world in following Allah without any impediment. Until the hidden imam reappears, leaders within the Shiite community will be guiding the people. In his article in the *International Bulletin of Missionary Research*, Kenneth Cragg summarizes the historic belief of the Shiites and the political practices of some Muslim nations.

> Since the ninth century C.E. the majority of Shiites believes that the twelfth imam in succession to Ali exists in the invisible state of occultation (rayba), hidden from sight as the sun behind a cloud, but no less the source of light and spiritual guidance. The theory of Shiite religous leadership involves a hierarchy of 'clergy' who receive and apply the guidance of the Hidden Imam as the infallible source of quranic interpretation for the direction of the Muslim community. This will pertain until the coming messianic age, when the imam will return to earth to establish a truly righteous society before the arrival of the Last Day.

> At the end of this clerical hierarchy…stand the ayatollahs-the 'signs of God' upon the earth. The most senior ayatollahs reside in the Shiite holy places in Iraq, associated with the martyrdom of Ali's son Hussain, killed by a Sunni army. It was during his exile in Iraq that Ayatollah Khomeini gave a famous series of lectures in which he developed his politicojuristic doctrine of the vilaya *al-Faqih*, or 'authority of the religious jurist,' in which he advocated the subordination of the religious scholar *(Faqih)*. His later success in marshalling Iranian resentments in revolution against the shah returned him triumphantly to Iran in 1979, and the new Islamic constitution established this doctrine at its core.[10]

---

9. Jaroslav Krejci, *The Human Predicament : Its Changing Image (A Study in Comparative Religion and History)*, (New York: St. Martin's Press, 1991), p.72.

10. Kenneth Cragg, "The Riddle of Man and the Silence of God; A Christian Perception of Muslim Response", *International Bulletin of Missionary Research*, October 1993, pp. 171-172.

The Shiites today are scattered all over Asia as active minority communities with large pockets of population living in Iran, Iraq, India, and Lebanon. The Shiites make up about ten percent of the entire Muslim population. Each of these scattered groups, at one time or another, had their glory, and dominated the political and cultural spheres of the Middle East. The most prominent are the Fatimids of the tenth and eleventh centuries, the Druses of modern Lebanon and Syria, the followers of Agha Khan, or the Nizarite Ismailians of Pakistan, India, and East Africa.

The two notable groups that existed within Fatimids were the Bhoras and the Ismailites under the Agha Khan. The groups came into being in the eleventh century A.D. when the question of succession rose among the ranks of Ismailites. One group supported the claims of al-Mustali as the successor of his father and in becoming Fatimid Caliph of Egypt. And another group supported his brother, Nizar. Those two groups were most powerful during the Middle Ages and they kept the vast Muslim empire under their control for several centuries.

The Shiite groups attribute superhuman qualities to their Imams and believe they were uniquely created by God. The Imams are held in high esteem as they are considered the successors of the prophets who share in the praise and blessing with God. Mahmoud Ayoub says :

> [The Imams were created] as a principle of order, harmony and goodness in the world; then they were made substantial as luminous entities or conventicles of light transmitted in the loins of prophets and wombs of holy women until they reached actualization in the Prophet Muhammad. They were then born as men through the 'prince of the Faithful' and first Imam, Ali, and his wife, Fatimah, the daughter of Muhammad...Unlike other men, the imams were shaped not of the dust of the earth, but were first created as forms of light singing the praises of God long before the material world came into being.[11]

The Imams guide the believers by interpreting the law of God and directing the community to deeper spiritual paths of Islam. The spiritual leaders of the Shiites teach that an Imam will be present in the world until the end of time and will continue to receive inspiration (rather than revelation) from God so that they might watch over the umma and guide them in truth.

---

11. Mahmoud Ayoub, *Redemptive Suffering in Islam : A Study of the Devotional Aspects of 'Ashura' in Twelver Shiism*, (New York: Mouton Publishers, 1979), pp.54-55.

The Imams are esteemed not only as sinless and the best of God's creation, but also pre-existent. Thus, according to Andrew Rippin, the Shiites take the Imams as "part of God's beneficence toward humanity [who] facilitate the salvation of God's creation by providing a sure guide in the world and a certain answer to issues of dispute."[12]

The modern day Shiites are divided on doctrinal and political grounds into several small sects. Jaroslav Krejci aptly summarizes the cause of the rift between the two major Islamic groups, the Fatimids and the Druses, in a larger theological and religious context.

> There is no other great religion in the world where a similar situation would receive such overriding consideration as to become a cause for schism. The rejection of Ali's descendants for the office of Caliph resulted not only in the recognition of another lineage of religious leaders, the imams, but in rejection of the whole *Sunna* tradition. In their frustration, the Shiites went so far as to extend the basic article of faith (that there is no other god than God and Muhammad is his Prophet) with the statement that 'Ali, the Prince of the faithful, is associate to God' *(Wali Allah).*[13]

The Sunnis, on the other hand, believe that the leadership in the umma should arise out of the consensus of the members of the community and the conduct outlined in the Sharia, the Law of Allah. Rippin recapitulates the beliefs and practices of Sunni Islam :

> The focal point of law in Islam is the sunna, the concept of the practice of Muhammad, as embodied in the hadith and transmitted faithfully by Muhammad's followers through the succeeding generations down to the present. The sunna presents, for the individual Muslim, the picture of the perfect way of life, the imitation of the precedent of Muhammad who was the perfect embodiment of the will of God. The hadith reports are the raw material of the sunna, and must be sifted through by jurists in order to enunciate the details of rightful practice; the sharia is the "way of life" for the Muslim which has been

---

12. Rippin, *Muslims: Their Religious Beliefs and Practices*, Vol.1, p.107.

13. Jaroslav Krejci, *The Human Predicament: Its Changing Image (A Study in Comparative Religion and History)*, (New York: St. Martin's Press, 1991), p.72.

developed by the Muslim jurists on the basis of certain jurisprudential principles, the *Usual al-Fiqh*.[14]

The Sunnis recognize the legitimacy of the first four caliphs, Abu Bakr, Umar, Uthman, and Ali. Before making any legal decision, the Sunnis consult the Quran, the tradition of the Prophet *(Sunna)*, the analogy *(Qiyas)*, and the unanimous counsel *(Ijma)* of the umma as interpreted by Islamic scholars, who have "the power to bind and to loosen." The Quran and the Sunna provide the material basis for the *Qiyas* to operate. Rippin says, "The vast majority of laws have, in fact, been fashioned by *Qiyas* because the Quran and the sunna provide a fairly limited selection of detailed legal provisions."[15]

Qiyas works only when the jurists find the commonality of a documented case and the case presented before them. The Sunni jurists have to use the method of deduction and present the evidence and case in point to the consensus of the umma, which upon approval of the community becomes the law. The Sunnis are divided into smaller groups, the predominant Hanafites, Shafites and Hanbalites.

The question of the authority and leadership has divided the modern Muslim world politically. Most of the Muslims in Iran are Shiites and a majority of Muslims in Iraq are Sunnis. The Shiites and Sunnis have developed their own brand of theological and legal institutions which continue to foster their religious ideologies to the umma around the world. The Sunnis and Shiites have many hadiths that are common to both traditions. The Shiites, however, have included a collection of traditions that contains stories about the Prophet Mohammed's family. Despite all the exiting differences between these two groups, one must bear in mind that both Shiites and Sunnis are Muslims. Both of them follow the same Quran, observe the identical Five Pillars of Islam, and practice the similar legal and liturgical instructions given by their Prophet.

14. Rippin, *Muslims: Their Religious Beliefs and Practices*, Vol.1, p.75.
15. Ibid., p.80

CHAPTER V
Islam and the Doctrine of God

The word Islam in Arabic means a practice of faith, not a precept or a set of beliefs. Islam is a culture of a community and an exercice of religion. Islam, according to the Muslims, is not a new religion but reckoning with God, a way of life, and a final revelation given to Mohammed to restore monotheism. The purpose of Islam, consequently, is to bring people back to worship the Creator God with whom the believers have made a covenant of allegiance *(Mithaq)*. The term Islam also means total submission to the will of Allah, who is the only true God. The term Muslim means the one who actively submits. The words Islam and Muslim do not represent the name of the founder of the religion or the place of its origin. The Muslims are prohibited to worship any idol and forbidden to bow before any human made image. They are instructed not to keep or revere the pictures or images of Mohammed or any other saint of Islam.

Islam is distinct from other religious faiths. Islam presents itself as the correction and fulfillment of the earlier revelations given to Jews and Christians (Sura 5:20, 3:48-49). Islamic religious practices are, therefore, defined against Judaism and Christianity. Consequently, Islam repudiates the Jewish and Christian scriptures, their religious ceremonies, and liturgical practices. Islam also disclaims the Christian notion of the Incarnation, the view of the Trinity, the doctrine of the Justification of believers by faith, the arrival of the Holy Spirit on the Day of Pentecost, the Christian notion of the Church and its administration of the Sacraments.

The Quran, however, does not totally reject the revelation given in the Bible. Rather, it professes to correct and perfect it. The Quran is acclaimed by Muslims to be the most sacred book on earth as it is an exact replica of a pre-existing heavenly tablet which the Prophet was able to read and recite with the help of angel Gabriel (Sura 13:38-39). This belief runs contrary to the revelation the Hebrew prophets and Jesus' apostles received from God. For instance, the ten commandments and the Law were revealed to Moses who wrote them down in his own words. So did the later prophets and apostles with the inspiration they received from God. Conversely, Islam asserts Mohammed was able to see the heavenly tablet, read, and recite God's words in its original form to his people, and hence his revelation was superior and sacred. Islam also maintains that the Arabic language is the most sacred language on earth as the Quran in heaven has been written in that language.

The Quran speaks in clear terms of the supremacy of Islam over all other religions and the universality of Mohammed's message over all other revelations. The Quran says :

> We have sent thee not, except to mankind entire, good tidings to bear , and warning; but most men do not know it (Sura 34:27).

In the Quran, the term Islam occurs twice in late Meccan Sura: first, in Sura 6:125 and secondly in Sura 39:23. The Medinite Suras emphasize the authenticity of Islam and the exaltation of its teachings. The Quran declares:

> The true religion with God is Islam *(Sura 3:17)*.
> Whoso desireth any other religion than Islam, that religion shall not be accepted from him *(Sura 3:79)*.
> It is my pleasure that Islam be your religion *(Sura 5.5)*.
> Who doth greater wrong than one who invents falsehood against Allah, even as he is being invited to Islam? And Allah guides not those who do wrong *(Sura 61.7)*.
> We profess Islam *(Sura 49.14)*.

Islam encompasses a complete way of life, and it does not dichotomize human life into secular and sacred, or private and public as God is ruler of every thing. Legislative sanctions to withstand the enemies of Allah are found in abundance in the Quran. It approves that any impediment to the Muslim way of life, religious or moral, must be met with as utmost disobedience.

Islam as a religion and a way of life is different from other faiths. Abd al-Rahman Azzam epitomizes the theological concept of Islam and summarizes the quintessence of Muslim practice.

> Islam is different from Judaism; Islam, being a universal submission to God, has no concept of a particular covenant or

a specially chosen people. It also differs from the Christian view of the Kingdom of God in heaven and the separate kingdom of Caesar on earth. And, it differs from other religions, such as Buddhism and Hinduism. Islam is a faith, a law, a way of life, a "nation," and a "state," with a system of jurisprudence that is constitutionally evolving for the administration of this world and the satisfaction of human needs under the sovereignty of our Creator. Islam's Kingdom of God on earth, with its faith, its laws, piety, rituals, society, and state, is the prelude and the means to the after life.[1]

The sovereignty of God and the freedom of will for humanity are affirmed in equal terms in Islam. Everything comes from God and human beings are free to choose whatever they would like to do. Human beings are, consequently, held accountable for their actions. Non-Muslims are the unbelievers who disobey Allah willfully, and they deceive both God and themselves. They will stand before God on the Day of Judgment and receive punishment for their sin of disobedience.

Anyone who worships Allah, who believes in the Quran, and who acknowledges the Prophethood of Mohammed is considered a Muslim. One does not have to go through any ritualistic initiation or submit to any ceremonious order of service in order to become a Muslim. Islam does not have sacraments, and therefore, it does not practice baptism. The following often quoted Quranic verse summarizes the faith and precept of the Muslim community :

> It is not righteousness that ye turn your faces toward East or West; but it is righteousness— to believe in God and the Last Day, and the angels, and the book, and the messengers; to spend of your substance, out of love for Him, for your kin, for orphans, for the needy, for the wayfarer, for those who ask, and for the ransom of slaves; to be steadfast in prayer, and practice regular charity; to fulfil the contracts which ye have made; and to be firm and patient, in pain (or suffering) and adversity and throughout all periods of panic. Such are the people of truth, the God-fearing (Sura 2:177).

The Allah of the Quran is "the Lord of the Worlds" and there is nothing outside the domain of his sovereign will. He is known by ninety-

---

1. Abd al-Rahman Azzam, *The Eternal Message of Muhammad*, trans. by Caesar E. Farah, (Cambridge : The Islamic Texts Society, 1993), pp.xix-xx.

nine other names and they are divided under four categories based on the personality of God: (a) Names of the qualities of God *(Asma As-Sijat)*; (b) Names of the essence of God, *(Asma Adh-Dhat);* (c) Names of majesty *(Jalal)*; and, (d) Names of beauty. All the above names are collectively known as "The Most Beautiful Names," *(Al-Asma As-Husna)*. The most frequently mentioned name for Allah in the Quran is "The Merciful One" which represents the person and character of Allah himself.

Islamic history shows that pledges, treaties, and agreements were often drawn in the name of Allah the Merciful. Mohammed was the one who gave the sub-title to God "Allah the merciful" on account of his immense mercy and enormous compassion upon his people.[2] Islam teaches six major articles of faith which serve as a guide to every God-fearing Muslim :

1. Belief in one God, Allah (divine unity, *Tawhid*).

2. Belief in angels who intercede for humanity.

3. Belief in the Quran.

4. Belief in the Prophets of Allah and the books that have been brought by them in the past. Accepting Mohammed as the Seal of the Prophets.

5. Belief in the resurrection, judgment, paradise, and hell.

6. Belief in divine decrees and predestination. No one but Allah knows how it operates. However, human beings are given enough freedom to make right or wrong decisions.

The Quran does not attempt to prove the existence of God; rather, it is regarded as self-evident. God is the creator of both celestial and terrestrial beings. The creation of angels out of light is a "strong tradition in Islam but it is not actually mentioned in the Quran".[3] The angels are immortal and sexless. They function as God's messengers and recorders. Some serve as bearers of the throne of God and others as agents to summon souls when their life on earth is over (Sura 40:7, 16:28-34). The angels also help the believers to win battles. Sura 3:124 says that the angels helped the Muslims to win the battle at Badr.

---

2. See Cyril Glasse, *The Concise Encyclopedia of Islam*, (San Francisco : Harper, 1991), p.37.

3. Rippin, *Muslims : Their Religious Beliefs and Practices*, vol.1. p.16.

The angels are categorized as Muslims and non-Muslims, who live in heaven or hell in accordance to their deeds (Sura 46:28-31). Angel Gabriel is called the Holy Spirit by the Muslims as he has been the instrument in bringing the divine message both to the prophets who lived before Mohammed and to the prophet himself. The Muslims also believe in the two guardian angels who accompany the believers all the time, on either side, both to protect and observe the believers' actions. Hence, the Muslims greet the angels on either side of them at the end of each prayer. However, no divine attributes nor any special honour have been offered to the angels so that they could be on par with Allah.

Next to the angels are ranked the jinns who are lower than the angels but higher than human beings. The jinns live in a different dimension. According to the Quran, unlike Adam, who was created out of clay (Sura 15:14, 26), the jinns were created out of fire (Sura 15:15, 27). The Quran says, "He created man from sounding clay like unto pottery, and He created jinns from fire free of smoke" (Sura 55:14, 15; &;12). Unlike the angels, jinns can take human form and behave like human beings. They may do good or evil, save or destroy, and be a friend or a foe. The jinns are also categorized as believers and unbelievers and they will also be judged by God on the Last Day

Like the Bible, the Quran also talks about the devil, the Great Satan, his rebellion against God, and his cunning devices to thwart God's order. Although Satan has been portrayed as the originator of evil in both the Bible and the Quran, the Quranic portrayal of Satan's interaction with Adam and Eve at the Garden of Eden is much different from the Genesis account. Satan is presented in the Quran as the leader of all fallen angels and jinns whom God will judge in the end of days.

The Quran discusses the last judgment, hell, and heaven in immense detail. Human beings will be judged by their actions. The Quran differentiates between hypocrites and true believers, and their respective kismet (fate) (Sura 2:263-267). The Quran vividly portrays the end result of people who obey and believe in God and those who trust in themselves (Sura 18:31-40). The end of days will be preceded by a short tumultuous period of persecution of the believers and restlessness of the inhabitants of the world. The believers will be abused and oppressed by the unbelievers. However, Allah will redeem his faithful and lead them to triumph in the end.

The advent of the final judgment will be accompanied by the sounding of the last trumpet, the bodily resurrection, the opening of books, the final verdict which are all explained in elaborate detail in the Quran. Heaven or hell would be the final destination for the jinns and humanity who did or did not do Allah's will. The Quran narrates, "And the trumpet shall be blown : That will be the day whereof warning (had been given). And there will come forth every soul: with each will be an (angel) to drive, and an (angel) to bear witness" (Sura 50:19,20). The final judgment will determine the ultimate fate of a human being.

The Islamic doctrine of eschatology emphasizes that the fate of individuals is decided right here on earth by the individuals themselves. Those who do "good deeds" and submit to Allah's commandments will share "the delights of Paradise." Those who fail to do so will suffer in a place where "the flare of sparks and fire" will torture them and "the seething bath" of hell will torment them night and day.

Human beings will be judged according to what is written in the Book of Deeds (Sura 45:29-30). The Quran uses the image of a scale which weighs the deeds of the believers and unbelievers (Sura 21:47). The Quran does not say explicitly if there will be an intercessor or a mediator available at paradise. However, some Muslim scholars claim that Mohammed will serve as an intercessor or at least as a mediator in the presence of Allah. They establish their argument based on the Quranic utterance, "No intercessor (can plead with him) except after his leave (hath been observed)" (Sura 10:3). Sufi theologian al-Ghazzali says that God has appointed Mohammed to intercede for whom he wills. Mohammed had accepted his position as an intercessor and declared that he would be the right person to intercede.[4]

Islam professes, all those who committed *Shirks* (the crime of setting other gods along side Allah) would suffer eternal damnation in the fires of hell. The Quran declares, "As those who reject faith…if they had everything on earth, and twice repeated, to give as ransom for the penalty of the Day of Judgment, it would never be accepted of them. Theirs would be a grievous penalty" (Sura 5:39). However, pardon is available for a sinner who repents and turns from his or her wicked ways to God "for God is oft-forgiving, Most Merciful" (Sura 5:42).

---

4. See Jane Idleman Smith, ed. *The Precious Pearl: A Transition from the Arabic*, (Missoula, Mt: Scholars Press, 1979), p.60.

Hell in the Quran is mentioned by different names : *Sair, Jahim, Jahannoh*. All of them in Arabic mean unquenchable pits of burning fire as defined in Sura 18:29. Commenting on the Sura, A. Yusuf Ali graphically illustrates the agonies of hell.

> Our choice in our limited free will involves a corresponding personal responsibility. We are offered the truth : again and again is it pressed as our attention. If we reject it, we must take all the terrible consequences which are prefigured in the fire of Hell. Its flames and roof will completely enclose us like a tent. Ordinarily there is water to quench the heat of thirst: here the only drink will be like molten brass, thick, heavy burning, sizzling. Before it reaches the mouth of the unfortunates, drops of it will scald their faces as it is poured out.[5]

Other forms of torture which will be inflicted upon the unbelievers include both mental and physical pain. The mental torment includes *Laza*, which stupefies the brain, and *Hutamah*, which gives agonizing mental torture. The Quran also refers to seven painful gates of hell through which the sinners will be led. There are nineteen wardens of hell who serve as posts to enable believers to choose hell or heaven.[6]

On the other hand, heaven is a place of joy and renunion. Heaven is explained in existential terms. Stuart Brown summarizes the Islamic understanding of heaven as a place where true believers will worship God :

> [They] will rest on silken couches with their wives of perfect purity and dark-eyed maidens, beside gardens watered by pleasant rivers. The Quran makes no promises specially to pious women except that the wine in Paradise is served by ever-youthful boys. Unbelievers and evil doers will be thrown into the fire of eternal torment. The most direct access to Paradise is martyrdom; otherwise, one must rely on God's mercy, which can be earned through repentance and right living. Muslims have always set great store by good works, principally observance of the duties prescribed by the Quran (prayer,

---

5. A. Yusuf Ali, *The Holy Quran : Text, Translation and Commentary*, p. 738.

6. Syed Mahmudunnasir, *Islam, Its Concept and History*, (New Delhi: Kitab Bhavan, 1981, pp. 30-32

fasting, alms, and prilgrimage) and abstention from such evils as wine, adultery, and usury.[7]

Of the blessings and the ecstasy of heaven, the Quran says:

> In Gardens of Bliss... (the believers will be) on thrones encrusted (with gold and precious stones), reclining on them, facing each other. Round about them will (serve) youths of perpetual freshness), with goblets, (shining beakers), and cups (filled) out of clean-flowing fountains : No after-ache will they receive therefrom, nor will they suffer intoxication. And with fruits, and that they may select; and the flesh of fowls, and that they may desire, and (there will be) companions with beautiful, big, and lustrous eyes... (They will be) among Lote-trees without thorns, among tall trees with flowers (or fruits) piled one above another, - in shade long extended, by water flowing constantly, and fruit in abundance... We have created (their companions) of special creation and made them virgin pure (and undefiled), beloved (by nature), equal in age,-for the companions of the Right hand (56:12-38).

The Quran uses "the garden" as a metaphor for paradise. The garden of the paradise is enclosed for believers and filled with rich foliage without any contaminating pollutant. Nothing harmful exists in the garden. No calamity will ever befall the believers who inhabit the place. The jubilation of the location is hard to imagine and difficult to articulate in words. Only those who experience the joys of paradise can fathom the exhilarating thrill of the garden's pleasure and the invigorating delight of its elation. Paradise is also referred to as the Garden of Eden where Adam and Eve lived prior to their Fall. The Quranic symbol of the Paradise with green shrubbery, flowering garden filled with flowing fountain and gentle breeze must indeed have been a soothing and refreshing experience to the Arabs who were always on the look-out for an oasis that would supply them rest and repose with cool water during their long trek across the scorching desert.

The inhabitants of the garden will enjoy the abundance of food, the pleasures of the family, and the plethora of entertainments in the natural setting of flowing rivers and splendid gardens. The Quran says that the

---

7. Stuart Brown, *The Nearest in Affection: Towards a Christian Understanding of Islam*, (Geneva: WCC Publications, 1994), p.11.

women (Hur) of the believers' family will also be in paradise.[8] The Arabic word, Hur has been translated by some as "beautiful damsels" and others as "our own wives". Contrary to the Christian concept of heaven as a place where no one marries nor given in marriage, the Quran offers an elaborate description of the material pleasures of Paradise.

Islamic Understanding of Christ and Allah

Islam upholds the One Eternal God who in Arabic is called Allah. Scholars of Islam argue that the English translation of Allah as God is inadequate. Allah is the Arabic word for God, and has been extensively used in pre-Islamic Arabia by all religious groups. The Arabic Christian Bible used Allah consistently when referring to God. The twelve million Arabic speaking Christians in the Middle East use Allah as an ordinary term for God, like Dieu in French or Gott in German.

Allah is provident and transcendent. No one can know him except to submit to his will and obey his commands as revealed in the Quran. The fundamental exercise of Islam, according to Endress is to acknowledge, "the glory and the inaccessible greatness of God... which includes both strict legal prescription and the mystical search for God".[9] The Quran says:

> God is the Light of the heavens and the earth. The parable of his light is as if there were a niche and within it a lamp. The lamp enclosed in glass. The glass is as if it were a brilliant star. Lit from a blessed tree, an olive, neither of the East nor of the West, whose oil is well-nigh luminous, though fire scarce touched it : Light upon light! God doth guide whom He will to his light : God doth set forth parables for men: and God doth know all things (Sura 24:35).

Allah is the Creator (al-khaliq), the Sustainer (al-razzaq) and the Sovereign God (al-malik). Since Allah has power (qadr) and authority (amr) over all of his creation, the Quran admonishes that the Muslims should accept Allah's supremacy and submit to his will (Sura 2:107, 217). Submission to Allah eliminates human loyalty to any other power in the world. By submitting to Allah, a believer acknowledges Islam's absolute monotheism and recognizes Muslims' unconditional loyalty to the

---

8. Hur can be translated as wives, sisters, mothers.

9. Endress, An Introduction to Islam, p.29.

teachings of the Quran. Yet, Islam affirms, this Sovereign God is also close to human beings. For the Quran says, God is nearer to believers "than the jugular veins" (Sura 50:15). The believers are admonished by Islamic leaders not to worship God to earn merits or to attain Paradise but for God's own sake. Therefore, Rabia, a female saint of Islam prayed:

> O God! if I worship Thee in fear of Hell, burn me in Hell; and if I worship Thee in hope of Paradise, exclude me from Paradise; but if I worship Thee for Thine own sake, withhold not Thine everlasting Beauty.[10]

As the Creator, Protector, and Sustainer of the world, Allah is actively involved in human history and he bestows compassion, mercy, and peace *(rahman and rahim)* to all of humanity (Sura 10:25). Human beings cannot know Allah, but Allah can see everything human beings do. The Quran states, "No vision can grasp Him, but His grasp is over all vision. He is above all comprehension, yet is acquainted with all things" (Sura 6:103). Muslims vehemently oppose the association of anything or anybody with Godhead, as it violates the fundamental tenet of Islam: "I witness there is no God but Allah."

Allah is the Creator and Sustainer of the universe and all that is in it. He created the universe in six days one by one with his command, "Be" and "there it was". "He is Who created the heavens and the earth in truth" (Sura 6:73).

> Lo! your Lord is Allah Who created the heavens and the earth in six days, then mounted He the Throne. He covereth the night with the day, which is in haste to follow it, and hath made the sun and the moon and the stars subservient by His command. His verily is all creation and commandment (Sura 7:54). He is Allah, the Creator, the Shaper out of naughts, the Fashioner. To Him belong the most beautiful names" (Sura 59:24).

Contrary to the Biblical creation narrative found in Genesis chapters 1 and 2, Allah did not rest on the seventh day after he originated the universe and everything in it in six days. The idea of God "resting" (Genesis 2:2) on the seventh day, according to Islamic teaching, reduces the potency of the Sovereign Lord of the universe into an ordinary creature who wears out in the end of performing a job.

---

10. Cited in Constance Padwick, *Muslim Devotions*, (London: S.P.C.K., 1961), p.5.

Allah has ordered everything according to season and needs. But, the kind and considerate Allah should be blessed and revered all the time. Human beings are expected to thank him for his generosity. Of the mercies of Allah, the Quran says:

> It is Allah Who has made the night for you, that you may rest therein, and the day, as that which helps (you) to see. Verily Allah is full of grace and bounty to men: "yet most men give no thanks" (Sura 40:61).

> It is Allah who made you the earth as a resting place and the sky as a canopy, and has given you shape and made your shapes beautiful, and has provided for you sustenance, of things pure and good; such is Allah your Lord. So glory to Allah, the Lord of the Worlds! (Sura 40:64).

The Creator of the universe is not a remote god who is totally cut off from the affairs of his creation. Rather, he cares about people who approach him in prayer and worship. He forgives those who turn to Him in repentance. "Allah will love you and forgive you your sins. For Allah is oft-forgiving, most Merciful" (Sura 3:31).

Allah gives or removes power to and from whom he wills. Allah is the "Grand Designer of human destiny." Allah alone is in-charge of the affairs of the universe. "Say: O Allah! Lord of Power (and Rule), Thou givest Power to whom Thou pleasest, and Thou strippest off Power from whom Thou pleasest: Thou enduest with honour whom Thou pleasest, and Thou bringest low whom Thou pleasest: In Thy hand is all good. Verily, over all things Thou hast power" (Sura 3:26). Therefore, the followers of Islam are instructed not to bow to earthly rulers in submission or adoration.[11]

In order to remind the believers about the nature of God and his concern for humanity, each chapter of the Quran begins with the appellation, "In the name of Allah, the Merciful and Compassionate." The Quran declares that Allah's mercy is showered upon every

---

11. Some scholars assume that this revelation was given to Mohammed mainly to warn the arrogant, mercantile Meccans of the impending judgment of God and his wrath upon them for their practice of polytheism. Mohammed's preaching against polytheism urged the merchants to repent of their evil conventions and return to praise only Allah's goodness, mercy and justice. Mohammed called the Meccans to exercise kindness and charity.

individual. "It is He who sends the winds like heralds of glad tidings, going before His mercy: when they have carried the heavy-laden clouds, We drive them to a land that is dead, make rain to descend thereon, and produce every kind of harvest therewith" (Sura 7:57). This Quranic reference comes very close to what Jesus has said in the Gospel that God sends "rain upon both the just and the unjust" (Matthew 5:45).

Words fall short in explaining Allah's attributes. He is eternal and self-subsisting. No anthropomorphic expressions could be attributed to Him. The magnificence of Allah is explained in the famous Quranic "*Verse of the Throne.*"

> God! There is no God, but He, - the Living, the self-subsisting eternal. No slumber can seize Him nor sleep. His are all things in the heavens and on earth. Who is there can intercede in his presence except as He permitteth?...His throne doth extend over the heavens and the earth, and He feeleth no fatigue in guarding and preserving them for he is the Most High, the supreme in glory (Sura 2:255).

The Quran does not make any reference to the ancient Asian religions such as Hinduism, Buddhism or Confucianism although Arabia had commercial and travel activities with the people of the East during Mohammed's time. For instance, the Syrians had their colonies in West India, which had a strong Hindu dynasty. Buddhism was present in Persia and the Oxus valley, and the caravan Meccans must have come in contact with them.

Nonetheless, those non-missionary ancient religions were confined, primarily, to the east of Arabia. Moreover, their scriptures were not popular outside of India or China, although some Indian fables of Bidpai had been translated into Persian. One must bear in mind, when Mohammed condemned the idolatrous practices in the Quran, he did not refer to the Hindu mythologies or their pantheon of gods but he referred mainly to the idols situated within the confines of the kaaba.

CHAPTER VI
Islam and Other Religious Faiths

When Muslims in Arabia became numerically large and politically powerful, the idolatrous Arabs renounced their traditional religions and accepted Islam as their own. Islam fostered a sense of national pride because of its successful military expeditions over the polytheists and the conquest of the powerful Christian quarters in the south, especially the Najran community. Muslims also nourished regional glory because God had revealed himself to one of their own. The umma gave a special identity to the formerly marginalized Bedouins and indigent rural Arabs in matters relating to religious, social, and political questions. Consequently, Islam became a fascinating religion to many in the oases and outskirts of Arabia.

Islam grew rapidly not only through conversion but also through political, diplomatic, and commercial means. After the death of Mohammed, Islam crossed the confines of Arabia and entered into Persia, Syria, Egypt, Turkey, North Africa through the Sudan and Ethiopia in the eighth century, and finally into Europe through Spain, Sicily and parts of France in eighth and ninth centuries. In the East, Islam spread its wings through commerce and military conquest. The Islamization of the East began with a unified front only when the leadership of the umma had passed from the hands of the Arabs into those of Turks, the Ottomans, after the annihilation of the Abbassid Caliphate in Baghdad. The Indian subcontinent was captured through military invasion.

The people in China, India, and Indonesia were intensely converted in the thirteenth and fourteenth centuries. The Hindus and Buddhists in India were denied of religious protection and they were forcefully converted as they were considered idolaters. Their temples were looted as they were perceived to nurse idol worship.

In India, many Hindus from the lower caste converted to Islam for fear of persecution from the hands of the Muslims as well as to escape from the oppressive forces of Hindu socio-religious hierarchy. However, the religious Hindus outnumbered the Muslim population. Consequently, the Muslim leaders had to seek the help of the high caste Hindus and appointed them to serve as officials and administrators in royal palaces and Muslim courts.

The high caste Hindus served as interpreters of local customs, religious laws, caste systems and social orders to the Muslim rulers. When the Muslim Mongols came to be rulers of the East from 1000 CE.-1500 CE., unlike their predecessors who were Arabs, the Mongols became more tolerant toward high caste Hindus and intermarried high caste Rajput princesses. Sequentially, Muslims became so tolerant of ancient religions in India that during the Mogul Emperor Akbar's time, he even attempted to create a syncretic religion called, *Din-Illahi*. Nonetheless, the Muslim tolerance of the local religions was short lived. Some of Akbar's successors like Aurangzeb were consumed with passion and zeal for Islam and once again began to persecute non-Muslims.

South East Asia (Malaysia, Indonesia, Brunei) and China were converted not by force but missionary and outreach efforts by the Muslim traders and itinerant preachers. One of the strongest groups of preachers who helped spread Islam in the South East Asia was the mystics (Sufis) of Islam. Their simple philosophy and popular belief in reaching the transcendent God through inner experience appealed to the vast majority of people in South and Far East Asia. In Singapore, Malaysia and Indonesia, conversion to Islam was carried out mainly through trade and marriage alliances. Indian Muslim traders (Gujaratis and Tamils) in Malaysia and Indonesia spread Islamic doctrines without disturbing the existing beliefs and traditions. It resulted in extensive inclination toward syncretism and tolerance for other beliefs.

During the expansion of Islam from the Middle East toward Far East Asia, the number of Christian communities on its path began to dwindle. The once strong Nestorian Church in the East, especially along the Silk Route, eventually disappeared. The church's long isolation from Byzantine and other major Christian centres, and the biblical ignorance of the members of the Nestorian Church had already eroded the Church to its foundation. Fear of persecution and discrimination in the hands of Muslim rulers also drove many Nestorian Christian communities to embrace Islam.

Believers of one religion persecuting the follower of another is not a mere Islamic phenomenon. Human history is replete with evidence of one religious group persecuting another religious group and forcibly converting them. When the Jews were briefly in power during the Hasmonean period during second century BCE., the Idumeans were persecuted and forcefully converted to Judaism. The Romans persecuted Jews and Christians on account of their monotheistic belief during the early Christian period. The persecution of Christians continued until Christianity was made an official Roman religion under Emperor Constantine in 391 C.E. During the medieval period Christian persecution of Jews and Muslims went to the extent of imposing social and economic restrictions on them. This religious phenomenon of one religious group persecuting another religious group is common among monotheists. Historian G.R. Elton writes :

> Religions spring from faith, endeavoring to maintain its own convictions, cannot permit the existence of rivals or dissenters. Thus religions organized in powerful churches and in command of their scence persecute as a matter of course and tend to regard toleration as a sign of weakness or even wickedness toward whatever deity they worship. Among the religious, toleration is demanded by the persecuted who need it if they are ever to become triumphant, when, all too often, they start to persecute in their turn.[1]

Monotheistic religions, in general, consider themselves superior to other revelations. The later their revelation, the stronger their conviction and affirmation over others have become. The Hebrew scriptures attest that Abrahamic religion claimed superiority over all polytheistic idol worshippers in the ancient Middle East. The prophets of Judaism were told to kill the idol worshippers and destroy their altar and worship places. Judaism claimed superiority over the existing idolatrous religions of the Middle East and dominated all the polytheistic religious groups. Christianity claimed superiority over Judaism by asserting that God had fully and once and for all revealed himself in the person of Jesus Christ. It imposed its values and beliefs upon others, especially upon Jews. Christianity's exclusive claim not only differentiated its belief from Judaism but also gave Christians the assurance that there would be no more "Gospel" to be revealed. When Islam appeared seven centuries

---

1. *Persecution and Toleration: Papers Read at the Twenty-Second Summer Meeting and the Twenty-Third Winter Meeting of the Ecclesiastical History Society*, ed., W.J. Sheils, (Oxford, 1984), p.xiii

later, it fostered the same affirmation Judaism and Christianity had been infused with. Islam abrogated all the earlier monotheistic religions and claimed that it was absoutely different from all earlier revelations and set out to maintain that it was the only authentic and legitimate religion God had given to humankind during the end of ages.

Islam's Treatment of People of Other Religious Faiths

Mohammed taught tolerance and forbearance toward the dhimmis at the early period of his ministry (Sura 22:40). He promised:

> Behold! those who have faith, and those who are Jews, and Christians and Sabians—those who trust in God and the Last Day, and do what is righteous, they shall have their reward; no fear shall come upon them, neither shall they grieve (Sura 2:62, 5:69).

This teaching, however, was soon obscured by hostility and intolerance when Islam became an organized religion and a political institution at Medina.

Mohammed gave legal, social, cultural, family, and spiritual instructions to Muslims and taught them how to live as the umma. He organized military expeditions, provided financial and political stability, taught how to negotiate with enemies, and helped them conquer all rival religious, political, and cultural institutions. In the midst of it all, when the Jews and Christians failed to support Mohammed's mission as a Prophet, he called them enemies of Allah and asked the Muslims to separate themselves from Jews and Christians.

Right from early on, Islam regarded itself as a legitimate religion and differentiated between *dhimmis*, those who worshipped One God (Jews, Christians, Zoroastrians) and "pagans", (those who worshipped idols). When Islam became a ruling power, the People of the Book were given three choices : Islam or poll tax with submission or death. The dhimmis were allowed to practice their faith as long as they submitted to Islamic power, paid poll tax, and did not proselytize the Muslims.

Although the people of the Book were given relatively more freedom to practice their faith under Islamic rule, the idolaters were forced to submit to Islamic teachings. The believers were strictly instructed neither to associate themselves with idolaters nor to marry them as they were considered unclean (Sura 9:28). The idolaters were given only two choices: Islam or death.

Muslims and Dhimmis

While the early period of Mohammed's ministry, his relationship with Christians was less antagonistic than with Jews. He established pacts and agreements with Christians and Jews.[2] Islam considered itself a close relative of Judaism, a friendly neighbour to Christianity, and "a complement to the Monophysite communities of Yemen and Ethiopia, the Nestorian churches of the Sassinid Empire and the Jacobites and the Melkites of the Byzantine Empire."[3] The Quran says of the Jews and Christians, whom it calls the People of the Book *(Ahl Al-Kitab)*, that they are also Muslims as they submit to the will of one God; and, their God and the Muslim God are the same one God. "We believe in that which was sent down to us and that which was sent down to you. Our God and your God is one God; to Him we are submitters (Muslims)" (Sura 29:46).

In 615, when Mohammed and his followers were persecuted in Mecca, he encouraged his followers to escape to Abyssinia, a Monophysite Christian country. Mohammed knew that they would be safer in a Christian community than in a pagan Meccan society. When the Muslim believers were told it was safe to return (the message later proved to be wrong), only a few came back to Mecca. Soon after Mohammed and his followers established a political state at Medina, Islam gave legal rights to the Jews and Christians and called them *Al-Dhimmah* (People of the Covenant). Although the Quran ordered warfare against non-Muslims, Jews and Christians were treated as tolerated minorites *(Al-Dhimmis)*, or least objectionable unbelievers.

The dhimmis were given freedom to continue their religious and domestic affairs. The Arab Jews and Christians found Muslim rule to be more benevolent than that of the Greeks, Romans, and even Persians who ruled Arabia before Mohammed arrived on the scene. The Byzantine rulers considered Arab Christians (the Nestorians, the Monophysites, the Jacobites, and the Coptics) heretics or schismatics and persecuted them. And the Persian empire proved to be over-bearing. The Muslims, on the other hand, were religiously tolerant, culturally amiable, racially closer, and politically charitable. They provided the dhimmis protection from outside aggression and exempted them from military services in exchange for a poll-tax *(Jizya)*.

---

2. See Azzam, *The Eternal Message of Muhammad*, p.128

3. Maurice Borrmans, Inter-religious Documents: Guidelines for Dialogue Between Christians and Muslims, tr. R. Marston Speight (Paulist Press : New York, 1990), p.13.

As the Muslims were fellow semites who shared similar cultural, social and linguistic setting, the dhimmis could conduct the business without fear of outside interference. At times, the dhimmis even helped the Muslim invaders in their effort to establish Islamic rule in certain parts of Arabia hoping that the Muslim rulers would be more benevolent than the alien oppressors. Francis E. Peters writes :

> The (Islamic) conquests destroyed little : what they did suppress were imperial rivalries and sectarian bloodletting among the newly subjected population. The Muslims tolerated Christianity, but they dis-established it; henceforward Christian life and liturgy, its endowments, politics and theology would be a private and not a public affair. By an exquisite irony, Islam reduced the status of Christians to that which the Christians had earlier thrust upon the Jews, with one difference. The reduction in Christian status was merely judicial; it was unaccompanied by either systematic persecution or a blood lust, and generally though not everywhere and at all times, unmarred by vexatious behaviour.[4]

Nevertheless, the freedom enjoyed by the dhimmis was short-lived. When Islam became a sole powerful force in Arabia and when the dhimmis refused to accept the teachings of the Prophet, they were forced to become second class citizens. Their religions were branded as corrupted faiths. They were strictly forbidden to engage in the evangelization of the Muslims. Islam was presented as a lofty religion which realized the fullness of God's revelation.[5]

The Muslims were instructed not to let the dhimmis do any harm to the umma. Unceasingly, the Prophet extended the invitation for the Jews and Christians to join "the true religion," Islam. He said:

> Had the followers of the Scriptures accepted Islam, it would surely have been better for them. Few of them are true believers, and most of them are evildoers. If they harm you, they can cause you no serious harm; and if they fight against you they will turn

---

4. Francis E. Peters, "The Early Muslim Empires: Umayyads, Abbasids, Fatimids", in Islam: *The Religious and Political Life of a World Community*, ed., Marjorie Kelly, (New York: Praeger, 1984), p.79.

5. The Quran also acknowledged the presence of some righteous people in those religions whom Allah knew.

their back and run away. Then there shall be none to help them. Ignominy shall attend them wherever they are found, unless they make a covenant with Allah or with man. They have incurred the wrath of Allah and have been utterly humbled : because they disbelieved His revelations and slew His prophets unjustly; and because they were rebels and transgressors. Yet they are not all alike. There are among the followers of the Scriptures some upright men who all night long recite the revelations of Allah and worship Him; who believe in Allah and the Last Day; who enjoin justice and forbid evil and vie with each other in good works. There are righteous men: whatever good they do, its reward shall not be denied them. Allah knows the righteous" (Sura 3:106-112).

In time, a large number of dhimmis embraced Islam, both by force and persuasion, and became one with the Arab Muslim tribes. Those new converts were called *Mawali* (new Muslims).

During the early history of Islam, no open rivalry existed between Muslims and Jews. The Jews and Muslims in Medina faced Jerusalem to pray. Monotheism was honoured and respected by both groups. The relationship between the two religious communities turned sour, however, when the Jewish tribes, which became a minority in Medina, allegedly sought the help of the powerful anti-Mohammed Meccan Qurayish tribe to aid them in fighting the Muslims. Although Mohammed had established a political pact with the Jews and granted them autonomy in internal religious affairs, they were accused of breaking the pact and conspiring against the Prophet. The Quran charges : "Why is it that whenever they [the Jews] make pacts, a group among them casts it aside unilaterally?" (2:100).

In consequence of the alleged Jewish conspiracy, the Muslims had to fight Meccan warriors in Badr and Uhud. After the battle, the Banu Qainuga tribe and Banu Nadir families were accused of treason and excommunicated. In 627 CE., after the battle of Ditch, the Jews of the Banu Qurayaz were condemned as traitors. They were denounced as renegades who had conspired against the Muslims. From then on [and to this day?], the mutual, trusting relationship between Muslims and Jews had been strained.

Strongest among men in enmity to the believers wilt thou find the Jews and pagans; and nearest among them in love to the believers wilt thou find those who say, "We are Christians"; because amongst these are men devoted to learning and men who have renounced the world, and they are not arrogant. And when they listen to the revelation received by the apostle, thou wilt see their eyes overflowing with tears, for they recognize the truth (Sura 5:85-86).

The Prophet hoped the Christians would accept him as a prophet and embrace his teachings. When they refused to acknowledge him as a prophet and continued to worship the Triune God, he accused them of committing *Shirk* and condemned them as infidels. The Prophet, subsequently, warned the Muslims to be careful of both Jews and Christians and imposed poll tax upon them.

Believers, take neither Jews nor Christians for your friends and protectors: they are but friends and protectors to each other. Whoever of you seeks their friendship shall become one of their number (Sura 5:51).

Fight those who believe not in God nor the last day, nor hold that forbidden by God and his apostle, nor acknowledge the religion of truth, (even if they are) of the People of the Book, until they pay the *Jizya* with willing submission, and feel themselves subdued (Sura 5:29).

The last part of the sura "until they pay the Jizya with willing submission and feel themselves subdued" has been hotly debated. Some interpretations have given way for Muslim leaders to subject dhimmis to humiliation and disgrace. After Mohammed, the burden of leading the umma and controlling the dhimmis rested upon the caliphs who followed their own interpretation of the texts. Nevertheless, the regulations governing the treatment of the dhimmis were clearly documented in Sharia.

The laws governing the conduct and the behaviour of the dhimmis took an extraordinary form in a document known as the Pact of Umar. Although the pact was attributed to Umar, the second caliph who ruled the umma from 634 to 644, the earliest documented pact can be traced only back to the 10th or 11th century. The document is a kind of agreement between Muslims and dhimmis.[6] However, the strong

---

6. Bernard Lewis, *Islam: From the Prophet Mohammed to the Capture of Constantinople*, (New York: Harper & Row, 1974), pp.217-219.

evidence to protect the dhimmis in exchange for poll tax can be found only in the Hadith. A saying ascribed to the dying Umar to his successor makes mention of the protection extended to the dhimmis. "I charge him with [sustaining] the protection of God and the protection of his messenger, that he should observe the agreement made with them and fight those that attack them and not overburden them [with excessive taxes] beyond their capacity."[7]

The tax imposed on the dhimmis was not a fixed amount and it varied from people to people. According to Abu Hanifa, the poor, females, children, slaves, monks, and hermits were exempted from paying jizya.[8] A Hadith says:

> One should be patient with [a poor dhimmi] until he finds the means to pay, and [meanwhile] nothing should be held against him. If he should become rich, it should be taken from him when he comes. If he is unable to comply with any part of the peace settlement to which he agreed, the burden should be lifted from him if his inability is confirmed, and the Imam shall assume the burden on his behalf.[9]

Many Muslim scholars say that the poll tax was only a compensation for protection from a marauding band of invaders and robbers, and a symbolic act of submission and commutation from the military service. In order to maintain stability and security to the umma amidst a vast majority of non-Muslims, the Muslim rulers distanced themselves from the dhimmis by imposing tax and making them feel that they are given protection from enemy invasion. Others argue that it was imposed to humiliate those who reflect God's message given through Mohammed. The Quran says, "[The Jews and Christians] were covered with humiliation and misery; they drew on themselves the wrath of God. This because they went on rejecting the signs of God and slaying his messengers without just cause. This is because they rebelled and went on transgressing."

---

7. Muhammad Muhsin Khan, *The Translation of the Meanings of Sahih al-Bukhari*, 6th ed. (Lahore, 1983), p.182.

8. See Ali, *The Holy Quran: Text Translation and Commentary*, p.447.

9. Quoted in Mark R. Cohen, *Under Crescent and Cross: The Jews in the Middle Ages*, (Princeton: Princeton University Press, 1994), p.56.

The manner in which the poll tax was collected varied from caliph to caliph, and place to place. Mahmud ibn 'Umar al-Zamakshani (1075-1144), a commentator of the Quran, says that the dhimmis should be humbled and humiliated when they come to pay poll tax. This treatment should continue until they embrace Islam. "The jizya shall be taken from them with belittlement and humiliation...[The dhimmis] shall come in person, walking not riding. When he pays, he shall stand, while the tax collector sits. The collector shall seize him by the scruff of the neck, shake him and say: 'Pay the jizya!', and when he pays it he shall be slapped on the nape of his neck".[10] Similar sentiment was shared by several other Muslim commentators also. Aby Yusuf writes:

> They should be imprisoned until they pay what they owe. They are not to be let out of custody until the jizya has been exacted from them in full. No governor may release any Christian, Jew, Zoroastrian, Sabian, or Samaritan unless the jizya is collected from him. He may not reduce anyone's payment by allowing a portion to be left unpaid. It is not permissible for one person to be exempted and for another to have to pay. That cannot be done, because their lives and possessions are guaranteed safety only upon payment of the jizya, which is comparable to tribute money.[11]

Islamic political policies and the process of Arab settlement in the Middle East gradually put pressure on non-Muslims to either become Muslims or to endure much humiliation at the hands of the leaders. Christian territories were conquered and annexed with Islamic lands. Iraq, (which had a large membership of the Nestorian Church), Syria, Palestine, and North Africa, were all incorporated under one caliph. Over time, the dhimmis were severely restricted in building new churches or synagogues. The existing structures were stringently made sure that they were not higher than mosques. The open display of crosses, the observance of outdoor worship services and ceremonies, the commemoration of public processions during Palm Sunday and Easter, the joy and jubilee of making loud noises either through musical instruments or through raising of voices, and the open exhibit of sacred books were strictly proscribed.

---

10. Quoted in Bernard Lewis, *Islam and Religions*, pp. 14, 15.

11. Ibid., pp. 16, 17

The dhimmis were forbidden to bear arms. They were refrained from mounting on saddles. They had to wear clothes with special emblems and rise in the presence of Muslims. The dhimmis were also barred from government and responsible administrative offices for fear of treason and treachery. During the ninth-century an edict issued by the Abbasid Caliph al-Mutawakkil (847-861) says that the Christians and the dhimmis were forced to wear distinct clothes, their newly built churches were destroyed, and denied supervisory role over the Muslims in employment places. Their children were refused schooling and instruction. Muslims were forbidden to have close contact with Christians and the dhimmis.[12]

---

12. Ibid., pp.25, 48-49.

CHAPTER VII
The Quran and Its Doctrine

The word Quran comes from the root *qr'*, meaning to "repeat", or "recite". It was probably the first command Mohammed received when he retreated to meditate in a cave outside of Mecca. Sura 96:1 says Mohammed was commanded to "Recite" *(Iqra)* what was revealed to him. Muslims believe the Quran as the foundation and cornerstone of Islam and the Prophet's revelation as the ultimate and final disclosure of God's will. This strong axiomatic conviction upon their sacred scripture and Holy Prophet has remained unchanged since the establishment of the first umma in Medina. The central message of the Quran is the Shahada (confession) : *"La Illaha Illa 'Illah Muhammadun Rasul Allah."* It means, "There is no god but Allah, and Mohammed is the prophet of Allah." The Shahada does not talk about other cardinal components of the Islamic faith. Shahada only encapsulates the Islamic faith into simple words and modest concepts so that even an unversed bedouin could comprehend and obey.

The Quran is not a book on theological discourse; rather a resource book for spiritual reflection and genuine worship. The Quran teaches that all Muslims must obey Allah's commands. Obedience is manifested in worshipping Allah five times a day and in adhering to the teachings of the Quran, particularly in witnessing to the oneness and unity of Allah. The Quran instructs:

> *Say :* He is Allah, the One Allah, the eternally besought of all! He begetteth not nor was begotten. And there is none comparable unto Him. Surely pure religion is for Allah only.
>
> (Sura 39:3)

> Choose not two gods. There is only One God. So of Me, Me only, be in awe.
>
> (Sure 16:51)

> There is no deity except Allah, and his names are finest names.
>
> (Sura 20:7)

The Quran and the Early Religious Faiths

The divine message about the one true God was a direct attack against polytheism which was commonly practiced by the tribals in Arabia with crudest rites. The message was also set in contrast to the Judeo-Christian traditions which were accused of making mere human beings into gods.

> The Jews call Uzair (Ezra) a son of God, and the Christians call Christ the Son of God. That is a saying from their mouth; (In this) they but imitate what the unbelievers of old used to say God's curse be on them : how they are deluded away from the truth. They take their priests and authorities to be their lords in derogation of God, and (they take as their Lord) Christ the son of Mary; yet they were commanded to worship One God. There is no god but He. Praise and glory to him: (Far is he) from having the partners they associate (with him).

The Quran does not establish clearly how the Jews made Ezra the son of God. The Hebrew scriptures talk about Ezra as only a prophet who revived the temple worship when the buried scriptures were found from the ruins of the Jerusalem temple and were read with delight both by the king and by the people. Similarly, the Quran condemns the Christians for deifying Jesus, a mere human being and a special messenger of God. However, the Quran does attribute special titles like "al-Masih," "Messenger", and "Son of Mary" to Jesus. Nevertheless, the titles do not have any theological implication.

The Quran also accuses the Christians of making the jinns and the saints, who are mere creatures, equal to God and worshipping them.

> Yet they make the jinns equals with God, though God did not create the jinns; and they falsely, having no knowledge, attribute to him sons and daughters. Praise and glory be to him! (for he is above) what they attribute to him! To him is due the primal origin of the heavens and the earth: How can he have a son when he hath no consort? He created all things, and he hath full knowledge of all things" (Sura 6:100, 101).

In his book, *Muhammad at Medina*, W. Montgomery Watt writes about the cultural and religious habits of the people of pre-Islamic Arabia and holds that much of Arabia prior to Mohammad was matrilineal and polytheistic.[1] Although there were signs of transition to patrilineality, the

---

1. W. Montgomery Watt, *Muhammad at Medina* (Oxford: Clarendon Press, 1956), 378-388.

Bedouin tribes of Arabia remained and practiced matrilineality. The Arabs worshipped goddesses and built sanctuaries for them. Some of those goddesses were considered daughters of Allah, the Supreme Arabian deity.

The relationship between Allah and the goddesses, Al-Uzza, Al-Manat, and Al-Lati is far from clear. As the female deities were popular and worshipped by powerful people like the Meccan Qurayish tribe, it has been alleged that Mohammed may have decided at one point to incorporate them in worship in order to gain the confidence of the Qurayish tribe and to win adherents from them. The hypothesis that Mohammed compromised his monotheistic belief to a dominant surrounding community was alluded to in the Quran in the Sura an-Najm. After analyzing the controversy encompassing the possibility of Mohammed's compromise of his belief, Watt concludes:

> The Quran thus fits in with what we learnt from the traditional accounts. Muhammed must have had sufficient success for the heads of Quraysh to take him seriously. Pressure was brought to bear on him to make some acknowledgment of the worship at the neighboring shrines. He was at first inclined to do so, both in view of the material advantages such a course offered and because it looked as if it would speedily result in a successful end to his mission. Eventually, however, through Divine guidance as he believed, he saw that this would be a fatal compromise, and he gave up the prospect of improving his outward circumstances in order to follow the truth as he saw it... If the stories of offers from the leading Quraysh are correct, then Muhammed must have been aware of the political aspects of his decisions, and in particular of his promulgation of the satanic verses and of the abrogating verses. Likewise he must have been aware, when he finally rejected compromise by repeating Surat-al-Kafirin, that there could be no peace with the Quraysh unless they accepted the validity of his mission... The mention of the goddesses is thus properly the beginning of the active opposition of Quraysh, and Surat al-Kafirin, which seems so purely religious, made it necessary for Muhammad to conquer Mecca.[2]

However, the Quranic verses in the Sura an-Najm have been abrogated and invalidated as the Satanic Verses. If Mohammed had made room for the three major goddesses in the kaaba, it was because of the prompting of Satan. The Quran contends Mohammed was indeed tempted by the devil to compromise the truth but the Prophet was never conquered.

And their purpose was to tempt thee away from that which We had revealed unto thee, to substitute in Our name something quite different : (in that case), behold! they would certainly have made thee (their) friend. And had We not given thee strength, thou wouldst nearly have inclined to them a little. In that case We should have made thee taste an equal portion (of punishment) in this life and an equal portion in death : and moreover thou wouldst have found none to help thee against Us! Their purpose was to scare thee off the land, in order to expel thee; but in that case they would not have stayed (therein) after thee, except for a little while. (This was Our) way with the apostles We sent before thee : thou wilt find no change in Our ways (Sura 27.73-77).

Never did We send an apostle or a prophet before thee, but, when he framed a desire, Satan threw some (vanity) into his desire : but God will cancel anything (vain) that Satan throws in, and God will confirm (and establish) His signs: for God is full of knowledge and wisdom (Sura 22.52).

Watt suggests that the compromise of acknowledging both Allah and the goddesses could have existed for a short period of time, anywhere from several weeks to a few months. When Mohammed became more influential as a leader in Arabia because of his military conquests and political victories, the monotheistic religion began to spread fast across the desert land and the need to compromise any iota of his conviction was absolutely abandoned.

After the death of Mohammed, Allah became the One, Supreme, and Eternal Ruler. Ninety nine names are used for God, which are called *al-asma' al-rusna* (the excellent names of God). The hundredth name is not given yet. Names like *al-Malik* (The King), *al-Mumim* (The Presence of Security), *al-Muhaymin* (The Protector), *al-Aziz* (The Mighty), *al-Jabbar* (The Overpowering), *al-Mutakabbir* (The Great in Majesty), *al-Qahhar* (The Dominant), *al-Kabir* (The Most Great), *al-*

Qadir (The Powerful), *al-Wali* (The Governor), *Malik al-Malik* (The Ruler of the Kingdom) were attributed to Allah.[3] Muslim traditions, however, refer to Allah in over five hundred names. The Quran mentions only about seventy names. Muslims can be often seen in public with a string of beads repeating the names of Allah as they run the beads between their right fingers. The most notable names attributed to God are "the Compassionate, the Merciful" *(al-rahman al-rahim)* as Islam strongly believes in the rich mercy and grace of God (Sura 6:147).

Allah's mercy reaches and "extends to all things" (Sura 7:156). His grace does not exclude any one as God is "the Lord of bounties unbounded" (Sura 3:74). He is the righteous judge and renders judgment according to the deeds of men and women. If any does good, the reward will be greater than the deed performed, but if any does evil, the punishment will be only to the extent of their deeds (Sura 38:84). Hence, the Quran concludes, God is a Merciful God who abounds in grace and love. Therefore, "That which ye lay out for charity, seeking the Countenance of God, will increase : it is these who will get a recompense multiplied" (Sura 30:39).[4] The followers of the Prophet carried forward the uncompromising message of absolute monotheism far and wide.

The Eternal and Uncreated Quran

The Quran is deemed the eternal and uncreated word of God which co-existed with him for eternity. Hence the Quran has a literal divine sanctity that is not found in the traditions of Judaism and Christianity. As the Quran was revealed to Mohammed in Arabic in order for people to recount, proper form of recitation, and appropriate manner of enunciation and intonation were considered indispensable. As liturgical recitation of the Quran makes up a major part of Muslim worship, each Muslim is encouraged to memorize and recite the entire Quran in its original Arabic form.

The Quran is frequently called the *Mushaf* (Scripture), *Al-furqan* (the discrimination between Real and Unreal), *Al-kitab* (the Book), *Adh-dhikr* (the Remembrance), and *Al-Quran*. The Quran was revealed to Mohammed over a period of about twenty years in the Arabic language, which was spoken by the Qurayish tribe of Mecca. Muslims believe that

---

3. S.G.F. Brandon, *A Dictionary of Comparative Religion* (New York: Macmillan, 1970), 306-307.

4. See Yusuf A. Ali, *The Holy Quran: Text, Translation, and Commentary*, (Brentwood, Maryland: Amana Corp., 1983), p.1465.

the Quran's language cannot be equated to any spoken language as the Book has a unique message standard of its own. The literary style of the Quranic message revealed to Mohammed while he was in Mecca has poetic style of pre-Islamic Arabic called *Saj* with rhymes and rhythms. Although some Meccan verses can be categorized as verses standing between poetry and prose, several verses found in the whole of the Quran have neither. The line-lengths, the metres of the later revelation frequently shift to varying pattern. Stuart Brown writes :

> The most consistent stylistic quality of the Quran is a pattern of shifting stresses, reflected in some translations. Each measured unit must be recited in a single breath, and official reciters have developed several different modes of expression for their work. There are few long stories, but a number of loosely connected scenes; and references to individuals like Abraham or Jesus are dispersed through the body of the text. Some verses seem to be responses to particular issues of concern to the Muslims, and many are injunctions recommending or prescribing particular actions. Apart from commenting on the ephemeral character of the works of humankind, the Quran makes no historical references beyond the contemporary life of the Muslim community and a solitary mention of the Persian victory over Byzantium (30:2). The Quran is not a text book, but a source book for worship and pious reflection.[5]

Muslims believe the translation of the Quran from the Arabic language does not convey the profound meaning of the original, divine message. For instance, "Allah" does not merely mean God as translated in English; rather, it means the One, Unique, Eternal and Merciful God. The call to worship in non-Arabic languages meanders with winding stream of words without offering a direct summons and a personal invitation to worship Allah five times a day. Cyril Glasse says:

> The substance of the Koran is completely wedded to its Arabic form. Because the Koran is what is called in Sanskrit *Sruti* ("primary revelation" or God Himself speaking) - unlike much of the New Testament which is *Smrti* ("secondary revelation") - and because of the nature of Arabic as a sacred language, a language capable of transmitting *sruti*, it is completely

    5. Brown, *The Nearest in Affection: Towards a Christian Understanding of Islam*, p.11.

impossible to translate the koran in its reality into another
language. Translations are therefore unusable for ritual and
liturgical purposes. The sound itself, of inimitable sonority and
rhythmic power, is numinous and sacramental.[6]

Muslims do recognize, however, the significance of sacred scriptures
of other religions, particularly the Jewish and Christian revelations, and
call them "the Book". The Quran attests to the revelation of the
Pentateuch of the Hebrew Scriptures:

> Surely We sent down the Torah, wherein is guidance and light;
> thereby the Prophets who had surrendered themselves gave
> judgment for those of Jewry, as did the masters and rabbis,
> following the portion of God's book as they were given to keep
> and were witness to (Sura 5:47).

However, the Muslims hasten to add that the Hebrew and Christian
Scriptures in their present form are corrupt. They have been defiled by
the inclusion of extraneous and non-Biblical materials such as rituals,
ceremonies and prayers to saints by enthusiastic Jews and Christians into
the original revelation and hence God had to give the revelation of his
message one final time to Mohammed. Islam acknowledges the validity
of four sacred Books of God which contain Allah's message to humanity.
Of which the Quran testifies :

> It is He Who sent down to thee (step by step), in truth, the Book,
> confirming what went before it; and He sent down the Law (of
> Moses) and the Gospel (of Jesus) before this, as a guide to
> mankind, and he sent down the criterion (of judgment between
> right and wrong) (Sura 3:3-4a).

Those four books are: the Taurat (the Torah), the first five books of
the Bible revealed to Prophet Musa (Moses), the Zabur (Psalms) revealed
to the Prophet Daud (David), the Injil (the Gospels) revealed to the
Prophet Isa (Jesus), and the Quran (means reading or preaching) revealed
to Prophet Mohammed as the final message of God. Nevertheless,
according to Muslims, of the four sacred books, only the Quran remains
scrupulous and intact.

---

6. Cyril Glasse, *The Concise Encyclopedia of Islam*, (New York: Harper Collins,
1989), p.231.

The Compilation of the Quran

It is hard to follow the Quran chapter by chapter and understand the chronological order in which Mohammed received his revelation. The Islamic scholars divide the suras of the Quran under two broad periods: (a) revelation given to the Prophet when he was a Messenger at Mecca; and (b) revelation given to the Prophet when he emigrated to Medina and was called to be the sole leader of the umma. The Meccan revelations are characterized by vivid descriptions of the final judgment, the punishment of disobedient sinners, and the rewards of the righteous. The Medinan suras also are interspersed with the same Meccan theme along with some newly introduced legal, political, moral, and spiritual matters in relation to the Islamic umma. At Mecca, the Prophet was more concerned about monotheistic worship and defending his call as Allah's Messenger. At Medina, the prophet was more concerned about the umma and its mission in the world.

Some of the themes which are common both in Meccan and Medinan suras are the Oneness of God, the final judgment and the acknowledgment of Mohammed as prophet. Since these are the fundamental and uncompromising tenents of Islam, they are repeated throughout the Quran in several ways. The so-called *"Throne Verses"* (Sura 2:255) of the Meccan period and the *"Light Verses"* (Sura 24:35) of the Medinan period demonstrate how seriously the Prophet was committed to his mission as Allah's messenger.

The Quran probably was the first book to be written in Arabic. During the time of Mohammed, the entire Quran was not written down. In the middle of seventh century, the oral and written traditions of the Quran were collected and arranged in the book form. Traditions say Uthman, the third Caliph, was the one who compiled a complete and unified book. The Quran, prior to Uthman, was transmitted separately. The suras and ayas were written on scrolls, bones, and parchments by the friends and companions of the Prophet. When the community of believers felt the need for the unity of belief and oneness in confession, Uthman ordered the scholars to collect various versions of the Quran in circulation and asked them to compile a canonical version.

The chapters (suras) were collected and compiled, all 114 of them, and arranged in order of length except the first chapter, *Fatiha*, which contains a short prayer. The chapters vary in length and contain from a few to over 200 verses (ayas) in a chapter. The second chapter is the longest chapter with 286 verses. The last chapters are the smallest ones with three to six verses. With the exception of Sura 9, each sura is prefaced with the basmalla, the statement "In the name of God, the Compassionate, the Merciful." In the Arabic text of the Quran, the number of each sura is placed after the text as the Muslim scholars believe that nothing ordinary should be placed before the revealed text.

With the exception of the first sura, all the suras are arranged not in chronological order but according to their lengths. Even the order of revelation or the chronology of revelation is not alluded to with certainty. While reading the Quran, one can only guess which verses were revealed at Medina or earlier and which verses were revealed at Mecca and later. For the Muslim community, the date or the chronology of the Quran is not as important a matter as the source of the text is, which is Allah himself. The Muslims strongly believe not only the revelation of the Quran but also the compilation of the Book being divinely ordained. Endress observes:

> [To the Muslims] the Koran is not only theophany and law; it is also a faithful mirror of their road to God, of the struggles of a man who seeks, goes astray and despairs, who disputes with God, is put back on the right way and consoled by Him and who corrects and justifies himself. The great themes of the Koran can be seen as reflection of this personality.[7]

The major themes of Islam are repeated in different ways throughout the Quran. In certain places, new subjects or characters are introduced without any prior introduction or any preliminary reference to historic background.[8] Hence, according to Endress, "it is not really possible to understand either the message in its entirety or many of the details of, and allusions to, its enviornment".[9] Occasionally, the Quran appears to be tediously repetitive as it covers the same theme over and over again. Muslim clerics argue that the repetition is meant only to make the believer grasp the central message of the Quran thoroughly. Moreover, unlike the Bible, the Quran was intended for liturgical recitation not for private meditation.

---

7. Endress, *An Introduction To Islam*, p.27.

8. The original Arabic text did not have the division of chapters (suras) and verses (ayats). They were introduced later for literary convenience.

9. Ibid., p.23.

The Quran has a unique literary style with a special phonetic intonation. The Quran satisfies the aesthetic sense of Muslims and generates reverence and admiration from the listeners. On account of its unparalleled nature of style and revelation, the Muslims uphold the Quran as the Word of God made "incarnate," as is the Jesus of Christianity. The formation of the Quran is a miracle *(Mujiza)* and forever inimitable. The Quran itself testifies, "Say: If the whole of mankind and Jinns were to gather together to produce a like of this Quran, they could not produce the like thereof, even if they backed up each other with help and support" (Sura 17:88). The Quran represents a "Real Presence of the Divine" like those Christians who believe in the "Real Presence of Christ in the Eucharist".

John Bagot Glubb writes that the reading or even the listening of the Quran has a transforming effect upon some believers. In his book *The Life and Times of Muhammad* Glubb observes:

> When the Quran was read aloud, the listeners were at times overcome with fear and trembling. Bearded warriors burst into tears, fainted or fell into a spiritual ecstasy, in which they temporarily lost consciousness of the world around them. Many stories have come down to us of men falling dead when they heard some verse describing the fate of the wicked in hell.[10]

The Quran is the focal point of the Islamic faith. Many Muslims believe, if the Quran is recited properly, God's presence could rest upon them in the form of tranquility *(Shekinah)* to guide and preserve them. Hence, Muslims revere the printed pages of the Quran with deference and high esteem, and honour the words of the Quran literally. Rippin observes, the Quran not only gives directions for living but also proffers magical power to some to heal the sick and deliver the possessed. The Fatiha is given much adoration during times of sickness and need. The Fatiha is widely believed to have a magical effect. Some traditions say that people who have been bitten by scorpions have found healing when they recited the Fatiha. Suras 113 and 114 are believed to be effective in healing sickness. Believers are taught, if certain verses are recited, for instance the last two verses of Sura 2, they will be protected from the evil darts of Satan at night. Suras 18, 48 and 112 will bring abundant blessings and substantial prosperity, if they are recited regularly. Rippin

---

10. John Bagot Glubb, *The Life and times of Muhammad*, (New York: Stein and Day, 1970), p.95.

remarks, "The Quran has been the central symbol of Islam as well as its vital source and, as is true of Jesus in Christianity, its power and effect to move and motivate individuals has never been underestimated by Muslims."[11]

As the Quran forbids idol worship in any form, the mosques and Muslim places of residence are devoid of figures and pictures of saints. Nonetheless, the inner longing and human desire for artistic expression of thought and the embellishment of the place of worship has been revealed through calligraphy and architecture. These are manifested in the printed and written pages of the Quran, the construction of majestic buildings, and the grand designing of magnificent mosques. Even the appearance of the Arabic script was constantly improved and its grace and grandeur fascinated the Turks and Persians and incited them to adopt the language. In fact, Islamic architecture became so exquisite and so elegant that during the Middle Ages, it became immensely popular and spread westward in contrast to the Christian gothic edifices of the west.

The Islamic civilization, by and large, is based on the teachings of the Quran and its tradition. The Quran has served as a major resource for the development of Islamic culture, oneness of the Muslim community and the improvement of Arabic grammar and language. Philip K. Hitti notices:

> In length the Koran is no more than four-fifths that of the New Testament, but in use it far exceeds it. Not only is it the basis of the religion, the canon of ethical and moral life, but also the text book in which the Moslem begins his study of language, science, theology, and jurisprudence. Its literary influence has been incalculable and enduring. The first prose book in Arabic, it set the style for future products. It kept the language uniform. So that whereas today a Moroccan uses a dialect different from that used by an Arabian or an Iraqi, all write in the same style.[12]

The Quran contains enough directions to guide both secular and sacred realms. The revealed scriptures of other religious faiths are appraised as imperfect as they have been confined either to a specific period of time, a particular community of people, or to a limited geographical location. Islam accuses that the divine message revealed

---

11. Rippin, *Muslims: Their Religious Beliefs and Practices*, vol.1, p.29.

12. Philip K. Hitti, *Islam: A Way of Life*, (New York: Henry Regenry, 1971), 27.

in Jewish and Christian scriptures contains a mixture of human and divine personalities, human and divine history, and partial revelation of God. Those scriptures do not contain an incorrupt and pure message from God. Human and divine messages are put together in a confused form, and hence, one finds it highly difficult to separate truth from fiction, or divine from human.

The Quran has incorporated stories such as the accounts of creation, flood, Abraham, Ishmail, Moses, Solomon, and others from Biblical and extra-Biblical sources. The Quran also contains stories from Arab's own history, such as those of Hud and Salih. Although some of the Quranic accounts agree with the Biblical narrative, often they are presented in a different form. The major doctrines and beliefs of Judaism and Christianity are portrayed in a form which is considered heretical both by Jews and Christians. The Quran's illustration of Jewish beliefs (sin, salvation, and Satan's rebellion) and the Christian doctrines (the incarnation, the crucifixion, the redemption, the resurrection, and the Trinity) come close to the teachings espoused and fostered by the pre-Islamic Gnostics, Docetics, and Christian heretics who were living in the deserts of Arabia and far from Judeo-Christian religious centres. Therefore, some Jewish and Christian scholars claim that Mohammed must have received some religious instructions, or atleast, listened to those desert dwelling itinerant preachers. Since Mohammed had an imperfect and faulty knowledge about their religious doctrines, the Prophet's Jewish and Christian critics maintain that the revelation Mohammed claimed to have received from Allah was not an authentic or original one.

As for the similarities between the Bible and the Quran, Muslims affirm that both are revelations from God. Nonetheless, only the Quran contains the final and authentic revelation from God and hence it is superior to the Bible. Muslims are ardent in their belief that the Quran was original and had borrowed nothing from other scriptures. If the Quranic revelation agrees with the earlier revelations, one can agree that both have a common origin. If the Quranic revelation does contradict the earlier revelation given in the Jewish and Christian scriptures, the Quran stands supreme and accurate. After all, "that which is superior cannot depend on that which is inferior."[13] Above all, for Muslims, originality is not important, but monotheism is.

---

13. Michael Nazir Ali, *Frontiers in Muslim-Christian Encounter*, (Oxford: Regnum Books, 1987), p.17.

The speaker of the Quran, usually, is Allah Himself. At times, Allah speaks directly to Mohammed, and at other times, Allah speaks to people through the mediation of the Prophet or the angel (Gabriel). When Allah speaks, he uses first person plural; when either the angel or Mohammed speaks, he uses first person singular. So, a reader has to first identify the grammar of the Quran in order to find out who the speaker of the message is. For instance, when Allah speaks, his message is loaded with first person plural "We" as it is found in the verse, "Verily this is a revelation from the Lord of the worlds: ...We revealed it...We caused it...We never are unjust" (Sura 26:192-209). The idea of God speaking directly to human beings is an alien Judeo-Christian concept. In the Bible, God rarely speaks in first person plural, although two biblical allusions, from the books of Genesis and Revelation, come close to it:

> Then God said, "Let us make man in our image, after our likeness; and let them have dominion over the fish of the sea, and over the birds of the air, and over the cattle, and over all the earth, and over every creeping thing that creeps upon the earth (Gen. 1:26).

> And he who sat upon the throne said, "Behold, I make all things new". Also, he said, "Write this, for these words are trustworthy and true." And he said to me, "It is done! I am the Alpha and the Omega, the beginning and the end. To the thirsty I will give from the fountain of the water of life without payment. He who conquers shall have this heritage, and I will be his God and he shall be my son. But as for the cowardly, the faithless, the polluted, as for murderers, fornicators, sorcerers, idolaters, and all liars, their lot shall be in the lake that burns with fire and sulphur, which is the second death (Rev. 21:5-8).

The Doctrinal Teachings of the Quran

The Fatiha of the Quran is estimated by many Muslims and Christians something tantamount to the Lord's Prayer of Christianity. The Muslims recite the Fatiha on almost all occasions and in each cycle of the salat in Muslim worship. The Fatiha comprises the following prayer :

> In the name of God, the Cherisher and Sustainer of the worlds, Most Gracious, Most Merciful; Master of the Day of judgment. Thee do we worship, and thine do we seek. Show us the straight way, the way of those on whom thou has bestowed thy grace, those whose (portion) is not wrath, and who go not astray. (Sura 1:1-7).

Islam places all human beings on the same level. Islam strictly forbids inequality to exist among its believers. A true Muslim is indeed a liberated and free individual. He or she is not in any way inferior or superior to other believers. James L. Barton contrasts Islamic doctrine of equality with the Indian Hindu religious caste system which divides humanity into unequal classes and states that equality is built into Islamic faith. Barton writes:

> The abolition of caste in India wherever the [Muslims] faith spread is evidence of the sense of brotherhood permeating the entire body...Islam recognizes no race, no color, no rank, and no caste; whoever is a true follower of the Prophet is a brother of every other follower and as such can claim his protection and hospitality.[14]

Islam's stance on impartiality regardless of colour or race or nationality has been strictly put into practice. The Prophet is reported to have said, "No Arab has any superiority over a non-Arab, nor does a non-Arab have any superiority over a black man, or the black man over the white man. You are all the children of Adam, and Adam was created from clay."[15]

The Creation of Adam, the Fall of Satan, and the Entry of Sin

According to the Quran, when God created the earth, he created Adam out of clay, and appointed him as his khalifa (vicegerent) on earth to take care of God's creation and live according to his guidance. The Quran does not say how Eve was created. The Quran does not mention the name of Adam's wife, only the Hadith does. The Quranic creation account says Allah formed Adam and his wife at heavenly places and gave them the gift of learning, discernment, freedom of will, and power over all of Allah's creation and sent them to earth for a fixed period to test their devotion and loyalty to Allah. The Quran teaches that Adam and Eve were not created in ignorance and in dependency, but in full autonomy and independence.

The Quran further explains that when Allah revealed his intention of creating Adam to the angels, they were not pleased with God's idea. The angels were afraid human beings would become violent and cause havoc to God's creation.

---

14. James Barton, *The Christian Approach to Islam* (Boston: Pilgrim, 1918), pp. 160-161.

15. Quote taken from Abdul ala Mawdudi, *Human Rights in Islam*, (Leicester, : Islamic Foundation, 1980), p.10.

Behold, thy Lord said to the angels: "I will create a vicegerent on earth." They said : "Wilt thou place therein one who will make mischief therein and shed blood?- whilst we do celebrate thy praises and glorify thy holy (name)?" He said: "I know what ye know not" (Sura 2:30).

The story of creation says that Adam was created out of clay and endowed with knowledge superior to that of angels. The Quran exalts Adam as the best of creation, but not as one who was created in the image of God. When God breathed into Adam's nostrils, God-like knowledge and resolution entered him. As a human being created by God, Adam was made special and superior to the rest of God's creation by virtue of his God-given knowledge and the uniqueness of his creation. As a carrier of God's spirit, Adam would be able to discern between good and evil. He could choose freely between right and wrong, and take care of the affairs of the earth.

Immediately after Adam was created, Allah taught Adam the name of all animals and birds on earth. When the angels were asked to name God's creation on earth, they were not able to recall a single one. On the other hand, Adam was so swift and correct in reciting the appropriate names of all of God's creatures that Adam amazed the angels. Then Allah ordered all his angels to bow before Adam which all of them did except Satan (Iblis). Since then Satan became jealous of Adam and became an enemy of God. After this incident, Allah created Eve (Hauwa), a companion for Adam and said to Adam, "O Adam! dwell thou and thy wife in the garden, and eat of the bountiful things therein as ye will; but approach not this tree, or ye run into harm and transgression" (Sura 2:35).

The Quran says Adam was the first Muslim and the first prophet of God. Islam teaches Adam and Eve were living in the Heavenly Garden when they were tempted and misguided by Satan to eat the forbidden fruit. As a result of Satan's deception and the disobedience of Adam and Eve of God's command, they were sent to earth. However, before they left the Heavenly Garden, both Adam and Eve sought the forgiveness and mercy of Allah.

The Quran narrates the penitent prayer of Adam and Eve : "Our Lord! We have wronged ourselves. If thou forgive us not and have not mercy on us, surely we are of the lost" (Sura 7:23). God forgave them, supplied them necessary guidance, and made Adam the first Prophet of Allah (Sura 2:36). The Quran says, "Then Adam received from his Lord words (of forgiveness), and he relented toward him. Lo! He is the Relenting, the Merciful" (Sura 2:37). After they obtained forgiveness, God sent them forth to earth.

When Adam and Eve left the heavenly place, God gave Adam a special guidance so that Adam, his family and descendants might obey Allah and re-enter Paradise. "Get ye down all from here; and if, as is sure, there comes to you guidance from me, whosoever follows My guidance, on them shall be no fear, nor shall they grieve" (Sura 2:38).

The Quran denies any concept of original sin. Islam insists that human beings become sinful only by the influence of external surroundings in which they are being reared. Since God has breathed his Spirit into the human body, no child born in this world is sinful. Adam's sin of disobedience was not passed on to his succeeding generations. In other words, sin is not inherent, as the Bible says. It is only acquired.[16]

According to Islam, the original source of evil is traced back to the disobedience and deception of Satan not Adam. Satan's disobedience can be traced back to his jealousy and resentment against God's special creation : Adam. The Quran explains the origin of sin:

> Behold! thy Lord said to the angels : "I am about to create man, from sounding clay from mud moulded into shape. When I have fashioned him (in due proportion) and breathed into him of My spirit, fall ye down in obeisance unto him." So the angels prostrated themselves, all of them together. Not so Iblis: he refused to be among those who prostrated themselves. Allah said : "O Iblis! what is your reason for not being among those who prostrated themselves?" Iblis said : "I am not one to prostrate myself to man, whom Thou didst create from sounding clay, from mud moulded into shape." (Allah) said : "Then get thee out from here; for thou art rejected, accursed. And the curse shall be on thee till the Day of Judgment." (Iblis) said: "O my Lord! give me then respite till the Day of the (dead) are raised." (Allah) said: "Respite is granted thee till the day of the time appointed." (Iblis) said: "O my Lord! because Thou hast put me in the wrong, I will make (wrong) fair seeming to them on

---

16. The concept of Sin and Salvation has been discussed elaborately in the last chapter of the book.

the earth, and I will put them all in the wrong, except Thy servants among them, sincere and purified (by Thy grace)." (Allah) said; "This (way of My sincere servants) is indeed a way that leads straight to Me. For over My servants no authority shalt thou have, except such as put themselves in the wrong and follow thee (Sura 7:11-18).

The Quranic portrayal of sin's entry into the world was through the disobedient act of Satan when he was commanded to fall prostrate before a human being. Satan became the arch enemy of God, attempted to thwart God's plans for his creation and intended to destroy the blissful life of Adam and Eve in the Heavenly Garden all because he was ordered to bow before Adam. This narration differs from the Hebrew Scriptures' account of Satan's rebellion.

The book of Isaiah says that Satan was trying to make himself equal to God and to reign supreme, and hence he was cast out of God's presence. The Book of Isaiah says:

> How you are fallen from heaven, O Day Star, son of Dawn! How you are cut down to the ground, you who laid the nations low! You said in your heart, 'I will ascend to heaven; above the stars of God I will set my throne on high; I will sit on the mount of assembly in the far north; I will ascend above the heights of the clouds, I will make myself like the Most High.' But you are brought down to Sheol, to the depths of the Pit. Those who see you will stare at you, and ponder over you : 'Is this the man who made the earth tremble, who shook kingdoms, who made the world like a desert and overthrew its cities, who did not let his prisoners go home?' (Isaiah 14:12-17).

Critics contend that Mohammed probably listened to oral accounts from Jews and Christians of Arabia of the Biblical story of Satan's disobedience and misconstrued the entire narrative.

Thus the Quran presents Adam and Eve as victims of Satan's deceit and temptation. Their Fall did not separate them from their contact with God. They were sent from heavenly garden to earthly garden only for a short while. The Quran narrates the disobedience of Adam and Eve the following way :

> Then began Satan to whisper suggestions to them, bringing openly before their minds all their shame that was hidden from

them (before). He said : "Your Lord only forbade you this tree, lest ye should become angels or such beings as live for ever. And he swore to them both, that he was their sincere adviser (Sura 7:20-21).

By cunning deception, Satan led them in eating the forbidden fruit and brought about their fall. When God summoned Adam and Eve, they did not hide from him but they prayed for God's forgiveness. They said:

Our Lord! We have wronged our own souls: If Thou forgive us not and bestow not upon us Thy mercy, we shall certainly be lost." (Allah) said : "Get ye down, with enmity between yourselves. On earth will be your dwelling place and your means of livelihood, for a time." God, in His abundant mercy, forgave them, and sent Adam and Eve and their enemy Satan to earth (Sura 7:23, 24).

Unlike the Hebrew Scriptures narrative of the Fall, the Quran presents that Adam not Eve was tempted by Satan. There is no perpetual curse or endless shame involved in his disobedience. Yielding to the devil's temptation was only a human failure showing only the weak, vulnerable and human nature of Adam and Eve. The Quran repeatedly asserts and demonstrates God's Nature and humanity's need for God's mercy. Adam's submission to temptation, his sincere repentance, and God's abundant forgiveness summarize Islam's paradigm of sin and salvation.

Sin, in Islam, is not so much the doing of something that is morally reprehensible, but rather the doing of that which is prohibited by the Quran. The greatest sin one can commit is by dividing the unity of God and giving an associate to God himself. "God forgiveth not (the sin of) joining other gods with him; but he forgiveth whom he pleaseth other sins than this: one who joins other gods with God, hath strayed far, far away (from the right)" (Sura 4:116).

The God of the Quran is Almighty and Merciful. His mercy and forgiveness are available to all who turn to him in repentance and worship. Satan has no power over those who are sincere in obeying the commands of God. Faithful Muslims may falter but they can always seek the forgiveness of the Merciful and Compassionate Allah through worship.

Islam makes ample provisions for Muslims who have failed in their duties by allowing compensatory acts to cancel out their sins. Such acts include : prayers, alms-giving, fast, and pilgrimage. The believers also build up *Thawab* (eternal merit) when they practice those good deeds.

Mohammed taught that the whole world is a *Masjid* (in English it is called mosque, a place of prostration before Allah). As human beings are given the freedom of will, they can choose to obey or disobey Allah. However, human response to Allah's call to submission has eternal consequences. Maudidi writes that life beyond the grave is an extension of life here on earth.

> The world and the hereafter are not two separate things but a continuous process whose beginning is the world and the end, hereafter. The relation between the two is the same as between cultivation and crop. You plough the land, then sow the seeds, then irrigate, then look after the field till such time as the crop is ready. Then after reaping it you feed yourself with it comfortably throughout the year. You will naturally reap whatever you have cultivated in the land. If you sow wheat, only wheat will grow. If thorns are sown, only thorns will grow. If nothing is sown, nothing will grow... This is exactly the position in respect of this world and the hereafter.[17]

The Quran supprts Maududi's view of life beyond. "And seek the other world in that which God bestows upon you in this world. Do not therefore forsake your share of this world. Do good to others as God has done good to you. Do not seek corruption, or allow it to happen to earth. God does not love corrupters" (Sura 28:77). This view contradicts the Christian teachings of life after death. Christianity affirms that the believers will be rewarded not by the merits of one's deeds but by the grace of God manifested in Christ Jesus. Faith in Jesus Christ, the Saviour of human kind, is the key to life beyond.

In short, Islam emphasizes that Satan's not Adam's disobedience was the root cause of all evil. Sin is not hereditary because human beings are not inherently evil. Each man or woman chooses to either follow Allah or Satan when he or she grows up. The gravest sin one can commit in Islam is to worship an idol or to substitute something or someone in the place of Allah. The rewards or punishments of life beyond death greatly depend upon the kind of life one lives here on earth.

---

17. S. Abdul A'la Maududi, *Fundamentals of Islam*, (Lahore: Islamic Publications, 1975), p. 43.

CHAPTER VIII
Five Pillars of Islam

The Quran talks about five essential and obligatory practices of every Muslim which are generally known as the five pillars of Islam. These mandatory practices bring the Muslim community together in unity and camaraderie. The imperative practice of the five pillars of Islam have some similarities with Christian theology and its ecclesiastical practice. Harvey Cox in his book *Many Mansions: A Christian's Encounter with Other Faiths* argues that the five pillars of Islam have strong Christian underpinning.

> Despite its firm refusal to recognize any divine being except God (which is the basis for its rejection of Christ's divinity), Islam appears sometimes to be a pastiche of elements from disparate forms of Christianity moulded into a potent unity. Take the Calvinist emphasis on faith in an omnipotent deity, the pietistic cultivation of daily personal prayer, the medieval teaching on charity, the folk Catholic fascination with pilgrimage, and the monastic practice of fasting, and you have all the ingredients of Islam.[1]

The five pillars of Islam are not unique characteristics of Islamic faith alone. Hinduism, Buddhism, Jainism, and Sikhism have already incorporated them into their very religious worship, in different forms. In Islam the five pillars serve as Pentalogue.

1. Call to Prayer

The first of the five pillars is call to prayer. When the Muezzin (the caller to prayer) from the minaret invites the faithful to pray five times a day, every Muslim must testify there is no god but Allah and Mohammed is his messenger. The public testimony of a Muslim affirms his or her trust

---

1. Harvey Cox, *Many Mansions : A Christian's Encounter With Other Faiths*, (Boston : Beacon Press, 1985), p.27.

in Allah. This affirmation in public reminds Muslims of their absolute commitment to monotheism.

The phrase, "there is no god but Allah" gives clarity to believers and upholds the mystery and sovereignty of Allah. When worldly power and societal demands undermine Muslims' commitment to Allah, this phrase in *Shahada* serves as an affirmation of their refusal to follow leaders who are hostile to the practices of Islam and whose values are contrary to the teachings of Islam. This resistance to submit to a spiritually malevolent environment has often been enforced by the Islamic community when foreign, particularly Western, political power tried to control the Arab national politics during colonial times. The public confession is also to remind the faithful that Mohammed was only a prophet and he should not be worshipped in the place of Allah. This ritual, according to the Hadith, was set up during the time of Mohammed.

> Narrated Ibn Umar: When the Muslims arrived at Medina, they used to assemble for prayer, and used to guess the time for it. During those days, the practice of Adhan [call to prayer] for the prayers had not yet been introduced. One time they discussed this problem regarding the call to prayer. Some people suggested the use of a bell like the Christians, others proposed a trumpet like the horn used by the Jews, but Umar was the first to suggest that a man should call (the believers) for prayer; so Allah's Apostle ordered Bilal to get up and pronounce the Adhan for prayer (1:334-35; 11.1.578).

During worship, the Muslims stand in a perfect line, whether the prayer of worship is held inside the building or in the open-air, and say their prayers. This tradition is also traced back to the time of the Prophet.

> Narrated Ana Malik : The Prophet said, "Straighten your rows as the straightening of rows is essential for perfect and correct prayer" (1:388; 11.73.690).

2. Salat

Every Muslim must face Mecca and pray five times a day (salat), when the call to prayer is given from the Minaret. According to the Islamic tradition, the command to pray five times a day was given by Allah to Mohammed when he was taken to Allah's throne during his night journey to Jerusalem. Armstrong refers to a legend that had been popularized by Ibn Ishaq.

When [Muhammad] reached the divine throne, God told
Muhammad that the Muslims must make *Salat* fifty times a day,
but on his way down Moses told Muhammad to go back and
get the number reduced. Moses kept sending Muhammad back
until the number of prescribed prayers was reduced to five,
which he still felt was excessive, but Muhammad was too
ashamed to ask for a further reduction.[2]

In beautiful rhythm the muezzin would begin the call to prayer in Arabic:
"God is most great (Allahu Akbar), God is most great, God is most great,
I witness that there is no god but Allah. I witness that Mohammed is his
messenger. I witness that Mohammed is His messenger. Come to prayer,
come to prayer. Come to prosperity, come to prosperity. God is most
great. God is most great. There is no god but Allah." Corresponding to
the important turns of the day: dawn, noon, afternoon, sunset, and
evening the Muslims have to pray.

Each of the five daily prayers is comprised of an elementary prayer.
Each prayer is represented with minor variation. The first prayer begins
at the end of night and beginning of day which is called *Al-Fajr*, the dawn
prayer. The prayer is repeated twice at dawn. The noon prayer is the
second which is said when the sun is past the zenith and at this time the
prayer is repeated three times. The noon prayer is called *Al-Zuhr*. At the
middle of the afternoon is said the third prayer which is called *Al-Asr*, and
during this time, the prayer is repeated four times. The fourth prayer is
said soon after sunset which is called *Al-Maghrib*, the evening prayer.
In the evening the prayer is repeated three times. The last prayer is said
nearly two hours after sunset, called *Al-Isha*, the night prayer. During this
time, the prayer is repeated four times.

Although children are not bound by the law to pray five times a day,
they are often instructed and trained into ritual prayer from early on.
Some Imams recommend children should start praying from the age of
ten. Men and women are bound by the law to offer private prayer.
Women are excused temporarily during menstruation, which, as was the
Jewish custom during the Old Testament times, is considered a time of
impurity.

Whether one is alone or in a group, the call to prayer must be heard.
If one is alone, the individual must give the call to himself or herself at

2. Armstrong, *Muhammad: A Biography of the Prophet*, p.139.

stated times and do salat. The time and rituals were established by the Prophet, not by the Quran.[3] Salat is regulated by ritual purification beforehand, similar to the ancient Israelite practice. The purification is partial or complete depending upon the external impurity of the worshippers.

Minor impurities acquired while relieving oneself, slight foulness procured through any kind of physical contact with the skin of another human being who is not a relative (like shaking hands), negligible amount of dust, dirt, and sweat accumulated from work place, require minor ablutions. The worshipper is expected to pour water on the feet, forearms, hands, face, head, mouth, nose and ears and wipe off the dirt from the body. Greater impurities like those of sexual origin demands total ablutions of the body before offering the prayer or entering the mosque. Salat without ritual purification is considered invalid.[4]

Salat contains recitation of certain Quranic verses and a predetermined number of prostrations and genuflections. During the early days of Islam, prostration was considered low and beneath one's dignity by the proud Meccan Qurayish. Mohammed made it a new symbol of pride (as Jesus demonstrated the authentic sign of a master by washing his disciples' feet or as the early Christians who made the accursed Roman cross a symbol of victory) in absolute submission before Allah.

In the mosque or public places, salat is led by an Imam[5] or a selected believer. Since Islam is a religion of lay people without any hierarchy, any male who is well versed in the Quran can lead the service. A female is not permitted to lead the congregation in worship. Men are forbidden to pray behind a woman who stands before the congregation.

In salat, the Muslims present themselves before Allah with fear and commitment. No offering plates are passed during the worship. Muslims give their gifts by mailing their cheques to the office of the mosque or by dropping their offering candidly in the box set by the doors. In worship, a believer acknowledges the greatness of Allah (Allahu Akbar), abolishes temptation to commit sin, commences the purification of soul,

3. The Hebrew Scriptures record David and Daniel prayed to God five times a day facing Jerusalem.

4. Exodus 19 talks about purification such as washing of garments and abstinence from sexual intercourse, as part of the preparation of the worship.

5. Literally it means the one who is in the front or the leader.

obtains the forgiveness of sin, and receives strength to perform duty (Sura 2:45, 153). In short, a believer draws closer to God in prayer and worship, and receives rewards and blessings from him in return. The Quran assures the believers of the blessings of salat:

> When my servants ask thee concerning me, I am indeed close (to them) : I listen to the prayer of every suppliant when he calleth on me : Let them also, with a will, listen to my call, and believe in me: that they may walk in the right way" (Sura 2:186).

Salat does not have room for personal request or personal favour from Allah, neither does it accommodate a distinct supplication for forgiveness. Salat is accepted as a good deed; therefore, God's blessings will rest upon the believers. It is generally assumed that Allah the Compassionate and Merciful God, forgives sins when the believers are engaged in salat. It can be offered either in the privacy of home, in public places, or at mosques.

The believers are encouraged to go to the mosque on Fridays for community worship as it strengthens the bonds with fellow believers. Salat reminds the worshippers that all Muslims are Allah's children and they are all equal in his sight. Turning toward the kaaba in Mecca and praying to Allah strengthens the sense of unity among Muslims and fosters a uniform level of worship around the world which no other religion has accomplished.

The Quran calls for its umma to stick together and support one another. As fellow believers in Allah, the Muslims must find support, encouragement, and nourishment within the umma. Therefore, the Quran instructs the Muslims to "Hold fast, all of you together, to the call of Allah, and do not separate. And remember Allah's favour unto you" (Sura 3:103). Strength and unity among the believers can be obtained only if they bind together as a community in worship. Hence, Friday worship in the mosque is considered imperative.

Muslims call the kaaba the House of God and the pilgrims his guests, and there is no inequality among God's guests. Kaaba is attached to a sense of very powerful and real divine presence. Pilgrims who go to the kaaba in Saudi Arabia must be Muslims. All non-Muslims are considered unbelievers and, therefore, forbidden to go near the sacred site. Even airlines are prohibited from flying over Mecca fearing that the presence of the unbelievers on the plane would desecrate the purity of the holy city.

Uniformity in worship and homogeneity in values create an identical Islamic culture and society. Syed Abdul Latif points out that the Muslims' way of worship serves as a catalyst to Islamic culture.

> This sense of equality, this standing shoulder to shoulder without regard for colour or race or station in life, this standing and kneeling and sitting together in a common worship before one common language of devotion, expressing one common wish, this sense of equality or its manifestations is the culture of the [Muslims].[6]

During Salat, the worshippers stand in rows of straight lines on clean ground with clean feet facing the *Mithrab*, the niche, which indicates the direction of kaaba. The worship place in the mosque will not contain any furniture except, perhaps, a pulpit. The floors of the mosques are usually covered by a clean, special carpet. Muslims pray with their eyes open. Hence, the mosque does not contain any image, picture, or object of worship. The presence of such objects would distract the hearts and minds of the believers from concentrating on Allah. One can only see the suras of the Quran written in adorning calligraphy all over the walls. Some mosques are known for their beautiful architecture, massive domes, large pillars resembling tree trunks, flowing fountains, and bubbling pools. All these represent a foretaste of paradise on earth. Most of the mosques have a minaret at the top from which the muezzin invites the faithful to pray five times a day. The minaret is also a universal symbol of Islamic faith.

Whenever the Muslims gather to pray, an absolute concentration of mind is expected. The prayer model set by the Prophet is emulated by the believers. A Hadith says of the diligent observance of prayer by the Prophet:

> Abdullah stated : While the Prophet was in the state of prostration, surrounded by a group of people from Quraish pagans, 'Uqba bin Abi Muait came and brought the intestines of a camel and threw them on the back of the Prophet. The Prophet did not raise his head from prostration till Fatima [his daughter] came and removed those intestines from his back, and invoked evil on whoever had done [the evil deed]. The Prophet said, "O Allah! Destroy the chiefs of Quraish (4:274; 53.40.409).

---

6. Syed Abdul Latif, *Islamic Cultural Studies* (Lahore: Shaikh Muhammad Ashraf, 1947), p.42.

The Muslims have a congregational prayer on Friday at noon, which is led by the Imam, and this is followed by a sermon. Friday is not a day of rest, but a day of worship at the mosque. Usually men go to the mosque to worship. If women are present, they are isolated from men by a curtain or a wall. The separation is for reasons of modesty due to the prostration and genuflections involved in the act of worship. Women are forbidden to wear perfume or adorn themselves with jewellery.

Prostration was common in the early Church and among the Jews (II Sam. 7:18, Ps. 95:6). Leviticus 9:24 says that the Israelites also fell on their faces and bowed before God: "And fire came forth from before the Lord and consumed the burnt offering and the fat upon the altar; and when all the people saw it, they shouted, and fell on their faces." Even today Christians in the Church of South India and many other denominations fall prostrate before God and worship him during prayer. Sitting on the heels or the inside of the feet during worship is not an uncommon sight in Asian culture.

The Muslims give great respect to a worshipper who has a callous mark on the forehead as a result of years of prostration. The mark symbolizes the worshipper's piety and devotion to Allah. The Quran itself attests:

> On their faces are their marks (being) the traces of their prostration. This is their similitude in the Taurat; and their similitude in the Gospels is... God has promised those among them who believe and do righteous deeds forgiveness, and a great reward (Sura 48.29).

The mosque plays a vital role in strengthening the community by taking care of the temporal and spiritual needs of its members. It serves as a centre of all communal activities. Erich W. Bethmann writes:

> The mosque has become the centre of community life. And here probably lies the secret of that marvelous influence of Islam, the mosque, the place of worship, where the faithful join in prayer five times a day, and the simple *"Kuttab"* school attached to every mosque, where the Quran was taught exclusively, have welded the heterogeneous elements of so many alien nations into one big fraternity—the fraternity of Islam.[7]

---

7. Erich W. Bethmann, *Bridge to Islam* (Nashville: Southern Publishing Association, 1950), pp. 98-99.

When the believers perform the salat, they are instructed to turn towards kaaba and pray five times a day. During his early ministry in Medina (622), the point of orientation established by the Prophet was Jerusalem. After the battle of Badr in 624, he changed the point of orientation to Mecca, and more particularly the kaaba. Scholars still debate and wonder what exactly prompted the Prophet to make such an abrupt change. Did he naively expect the Jews and Christians to support him, when he claimed to be standing on the tradition of Abraham, Moses, and Jesus? Did Mohammed try to please the Jews and Christians, when he first chose Jerusalem as *Qiblah* for the believers? They are difficult questions to answer. Some scholars argue, when the People of the Book refused to accept Mohammed's claim to prophethood and, particularly, when they joined the Meccan Qurayish tribe to fight Mohammed's army in Medina, Mohammed, in a fit of resentment and indignation turned the focus of the prayers toward the kaaba, the spiritual centre of the Arabs.

In his book, *Islam,* Fazlur Rahman gives another reason for making kaaba the point of orientation. He says, Mohammed's cousins of Abd-Shams were making the kaaba a hub of pagan pantheon and centre for pilgrims for the Arab tribes. They were making it a political and pagan-spiritual establishment. In order to thwart their ambition, Mohammed set Jerusalem as the direction of prayer. It was merely a political tactic Mohammed had to adopt at the early part of his ministry. Jerusalem as the direction of prayer had nothing to do with Mohammed's expectation from the People of the Book. After the victory of Badr, Rahman argues, Mohammed gave up the ruse, since he was confident of his victory over the Meccans, the destruction of idol worship and the removal of his political and spiritual enemies. And he, therefore, felt free to reinstate the point of orientation toward kaaba.[8] Kenneth Cragg validates Rahman's thesis and says Mohammed's conquest of Mecca indeed destroyed paganism, reformed Mecca, established the kaaba as a unitarian symbol and "rehabilitated the familiarly sacred territory (of paganism) itself, Islamized, as it were, the very symbol of the struggle, making the triumph complete."[9]

Another legend says, in 622, when a group of pilgrims went to Mecca from Medina at the time of the Hajj (the greater canonical

8. Fazlur Rahman, *Islam* (New York: Double Day and Co., 1968), pp. 19-20.

9. Kenneth Cragg, *The House of Islam,* 2nd edition, (Encino, Ca: Dickenson, 1975), p.64.

pilgrimage, one of the five pillars), Al-Bara ibn Ma'rar, one of the chiefs of Khasraj, faintheartedly suggested to the fellow pilgrims that for the time period they should change the *Qiblah* from Jerusalem to Mecca where all the sacred shrines had been situated. Although others objected to his suggestion, Bara made Mecca his *Qiblah* during the pilgrimage. When the matter was reported to Mohammed, he did not seem to be concerned. Then Bara died. Two years after that incident, Mohammed was leading prayers in a mosque built in the region of the clan of the late Bara. Being inspired by a distinctive revelation, he made the worshippers turn around and pray facing Mecca instead of Jerusalem.[10] Of the change of direction, the Quran says:

> The fools among the people will say; "What hath turned them from the Qibla to which they were used? 'Say: to Allah belong both East and West: He guided them whom He will to a way that is straight...We see the turning of thy face (for guidance) to the heavens: now shall We turn thee to a Qibla that shall please thee. Turn then thy face in the direction of the sacred mosque: Wherever ye are, turn your faces in that direction'." (Sura 2.142-144).

3. Giving Alms *(Zakat)*

Zakat in Arabic means "purification". Over the centuries, the word has taken on the meaning of alms-giving. The connection between purity and alms-giving has Biblical roots. Jesus said, according to the Gospel of Luke 11:41, "But give for alms those things which are within; and behold, everything is clean." In the early Islamic period, zakat was implemented and practiced as a law to help the poor, and build or finance projects such as road construction and bridge building, which were useful to the general public. Zakat was considered a kind of charitable tax and those who refused to pay were subjected to harsh treatment such as flogging.

Zakat is still practiced in Saudi Arabia. In other Islamic nations, state taxation is considered zakat, as it addresses the needs of all people and functions as a funding program to alleviate the misery of everyone. However, Muslims who strictly adhere to the law practice zakat in their everyday personal lives.

The Muslims are mandated in the Quran to give zakat to the poor and the needy because it is the latter's right to receive from those who

---

10. Armstrong, *Muhammad*, pp. 149-150, 161-162.

are fortunate (Sura 51:19). The poor does not necessarily have to be economically poor. Any one who is in want of anything is considered poor. The slaves, the travellers, the orphans, the widows, and the helpless are also considered poor. The Quran mandates, "Give what is due to kindred, the needy, and the wayfarer. That is best for those who seek the countenance of God, and it is they who will prosper" (Sura 30:38). Muslims are instructed to give at least 2.5% of their overall wealth and assets, not just 2.5% of their net income.

A few other sources of income entail a higher percentage of giving. If a farmer obtains his harvest only by depending upon rain water, the farmer should give 10% of his income to charity. If the water for his farm is drawn from the ground or other means, the giving should be five percent. The percentage also varies according to trade. For example, a camel herdsman must give one camel to meet the needs of the poor for every forty camels the owner has. A modern commodity broker or a real estate agent or an engineer or a clerk should give two and a half percent of their cash income.

Zakat teaches the Muslims that all material blessings come from God. The rich and the privileged must meet the physical needs of the less fortunate in the umma. The Quran says:

> The alms (Zakat) are for the poor and needy, those who work to collect them, those whose hearts are to be reconciled, the ransoming of slaves and debtors, and for the cause of God, and for travellers (Sura 9:60).

The Quran also gives stipulations regarding the just treatment of widows, debtors, orphans, and the poor (Sura 90: 13-16). The Muslims are encouraged to redress economic inequalities and fight social evils. All those who are blessed by Allah must attend to the needs of the umma as all Muslims are equal in the sight of Allah. However, alms-giving done in secret is much better and its reward will be a place in paradise.

> As the righteous, they will be in the midst of gardens and springs. Taking joy in the things which their Lord gives them, because, before then, they lived a good life. They were in the habit of sleeping but little by night, and in the hours of early dawn, they (were found) praying for forgiveness; and in their wealth and possessions (was remembered) the right of the (need), Him who asked, and him who (for some reason) was prevented (from asking) (Sura 51:15-19).

The Quran says that those who refuse to give to the poor and those who refuse to obey the commandments of the Quran will be cast into the fires of hell (Sura 74:38-56). Those who help the poor and needy give a loan to God, who will repay the givers in manifold. The exploiters and freeloaders of society are vividly condemned and warned by the Quran. They will incur the wrath and "war from God and His Prophet" (Sura 2:279). Not only the individual believers but also the governments are expected to help and aid the needy. One of the reasons for the rapid multiplication of Islamic institutions and the vast expansion of new mosques around the world is because of billions of petro-dollars being spent by Muslim governments for the Muslim World Mission and the establishment of Islamic umma.

The Quran mandates, the beneficiaries of *Zakat* should only be the members of umma or Islam. The fruits of Muslims should benefit only Muslims.

> Alms are for the poor and the needy, and those employed to administer the funds; for those whose hearts have been recently reconciled to truth; for those in bondage and in debt; in the cause of God; and for the wayfarer: Thus is it ordained by God, and God is full of knowledge and wisdom (Sura 9:60).

4. Fast *(Siyam)*

The Muslims are commanded to fast in the ninth lunar month of Ramadan, the month when the Quran was revealed to Mohammed. As for the formation of the Muslim calendar, Philip K. Hitti writes in *History of the Arabs*, "The Muslim calendar is based on twelve lunar months, and therefore, it is approximately eleven days shorter than the solar year, and goes full cycle through the Gregorian (Western) calendar about every thirty-three years".[11] The month long fasting purifies one's inner self. The Hadith says fast is a major spiritual discipline.

> Narrated Abu Huraira: Allah's Apostle said, "Fasting is a shield or protection from the fire and from committing sins. If one of you is fasting, he should avoid sexual relation with his wife and quarrelling, and if somebody should fight or quarrel with him, he should say, "I am fasting" (3:71; 3.9.128).

The Quran compares the fast with those of earlier religions. The fast prescribed in the Quran during the ninth lunar month is not found in the

---

11. Philip K. Hitti, *History of the Arabs*, p. 458.

Hebrew or Christian tradition. The Christians fasted for forty days before Easter in remembrance of Christ's fast, which excluded Sundays. It is highly speculative which former religions the Quran is referring to when it makes mention of the fast during the lunar month. It is known that the Manichaens and the Sabaeans observed a continuous fast of one lunar month. We do not know if any other sects or groups in Arabia observed a fast during the lunar month. The Quran legislates on this fast:

> O ye who believe! Fasting is prescribed to you as it was prescribed to those before you, that ye may learn self-restraint. Fasting for a fixed number of days; but if any of you is ill, or on a journey, the prescribed number (should be made up) from days later. For those who can do it (with hardship), is a ransom, the feeding of one that is indigent. But he that will give more, of his own free will, - it is better for him. And it is better for you that ye fast, if ye only knew. Ramadhan is the (month) in which was sent down the Quran, as a guide to mankind, also clear (signs) for guidance and judgment between right and wrong... When My servants ask thee concerning Me, I am indeed close (to them): I listen to the prayer of every suppliant when he calleth Me: Let them also, with a will, listen to my call, and believe in Me. (Sura 2:183-186).

Fasting draws believers closer to Allah to seek his forgiveness for sins committed and to acknowledge his blessings upon life. It also helps focus one's mind from material things and pay more attention to the all-encompassing love and mercies of the Sovereign God. Fasting helps the believers experience hunger, thirst, and abstinence which are the basic human instincts. Fasting reminds the Muslims that they are mortal and every good thing comes from God. Fasting is also considered an offering to God. Fasting and deprivation of food create an awareness of the plight of the needy and less fortunate, and thus all Muslims are brought together in unity by a common human experience of hunger and thirst.

Hammudah Abd-al Ati testifies how the mandatory practices, particularly fasting, established by the prophet bring the Muslim community to a common ground. Abd-al Ati states, with admiration, *Siyam* binds the members of the Islamic community together in a unique way which no other religion of the world has done. It is one of its kind.

> The fast originates in man the real Spirit of Social Belonging, of Unity and Brotherhood, of Equality before God as well as

before the Law. This spirit is the natural product of the fact that when man fasts, he feels that he is joining the whole Muslim society in observing the same duty in the same manner at the same time for the same motives to the same end. No sociologist can say that there has been at any period of history anything comparable to this fine institution of Islam. People have been crying throughout the ages for acceptable belonging, for unity, for brotherhood, for equality, but how echoless their voice has been, and how very little success they have met. Where can they find their goals without the guiding light of Islam?[12]

The sick, the menstruating women, and the travelers are excused from the fast, albeit, they have to make it up at a later period with as many days of fasting as they have missed. Menstruating women are considered ritually unpure as the Hebrew scriptures had taught. It was a belief shared both by Jews and Christians of Mohammed's days. During the fast, which begins from sunrise and ends at sunset, the believers take nothing into the digestive tract and the intestine. Not even water is drunk during the day time. After sun set, a special meal breaks the fast. Every Muslim who has attained puberty is encouraged to fast. Any kind of personal pleasure, particularly sexual activity, is forbidden during daytime. The Quran warns:

> It is made lawful for you to go unto your wives on the night of the fast. They are raiment for you and you are raiment for them. Allah is aware that you were deceiving yourselves in this respect and He has turned in mercy toward you and relieved you. So hold intercourse with them and seek that which Allah has ordained for you, and eat and drink until the white thread becomes distinct to you from the black thread of the dawn. Then strictly observe the fast till nightfall and touch them not, but be at your devotions in the mosques. These are the limits imposed by Allah, so approach them not (Sura 2:187).

Ramadan brings the community together to pray, meditate and submit to God. Kenneth Cragg says that Ramadan fosters the community's sense of belonging. He writes:

> Belonging in Ramadan can be a figure of men's involvement with each other. The whole power and theme of the fast is communal. Men in Islam participate because they are "in

---

12. Hammudah Abd-al Ati, *Islam in Focus*, (Indianapolis: American Trust Publications, 1977), p.88.

Islam". This is a form of their membership and the fact that others, with strong communal sanction, are fulfilling it also both commands and fosters the individuals' conformity. In a sense the realization that we live among fellows, among a common humanity, can become a force in the conquest of self-will. There is clearly an intimate connection between what the individual ought to do and the fact that he is part of a whole, a human whole.[13]

Ramadan is a time for celebration and socializing. Special food and meals are served after dusk. Communal and family celebrations are organized during this time of the year during late evenings. The Quran is studied, memorized, and recited at home and the mosque during this season. As total abstinence is encouraged during daylight hours, Muslim families rise before sunrise and eat heavy meals which might sustain them all day.

Ramadan is celebrated in conjunction with the revelation given to Mohammed. On the twenty seventh day of the festival, the Muslims observe the "Night of Power" in commemoration of the command to recite the Quran angel Gabriel gave the Prophet. The last day of Ramadan is celebrated with big feasts and festivities, which is called *Id al-Fitr* (commonly called Id), the Breaking of the Fast.

5 Pilgrimage to Mecca *(Hajj)*

The word *Hajj* comes from the Semitic root symbolizing the making of a circuit. The word is mentioned in the Hebrew Scriptures with reference to feasts in Exodus 23:14 and in Judges 21:19. Pilgrimage to Mecca makes a Muslim a complete Muslim. A Muslim is expected to undertake the pilgrimage, at least once in his lifetime. Only those who are not able to make the trip on account of financial or physical limitations are forgiven. Everyone who has means to go to Mecca but chooses not to commits a sin against Allah. Believers, usually go to Mecca during the last month of the Muslim year, Dhu-al-Hijjah, for seven days (days 7 through 13).

Mecca for the Muslims is like the New Jerusalem to Christians, although no such comparisons have been made in the Islamic literatures. Pilgrimage to Mecca teaches the Muslims the origin of their faith and

---

13. Kenneth Cragg, *The Dome and the Rock: Jerusalem Studies in Islam*, (London: S.P.C.K., 1964), p.29

the fulfillment of the act of prayer. Kaaba unites Muslims from all over the world as a single believing community. Non-Muslims are not allowed within the city limits. Every year, over two million Muslims from all over the world gather at Mecca to take part in the special celebration during the month of Ramadan. Some Muslims save money for years to make the pilgrimage. Travel to Mecca is undertaken between the eighth and the thirteenth days of the twelfth month of the Muslim lunar year. The Muslims do not go to worship a shrine or a statue in Mecca, rather, they gather together in an ancient and historic place, and worship the Eternal God.

When men go to Mecca, they shave their heads and wear a white garment called *Ithram*, which is made of two seamless pieces of unstitched cloth. No stitched clothing is allowed. This ritual clothing is the customary dress of the bedouins who used to live in the arid regions of pre-Islamic Arabia.[14] Women do not wear special clothing, but they do wear a long dress to cover their head and conceal their hair. They do not wear a veil, but their bodies are covered to the wrist and to the ankle. The ritual clothing reminds the believers of their humble origin from a rural, Bedouin community of believers to one of the largest spiritual, religious, and political forces in the world. The equality of human beings before God is made visible by this symbolic act.

No cosmetics or jewellery are to be used while on pilgrimage. Sexual activity is absolutely prohibited. Menstruation does not prohibit a woman to perform pilgrimage or to enter the Grand Mosque of Mecca *(Al-Masjid Al-Haram)*, in the centre of which stands the kaaba. While in Mecca, the pilgrims are forbidden to cut their hair, pare the nails, fell a green tree, kill an animal (except poisonous animals and rodents). Hence, the pilgrims do not have to worry about everyday routines of life but can focus on spiritual matters of life.

Modern air and sea travel facilities have made the pilgrimage much easier to undertake for Muslims who live far away from Mecca. When the pilgrims enter the city of Mecca, by whatever mode of transportation, they cry out a traditional prayer in Arabic, over and over again. The prayer is known as the *Talbiyah:*

> You call us, we are here, O Lord! We are here!
> We are here, there is no one beside You! We are here!
> Praise and good deeds belong to You, and the empire!
> There is none but You!

---

14. Some nomads in the deserts still wear it.

Another tradition has a much more personalized version:

At your call, O Lord, I come! At your call I come!
You who are peerless: At your call I come!
All praises and blessing be to you. Sovereignty too.
You who are peerless: At your call I come!

The background of the pilgrims and the translations from Arabic are responsible for variations of prayers.

When the pilgrims arrive at Mecca, they go straight to the Grand Mosque. The kaaba is a roughly cube-shaped building with a low door in its northeast side. At its eastern corner is the black stone, the sacred shrine, which is built into the wall about five feet above the ground. The pilgrims spend a few days praying at this place kissing the stone out of love and respect. A Hadith says:

Narrated Abis bin Rabi'a: Umar came near the Black Stone and kissed and said, "No doubt, I know that you are a stone and can neither benefit anyone nor harm anyone. Had I not seen Allah's Apostle kissing you I would not have kissed you" (2:390-91; 26.49.667).

The kaaba, according to Islamic belief, was established by Adam, the founder of true religion, who placed in its wall the sacred stone of Paradise which was given to him by the angel Gabriel. The stone was later given to Abraham and Ishmael. When Adam received the stone from Gabriel, it was white in colour but turned black over the years as it absorbed the evils of the world which were committed against Allah and the polytheistic worship which was practiced by the Arabs in rebellion against Abrahamic monotheistic religion. The stone is considered a symbol of God's covenant with Ishmael and his descendants who are the Arabs and followers of Allah. Critics say the black stone was a meteorite which fell on the desert centuries before Mohammed came.

On the last day, the Quran attests, God will gather all of humanity and judge them according to their deeds at this sacred site. As the pilgrims reach the kaaba, they circle seven times and do prostrations from a place Abraham supposedly stood. Circling the kaaba has been a practice since the days of Abraham and Ishmael. Islam strongly believes Abraham and Ishmael visited Mecca, observed salat, circumambulated the kaaba, and passed on those traditions to the succeeding generations. In time, over population, family feuds and tribal dissension made people move away from the kaaba. Many left for distant places in search of food and shelter, and others tried to stay away from warring situations. When they moved, the early Arabs carried with them a stone or a symbol from kaaba in its reverence and circumambulated them. This practice eventually led them to idolatry and polytheism. Of the people who lived before Mohammed and their religious practices, Ibn al-Kalbi writes:

> They forgot their ancient beliefs and changed their religion of Abraham and Ishmael for another. They worshipped idols and returned to the practices of the nations before them. After discovering the images which the people of Noah...worshipped, they adopted the worship of those which were remembered. Among the practices were some which came down from the time of Abraham and Ishmael, including the veneration and circumambulation of the temple (in Mecca), the pilgrimage, the visitation...the standing on 'Arafa, the rituals of Muzdalifa, offering sacrifices, and uttering the ritual formulae during the pilgrimage and visitation.[15]

After their worship at kaaba, the pilgrims run frantically between the hills of Safa and Marwa in celebration of Hagar's plea for water for her son Ishmael. Then they go to drink water from the spring of Zamzam. The spring is considered the source of water which was revealed to Hagar by an angel when she and her son Ishamel were sent out of Sarah's abode and were about to die of thrist in the wilderness (Genesis 21:15-21).

The water of Zamzam saved Hagar and her little son, Ishmael. Islamic traditon says that Hagar, then, settled at Mecca where Abraham came to visit her from time to time. Near the kaaba is a site called *Maqam*, a station of Abraham, which contains a stone on which Abraham's feet are reported to have left a mark. The site is still regarded as a sacred spot. Drinking water from Zamzam has a deep spiritual and metaphysical implication. The desperate longing for a thirst quenching water unites the pilgrims to their ancestral faith, reminds them of their long heritage, refreshes their soul from its weary search, and cleanses them of their sins.

Islam has several oral and literary traditions about the pilgrims' frantic run and search for water between the hills of Safa and Marwa.

---

15. Ibn al-Kalbi, *Kitab al-asham*, R. Klinke-Rosenberger, ed., (Leipzig: Otto Harrassowitz, 1941), pp. 3-4. Quote taken from Rippin, *Muslims: Their Religious Beliefs and Practices*, vol.1, pp.12,13.

The Quran makes mention of it in Sura 2:158. Yet, some scholars are not sure if indeed the pilgrims, prior to the arrival of Islam, ran frantically between the hills to re-enact their ancestors' search for water. Rippin cites two common Islamic stories which have dissenting details about the journey of the pilgrims between the hills.

> On Safa was the image of a man called Isaf, while on Marwa was the image of a woman called Na'la. The People of the Book [i.e., the Jews and Christians] claimed that these two had committed adultery in the Ka'ba [in Mecca] so God converted them into stone and placed them on Safa and Marwa in order to act as warning to others... The people of the jahiliyya stroked the idols when they circumambulated them [during their pilgrimage rituals]. When Islam came and the idols were broken, Muslims detested the circumambulation between the hills because of [their association with] the idols. So God revealed this verse.[16]

Another story says:

> 'Urwa ibn al-Zubayr said to 'A'isha: "I see no fault in someone who does not run between Sufa and Marwa, nor would it concern me if I did not run between them." 'A' isha answered: "Your are wrong, O son of my sister! Mohammed ran between them and so did the Muslims. Rather it was [the pagans] who sacrificed to Manat, the idol of Mushlal, who did not run between them. Then God sent down this verse. If it were as you say, the verse would read "there is no blame on whoever does not run between them."[17]

Although the two accounts give differing and conflictive historical descriptions, both of them justify the present day running between the hills.

An important part of the Hajj, pilgrimage to Mecca, is to go to the Plain of Araft which is fourteen miles east of Mecca and stand before God in front of the Mount of Mercy (Jabal-ur-Rahman) from noon to sunset in repentance. Since the pilgrimage is undertaken as a great

---

16. Michael Cook, "Early Islamic Dietary Law", Jerusalem Studies in Arabic and Islam, vol.7, (1986), pp.270-271. Quote taken from Rippin, Muslims: Their Religious Beliefs and Practices, vol 1, p.11.

17. Ibid.

penitential act to secure forgiveness of sins, the pilgrims ceaselessly read, memorize, recite the verses from the Quran and endlessly submit themselves before Allah. The pilgrims also hear invocations from the Imams to the glory of Allah and his prophet Mohammed. The fundamental and the major doctrines of Islam are recited and expounded in countless ways in order for pilgrims to grasp the deeper significance of their faith. No pilgrim can miss the standing ceremony of waiting in penitence before the Mount of Mercy to pray and to listen to the great teachers of Islam. If a pilgrim misses it, the entire trip to Mecca is rendered useless and the pilgrimage has to be repeated again.

Standing on the Plain of Arafat also symbolizes Abraham's steadfastness and the hosts of ancestors who listened to the master sermons preached from there by Allah's prophet. Mohammed also is believed to have preached his last sermon for peace and unity among the faithful from that hill. The Prophet's message is repeated here as a reminder to the pilgrims and Muslims around the world.

The pilgrimage formally ends on the morning of the tenth, the "Day of Slaughter" *(Yom-Un-Narh)*, while the pilgrims gather in the valley of Minah. At a site called "the stoning place of the stumbling block" *(Janrat-Ul 'Aqaba)*, the pilgrims throw stones at three carved pillars representing the "Great Satan". This ritual is to follow what Abraham had done when he was tempted by Satan not to listen to God in sacrificing his son but to let his son live. Abraham reacted to Satan's temptation to disobey God's command by picking up stones and throwing at the tempter three times.

After the ritual of stone throwing, the pilgrims sacrifice an animal and celebrate the Feast of Sacrifice *(Ad Al-Adha)*. The Feast commemorates God's command to Abraham to sacrifice his son. Islamic tradition says Abraham was asked to sacrifice Ishmael not Isaac as the book of Genesis portrays in chapter 22. The Quran, in fact, is silent about the name of that son.

When Abraham passed the test of his faith, according to the Quran, God gave Abraham a ram to be sacrificed as a substitute for his son. The pilgrims also sacrifice animals as a symbolic act of obedience to God. By doing so, they affirm they will sacrifice anything that is important to them in obedience to God's command. The celebration of the Feast and the break of the Fast formally conclude the canonical observation of the pilgrimage. The sacrificed animals are shared with fellow pilgrims and Muslims in nearby towns and cities. The present day Saudi Arabian government uses modern technology and conveniences to send the sacrificed and the leftover meat to Muslims in other parts of the world by means of airplane and refrigerated ships.

Before coming home, the pilgrims visit the first mosque ever built and the prophet's tomb, which are situated in Medina. Some will even go to Jerusalem, the third holiest city for Muslims, to visit the *Al-Aqsa* mosque from where Mohammed is said to have ascended into heaven and returned during his night journey. Those who are not able to go to Mecca during the festival season, can undertake the *Umrah*, the lesser pilgrimage, during other times of the year.

When the pilgrims go back to their respective communities, they are received by their relatives and fellow believers, and they are asked to lead the worship service at the local mosques. The returned pilgrims are usually given an honorary title *Hajji* before their names and treated with respect and reverence.

CHAPTER IX
Islam and Jesus

Judaism, Christianity, and Islam trace their origins back to the Middle East. They are all monotheistic religions which take the teachings of the Hebrew Scriptures about the One, Eternal, and Just God seriously. Moses said in Deuteronomy 6:4, "The Lord our God is one Lord; and you shall love the Lord your God with all your heart, and with all your soul, and with all your might." Thousands of years after Moses, when asked which was the first and the foremost of all commandments, Jesus affirmed Moses' message about the One God and of the human race's absolute commitment to him.

Islam likewise affirms the Oneness of God in its Shahada. The uncompromising monotheism, the oneness, and the Sovereignty of the Creator God are evident throughout the Quran. The most supportive verses for this are found in Sura 57.

> Whatever is in the heavens and on earth, -let it declare the praise and glory of God: for he is exalted in might, the wise. To him belongs the dominion of the heavens and the earth: it is he who gives life and death; and he has power over all things. He is the first, and the last, the evident and the immanent: and he has full knowledge of all things. He is who created the heavens and the earth. In six days, and is moreover firmly established on the throne (of authority). He knows what enters within the earth and what comes forth out of it, what comes down from heaven and what mounts up to it. And he is with you wheresoever you may be. And God sees well all that ye do (Sura 57:1-4).

The fundamental precepts of Islam were codified and passed on to succeeding generations by Islamic scholars and mystics. In the twelfth century, Al-Nasafi wrote the *Articles of Faith* in which he gave a philosophical discourse on the Quranic understanding of God.

In one of his articles, he explained the attributes of God and presented in simple, clear language who God is and who he is not.

> God Most High, the One, the Eternal, the Decreeing, the Knowing, the Seeing, the Hearing, the Willing: he is not an attribute, not a body, nor an essence, nor a thing formed, nor a thing bounded, nor a thing numbered, nor a thing divided, nor a thing compounded, nor a thing limited. He is not described by *mahiya* [what-ness], nor by *kaifiyyah* [howness], and He does not exist in place or time. There is nothing that resembles Him... He has qualities from all eternity, not belonging to the genus of sounds and letter, a quality that is incompatible with coming to silence.[1]

Islam's belief in the unity of God is based on the revelation given to Adam, the first prophet, and then to Abraham, "the friend of God" who was considered the first Muslim. When some of the descendants of Abraham failed to maintain monotheistic worship, God raised prophets from time to time and sent them into the world to bring people back to the "right way" of worship. The greatest of the prophets who came after Abraham was Jesus.

Jesus, according to the Quran, came in the succession of prophets, "to follow in their footsteps confirming that which was (revealed) before him, and We bestowed on him the Gospel wherein is guidance and a light" (5:46). The reason why the Quran calls Abraham a true Muslim is that he voluntarily submitted himself to God's will in absolute faith and in unconditional surrender. Islam affirms that a true Muslim is the one who says, "My welfare is only in Allah. In Him I trust and unto Him I turn (repentant)" (Sura 11:88).

Jesus and the Quran

Although, Muslims do not accept the Christian Scriptures in its present form, the Quran presents Jesus (whom the Quran calls with different names: Isa, Miriam, Son of Mary) in a respectful way. In fact, Islam is the only non-Christian religion that acknowledges the teachings and miraculous birth of Jesus. The Quran speaks about Jesus in 14 suras, 4

---

1. Duncan B. Macdonald, *Development of Muslim Theology, Jurisprudence and Constitutional Theory*, (Lahore: Premier Book House, 1964), pp.314-315. Quoted by Kenneth Cragg and R. Marston Speight in *The House of Islam*, Third Edition, (Belmont, Ca.: Wadsworth Publishing Co., 1988), p.15.

from the Meccan period when Mohammed was opposed by the Qurayish tribe and 10 from the Medinan period when the Jews and Christians challenged the origin of his message. Jesus, according to the Quran, was Allah's Prophet, and was sent with a message to the Israelites, the people of Jesus' time. Jesus, the messenger of God, is introduced in the Quran as the Messiah, a Spirit, a Mercy, and a Word from God who owed his existence to God's command. "God creates what He wills. When He decrees anything He only says to it "Be!" and it comes into being." The Quran emphasizes that Jesus was created by a Sovereign God, by His divine speech. "He simply said, 'Be!' and it is." This story comes very close to the creation story rendered in Genesis Chapter 1. According to the Quran, Jesus and Adam were created in like manner with celestial decree and divine power (Sura 2:10). "Jesus was no more than a mortal whom we favoured and made an example to the Israelites" (Sura 43:59). The Jesus of the Quran, therefore, is not the Word of God but word from God, a specially created being like Adam. The Quranic name Isa, probably came from the Syriac Yeshu, which in turn originated from the Hebrew, Yeshua.[2] The European Christians' use of the name Jesus has its origin from the Greek (Ieysous), an abbreviated form of Yehoshua. The meaning of Yehoshua is "YHWH is my salvation." The Arabic Bible, both modern and traditional, continue to use Yasu whenever it refers to Jesus.

Jesus : the Sign of God

The Quran acknowledges the miraculous birth of Jesus, which as explained above, is compared to that of Adam. Adam was born by Allah's Divine decree as a sign of God's care for the world. The angel who came from God announced the birth of Jesus to Mary (Miriam) before she conceived the child. He told her she would bear a son who would be "a revelation for mankind and a mercy from Us" (Sura 19:17-21). Both Jesus and Mary are sinless and they would be "a sign and a blessing from God" to the whole world (Sura 19:21). The early childhood of Jesus and his life with his parents are not mentioned anywhere in the Quran. There is only a slight and passing reference about the place of his birth, "We made the son of Mary and his mother a portent, and We gave them refuge on a height, a place of flocks and water-springs" (Sura 23:50).

---

2. One needs to remember Isa is not the Arabicized name for Jesus.

Islam teaches that Jesus received the Gospel from heaven by divine revelation. He received the message in the same manner as the earlier prophets like Moses and David received the ten commandments and Psalms (Sura 3:46-60). The Jesus of Islam is merely a prophet sent by God as a sign of God's power (aya) with a definite message to the people of his time, the Israelites (Sura 3:49-50).[3] His message to them was that they should worship the one, true God, and submit to him. The first words Jesus spoke from the cradle were already the words of a Muslim. From the very beginning of his birth Jesus knew that he was "only a servant" of Allah.

The Quran acknowledges that Jesus was conceived and born of a pious virgin, who was "a token for (all) peoples" (Sura 21:91). Mary was chosen by God because she was humble, obedient, and the Spirit of God dwelt within her (Sura 21:91, 66:12). Jesus is addressed as *Al-Masih*, the Messiah. Most importantly, the Quran says, the Prophet Jesus (Isa) is only a messenger of Allah, not a Redeemer; a servant not a Saviour. "Not one of the beings in the heavens and earth must come to (Allah) most gracious as servant" (Sura 19:93). After all, Allah is Supreme.

> His name (the name of the Word) is Messiah, Jesus the son of Mary, honourable in this world and the next, being among those who are nigh to God (Sura 3:40).

However, the title "Messiah" does not have any of the Biblical connotations of Messiah as a liberator from bondage or deliverer from sin. The Messiah of the Quran is simply a messenger of God, who preached about the sovereignty of Allah and who invited people to worship and submit to him (Sura 4:17).

The Quranic concept of anointing also differs from the Biblical notion. In the Quran, Jesus is referred to as the one who is anointed with honour, protected from Satan's power from birth (Sura 3:31-36), and blessed with Allah's favour to serve as a special Messenger. The messiahship of Jesus is established by the miracles he performed and the revelations he brought in the form of the Gospel (Sura 3:43-45). The Islamic concept of Messiah is very much confined to the equipping and commissioning of a servant of God for the prophethood and teaching of Allah's message. It has no redemptive feature.

---

3. *Aya* is used in many different ways in the Quran. The punishment of unbelievers (15:75), the reward for believers (29:24), the wonders of nature, and the prophets of Allah are seen as an *aya* of God. The greatest sign of God ever given to humankind is the Quran itself.

The Quranic narration of Jesus begins with the story of the mother of Mary, the wife of Imran. As soon as Mary was born, she was entrusted by her parents to Zechariah, a priest, who raised her in the closed enclaves of the temple called *Mithrab*. The word *Mithrab* could be translated as sanctuary, cell or niche. The Gospels do not say Mary was cared for by Zechariah, although during her pregnancy, Mary did go and stayed with Zechariah and Elizabeth for three months as recorded in Luke 1:40-57. Some of the narration of Mary's childhood as mentioned in the Quran comes nearer to what has been recorded in the apocryphal infancy gospels, particularly the Protevangelism of James.

In the Book of James, Mary was taken to the temple when she was three years old, where Zechariah was a priest. Mary was miraculously fed and given food from the hand of an angel. Traditions say that Mary was fed from heaven. Liberal Islamic scholars say that Mary was fed by fellow worshippers who brought gifts to the temple where she was living which by itself was a miracle.

The Quran stresses the virginity of Mary and the miraculous birth of Jesus without a biological father. The birth of Jesus begins with the chronicle of Mary's life along in the desert, far away from any human habitation. After her child was born, Mary returned to the community where her fidelity was questioned.[4] In order to clear his mother, the infant Jesus spoke from the cradle and defended his mother.

> (Jesus) said : I am indeed a servant of God. He hath given me revelation and made me a prophet. And he hath made me blessed wheresover I be, and hath enjoined on me prayer and charity as long as I live. (He) hath made me kind to my mother, and not overbearing or miserable. So peace is on me the day I was born, the day that I die, And the day that I shall be raised up to life (again) (Sura 19:30-33).

The Infancy Gospel mentions that Jesus spoke from the cradle to Mary, "I am Jesus, the Son of God, the Word, which you have borne as the angel Gabriel announced to you." Christian scholars contend that this story about Jesus must have been a very common tradition among Arab Christians during Mohammed's time.

---

4. Matthew Gospel talks about Joseph's hesitancy in accepting Mary as his wife when he came to know she was with a child. Matthew 1:19.

Islam and Mary

Islamic traditions say that Mohammed had a profound respect for Mary. The Quran calls her, "the daughter of Imran and Hanah, and "the sister of Aaron" (Sura 19:128). Mary's relationship with Aaron, the brother of Moses, who lived thousands of years before Mary, is interpreted by the Muslims as a kinship on a spiritual plane. Islamic literatures often present Mary with her honorific "our lady" (Sayyadátuna) just as the Prophets of Allah are addressed "our lord" (Sayyiduna).[5] Azraqi, a Muslim historian of Mecca, who died in 858 A.D., said that in the kaaba, on the pillar near the door was hanging a picture of Mary with Jesus on her knee. When Mohammed invaded Mecca and commanded his soldiers destroy all the idols and pictures in the kaaba and wash the sanctuary with water from the Zamzam well, he saw the picture of Mary and Jesus on the pillar, covered it with his hands and said to his soldiers, "Wash out all except what is below my hands".[6]

All the women in the Quran, except Mary, are called by the name of their husbands, e.g., the wife of Adam, the wife of Noah, the wife of Lot, the wife of Pharaoh, the queen of Sheba. Nowhere in the Quran is Joseph declared Mary's husband nor is Mary declared Joseph's wife. Jesus is often called "son of Mary", yet Mary has not been called "Mary, the mother of Jesus".

The Quran presents Jesus as a sinless human being, born of a virgin mother, Maryam (Mary), by Allah's decree. Hence Jesus is called Ibn Maryam (son of Mary) in the Quran. Ibn Maryam is one of the several titles attributed to Jesus, and is found 23 times in the Quran: 16 times as "Jesus, son of Mary", and seven times as "son of Mary" or with other titles. In contrast, the title son of Mary occurs only once in the Bible.

Some Muslim scholars argue that the title "Jesus, son of Mary" refers to the mortal and human nature of Jesus. A few others argue that children in those days were called after the father, and not the mother, except where the father was not known. Therefore, the angel's announcement to Mary was to let her know that Jesus would be born without a father.

Nevertheless, those arguments are highly speculative and unsubstantiated. Although, in pre-Islamic Arabia, it was not uncommon for children to be called after the father, it was also not that unusual to

5. Glasse, The Concise Encyclopedia of Islam, p.260.

6. Keppel Archibald Cameron Creswell, A Short History of Early Muslim Architecture, (Baltimore, Md.: Penguin Books, 1958), p.2.

be called after one's mother. Some poets, Ibn Aisha, Ibn Mayyada, and Mohammed's opponent Abu Jahl were known by their mothers' names. W. Montgomery Watt in his book *Mohammed at Medina* talks about the existence of a strong matrilineal idea in some Arabian families.[7] The fact that Jesus was called son of Mary defines his mother was a well-known woman who, according to the Quran, was "above the women of the worlds". The Quran does not make mention of Joseph, who according to Matthew's and Luke's Gospels, was the foster-father of Jesus. Mary "was a faithful woman", who "guarded her chastity". She was "one of the devout" and God chose her "above the women of the worlds" (Sura 5:75-79, 21:91, 66:12, 3:37, 42). Mary was sinless and virtuous. The angels said, "O Mary! Lo! Allah has chosen you and made pure, and has preferred you above (all) the women of creation" (Sura 3:42).

The Quran speaks of Mary's conception of Jesus, her withdrawal to the temple, the annuciation, the birth of Jesus, the calumny endured by Mary, and the miraculous child called Jesus in an elaborate way. The miraculous birth of Jesus is narrated in two different places in the Quran with slight variations: (Sura 3:42-53 and 19:16-36).

The Quranic reference to Mary's withdrawal to "a place eastward" and with a "veil" (or curtain) has been debated. The Book of James says that when the angel appeared, Mary was at home and wearing a veil for the temple. Contrary to the above report, neither the gospel account nor the Quran places the annunciation in the temple. A few Islamic scholars (for instance, Maulana Azad) interpret the "eastern place" as Nazareth which the gospels talk about.

Jesus and the Miracles

The Quran attests to some of the miracles Jesus performed from his childhood. The more prominent of his miracles are the creation of birds out of clay, healing of the blind, cleansing of the lepers, and raising of the dead.[8] At one time, in answer to his prayer, Jesus received from heaven a table filled with bounteous food (Sura 5:12, 114).[9]

---

7. Watt, *Mohammed at Medina*, p.374.

8. Stories about giving life to birds of clay is found in the Apocryphal Gospel of Thomas. Many words used in this narration are also found in the Old Testament creation story of Adam. See Genesis 3 and Sura 3:48, 49, 6:2, 32:9.

9. Some critics say that Mohammed was confused about Jesus' feeding of the five thousand as recorded in the Gospels. Others say it is the story of the Last Supper. Still others say it is a reference to the prayer he taught his disciples, "Give us this day our daily bread."

Some of the apocryphal literatures do narrate stories about the miracles Jesus performed as an infant. The Gospel of Pseudo-Matthew, a Latin script probably written in eight century C.E., says that during the Holy Family's flight into Egypt, Mary and Joseph were overcome with hunger and thirst and they were sitting under a tree. Infant Jesus, sitting on Mary's lap and having seen the plight of his earthly parents, ordered the tree to bend down and give its fruits to his mother. Then he said to the tree to give some of the water under its roots. The tree obeyed and the Holy Family was refreshed. The Arabic Infancy Gospel narrates another similar story. It says the family was resting under a sycamore tree at Matarieh and there Jesus caused a spring to gush out. His mother washed his clothes and the whole family got nourished by the fresh water.

The Quran does not talk about Jesus' control over nature nor the miracles he performed in controlling them. The first miracle Jesus performed at Cana of Galilee, the changing of water into wine, and the subsequent "nature" miracles, such as, stilling the storm, and walking on the water are not alluded to in the Quran.

The Holy Spirit and Ahmad

Muslims interpret the references to the Holy Spirit found in the Gospels as allusions to the coming of another prophet, Mohammed. One such allusion is given to a Syriac word meant for the Holy Spirit. Muslim scholars argue, in the Syriac lectionary the Greek word for the Holy Spirit (paraclete) had been translated as Munahhema (means, life-giver), which comes very near to the word "Mohammed". Others like Karen Armstrong, a former Roman Catholic nun who became a religious pluralist, contends:

> Other Arab Christians had read Periklytos instead of 'Paraclete', which can be translated by the Arabic 'Ahmad'. This was a common name in Arabia and, like 'Muhammad', it means 'the praised one'. Muhammad had obviously been made aware of this translation because the Quran refers to the belief that Jesus had foretold that another prophet, called 'Ahmad', would come after him and confirm his message.[10]

The Quran's reference to Ahmad in Sura 61:6 has generated considerable discussion among both Muslim and Christian scholars. Ahamd has generally been translated as Mohammed by the Muslims, whose coming had been foretold by Jesus.

---

10. Armstrong, *Muhammad: A Biography of the Prophet*, p.73

The word Comforter, as referred to in the Gospels, comes from the Greek word *Paraclete*. It always refers to the Holy Spirit, except once to Jesus (I John 2:1). Since *Paraclete* is a difficult word to understand and translate, many versions of the Christian Scriptures retained the same Greek word in their translations. Thus in the Syriac Gospel it is mentioned as *Paragleto* and in the Arabic version as *Faraqlit*. Christian scholars argue that the word *Parakletos*, which means Comforter, was indeed confused and misunderstood by the Muslims with the word *Periklutos*, which in fact means, "celebrated" or "praised one". As "celebrated" or "praised one" is the actual meaning of Ahmad, critics say that Muslim writers and commentators have assumed that the coming of Ahmad was foretold in the Gospels.

Muslims do not agree with the above thesis. They say that the prediction of the *Paraklete* was indeed applied to Mohammed even before the middle of the second century C.E. However, the terms used have been either the Greek *Parakletos* or its correct Aramaic translation *Menehhemana*.[11]

Christians argue that Jesus was only referring to the Holy Spirit, the Spirit of Truth, which was to come upon his disciples from the Day of Pentecost on, and bear witness to Christ everywhere, and guide them into deeper truth. The Holy Spirit is the Spirit of Christ himself who will abide with every believer all the time, unlike the Jesus who came in a physical body. The Gospel of John says:

> [Jesus said] I will pray to the Father, and he will give you another Counselor, to be with you for ever, even the Spirit of truth, whom the world cannot receive, because it neither sees him nor knows him; you know him, for he dwells with you, and will be in you. (John 14:16-18).

> But when the Counselor comes, whom I shall send to you from the Father, even the Spirit of truth, who proceeds from the Father, he will bear witness to me. (John 15:26). Nevertheless I tell you the truth: it is to your advantage that I go away, for if I do not go away, the Counselor will not come to you; but if I go, I will send him to you. (John 16:7).

---

11. See The Encylopaedia of Islam, (New York: E.J. Brill, 1987), I, p.267.

Debate on the Divinity of Jesus

The greatest stumbling blocks to Muslims in reference to Christ are his divinity, his Sonship, his vicarious death on the cross, the efficacy of his mediatorial office, and the doctrine of the Trinity. In rejecting the incarnation of Jesus, the Quran comes very close to Nestorius' teachings about Jesus. Some Christian scholars argue that Mohammed's concept of Allah as the One Sovereign God was influenced by Nestorianism.

> God cannot have a mother, [Nestorius] argued, and no creature could have engendered the Godhead; Mary bore a man the vehicle of divinity but not God. The Godhead cannot have been carried for nine months in a woman's womb, or have been wrapped in baby clothes, or have suffered, died and been buried.[12]

The Quran condemns any association of anthropomorphism to Allah or the sharing of his Godhead by a human being. Associating Jesus with God and narrating his birth as the Saviour of humankind limit God's sovereign power over his creation. God cannot come in the form of a human being. The Christians, by equating Jesus with God, have committed the gravest sin.

> They say God has begotten a Son. Praise His Holiness! No (Sura 2:116).

> The Nazarenes say with their mouth imitating those who formerly disbelieved. May God curse them. O how they pervert things (Sura 9:30).

The Quran insists that Jesus himself denied his divinity and claimed he was only Allah's servant and a messenger.

> And when Allah says: O Jesus, son of Mary! Did you say to mankind: Take me and my mother for two gods beside Allah? he says: Be glorified! It was not mine to utter that to which I had no right. If I used to say it, then You know it. You know what is in my mind. You, only You, are the Knower of Things Hidden. I spoke to them only what You commanded me, (saying) Worship Allah, my Lord and and your Lord. I was a witness of them and when You took me you were the Watcher

---

12. J.N.D. Kelly, *Early Christian Doctrines*, 3rd ed (Edinburgh: T.&᾽. Clark, 1965), p.311.

over them. You are Witness over all things. If you punish them, they are Your slaves, and if You forgive them (they are Your slaves). You, only You are the Mighty, the Wise (Sura 5:116-18).

Speaking of the Sovereignty of God and the humanity and the personality of Jesus, the Messiah, the Quran says:

O People of the Book! Commit no excesses in your religion... Christ Jesus the son of Mary was (no more than) an Apostle of God, and his word, which he bestowed on Mary, and a Spirit proceeding from him: so believe in God and his Apostles. Say not "Trinity" : desist (Sura 4:171).

In blasphemy indeed are those that say that Allah is Christ the son of Mary. Say : "Who then hath the least power against God, if his will were to destroy Christ the son of Mary, his mother, and all - everyone that is on earth? For to Allah belongeth the dominion of the heavens and the earth, and all that is between. He createth what he pleaseth. For God hath power over all things (Sura 5:17).

Nonetheless, the title Messiah given to Jesus is an honorific title without any historic, particularly Biblical, implications. Not only does the Quran deny the divinity of Jesus but it also asserts that he is no more than other prophets who transmitted God's revelation to humanity. The names attributed to Jesus as Son of God, Lamb of God, God's only begotten Son are blasphemous and a corruption of Allah's message revealed through Jesus. The Muslims take the title 'Son of God' literally and argue that the term undermines God's Sovereignty; Jesus, after all, is the son of Mary not the Son of God.

Christians are accused of shifting attention from the message to the messenger and elevating a mere prophet to the level of God. Christians have committed the worst crime against humanity and God by giving a partner to the Supreme God. The Quran incriminates them by saying:

They say : Allah has taken a son. Glorified be He! He has no needs! He is all that is in the heavens and all that is in the earth. You have no warrant for this. Do you tell concerning Allah what you do not know? (Sura 10:68).

> And they say: Allah has taken to Himself a son. Be He glorified!
> No! But whatever is in the heavens and the earth is His. All
> are subservient to Him. The Originator of the heavens and the
> earth! When he decrees a thing, He says to it only: Be! and it
> is (Sura 2:116-117).

> Allah says : It is not befitting to (Allah) that He should beget a
> son. Glory be to him, when he determines a matter, He only
> says to it 'Be' and it is there (Sura 5:75).

The Christian scholars argue that the gentile audience during the
days of the apostles could not comprehend the deeper theological and
soteriological effect of Jesus the Messiah or Christ. The title, Son of God,
enabled the disciples to bridge the gap between the Jewish-Christian and
Gentile-Christian religio-political thought. Commenting on the Matthew
Gospel, James D.G. Dunn observes:

> This Gospel was intended as something of a bridge document
> between a more narrowly defined Jewish Christianity on the one
> hand, and a Jewish Christianity much more informed by
> Hellenistic categories on the other... Why was this? Probably
> because the title "Son of God" was more meaningful to a
> Gentile audience than Messiah could ever be. Moreover, it could
> serve as a *good bridge between Jewish and Gentile thought*:
> both societies were familiar with the idea that a good or great
> man might be called a son of God, and in both societies "son
> of God" could have connotations of divinity.[13]

The Christian response to the debate of the incarnation and Jesus'
divinity is that the Bible does not talk about the physical relationship
between the Father and the Son, but the fellowship between God the
Creator and Jesus the Messiah, who was co-existent with God himself.
This fellowship neither divides the Oneness of Divine Unity nor
undermines the Sovereignty of the Eternal God. It only manifests a
complete self-expression of God's love for his creation.

The Jews and Christians are also accused of distorting God's
message of love and compassion and limiting the abundant mercy of God
to a specific group of people. According to Muslims, Jews and Christians
are not the only chosen people; rather, Islam affirms, everyone who draws
to God in submission belongs to him.

---

13. James D.G. Dunn, *Unity and Diversity in the New Testament*, (London: SCM
Press, Ltd., 1977), p.47 quoted by James R. Brady in *Jesus Christ: Divine Man or Son of
God*, (Lanham, Maryland: University Press of America, 1992), p.94.

And the Jews and Christians say, 'We are the sons of God, and His beloved ones.' Say: 'Why then does He chastise you for your sins? No you are mortals, of His creating: He forgives whom He will, and he chastises whom He will' (Sura 5:20).

Debate on the Authenticity of the Gospel

Muslims contend that the original Gospel, like the Quran, contained the summons to worship and serve One God; Jesus himself practiced *Salat* (ritual prayer) and *Zakat* (almsgiving) which are the two pillars of Islam. But the original Gospel and the earlier revelations were corrupted by the Christian and Jewish religious and political leaders. If one reads the Bible now, it is impossible to say which one is an original revelation and which one is human interpolation. Of the corruption of the Bible, the Quran says:

> O People of the Book! Come to common terms as between us and you: that we worship none but God; that we associate no partners with Him; that we erect not, from among ourselves, lords and patrons other than God (Sura 3:64).

> There is among them a section who distort the Book with their tongues. (As they read) you would think it is a part of the Book, but it is no part of the Book; and they say, 'That is from God'. But it is not from God: it is they who tell a lie against God, and (well) they know it! (Sura 3:75).

> But the transgessors among them changed the word from that which had been given them so we sent on them a plague from heaven. For that they repeatedly transgressed (Sura 7:162).

Paul of Tarsus and early Christian leaders, politicians, philosophers and popes have corrupted the texts of the Bible, and now it is hard to tell which is revealed and which is unrevealed. The Muslim polemicists argue that the Jews and Christians cannot point to an unbroken, authentic textual tradition which was revealed by God to the Hebrew Prophets. The successive tradition of Torah was broken at the time of the Babylonian exile, the authentic texts were lost during the alien invasion, and the divine revelation was obscured during life in captivity. The present form of the Hebrew Scriptures was put together by Ezra, the scribe, after returning from exile. Since Ezra was not a prophet, human errors crept into the Torah, and human inventions were added into the text which made the once revealed message unauthentic.

The Torah is the most correct of Books, and the most widely distributed among Jews and Christians. In spite of this, the text of the Samaritans is different from the text of the Jews and Christians, even to the very wording of the Ten Commandments... This shows that *Tabdil* (beliefs taught by prophets with innovated, human creations) has occurred in many copies of the books, for numerous copies exist among the Samaritans.[14]

The Muslims argue that the *Tabdil*, which occurred in the Gospels, is far worse than the corruption brought on the Torah. The Gospels were written by four different evangelists, of whom two were not disciples and did not know Christ personally. Paul's letters to churches, which make up two-third of the Christian Scriptures are not revealed messages, rather, they are the interpretations and teachings of an individual who had an encounter with a *jinn* (an angel) on his way to Damascus. Some of the Gospel narratives, the Muslims insist, are self-contradictory, and are riddled with human elements. An authentic revealed message should be mediated without human elements, and should come directly from God.

Some scholars like Sayyid Ahmad Khan and Geoffrey Parrinder take a cautious approach by saying the Quran does not accuse Jews and Christians of literally corrupting their scriptures; rather, the Quran only uses allegorical language. Khan observes:

> Early Muslim authorities recognize in theory two forms of 'tahrif,' corruption:viz., 'tahrif-i-lafzi,' which means verbal corruption or corruption of the text; and 'tahrif-i-manawi,' which indicates corruption of meaning or interpretation. The changes in the Quran are of the latter type, such as making verbal changes while reading to convey to the ear words different from those written; reading only some passages and omitting others; instructing people in a manner contrary to God's in His Holy Word and yet making them believe that this instruction is the true word; adopting an improper meaning of certain words of ambiguous or equivocal interpretation which does not suit the sense intended; misinterpreting passages that are mystical and allegorical.[15]

---

14. Ibn Taymiyya, *A Muslim Theologian's Response to Christianity*, ed. and trans. Thomas F. Michel, S.J. (Delmar, New York: Caravan Books, 1984), p.114.

15. Quoted in L. Bevan Jones, *The People of the Mosque* (London: Student Christian Movement Press, 1932), p.264.

Parrinder also shares Khan's view and observes that the Quran does not postulate that the Gospel in the present form is different from the one which was revealed to Jesus.[16]

Sacred message is always incorrupt, pure and eternal without any contradiction or human error. Divine message is given to the people through messengers sent by God himself. Revealed message, has to maintain textual fidelity. The Torah and the Gospels have come short of it, therefore, they are not blameless. Only the Quran has preserved its purity. Since the Torah and the Gospels are corrupted with comments, interpretation, rituals and stories, they can neither be rejected as fabrications, imaginations and inventions, nor accepted as sacred books handed down by the Prophets. The Christian Bible could be accepted only as *Hadith*. Ibn Taymiyya maintains:

> The gospels are therefore of the same status as the Muslim collections of hadith reports from Mohammed, which, although they contain true statements and teaching of Mohammed, may differ verbally and may contain erroneous material. Even the Torah, although it is assumed to be textually sounder than the gospel, must be treated as khabar from the prophet Moses because it has no indisputable attestation of textual accuracy.[17]

The Quran has been sent down to re-establish a pure religion that has been defiled by the Jews and Christians. The Quran, wherefore, summons the people of Israel to submit themselves to the will of God which is seen not as a new covenant but as an urgently needed restoration of the old. "Children of Israel, remember the favors I have bestowed upon you. Keep your covenant and I will be true to mine. Revere me. Have faith in my revelations, which confirm your Scriptures, and do not be the first to deny them" (Sura 2:40-41).

Jesus, according to the Muslims, had a specific mission to the Jewish people of his time. Mohammed, on the other hand, being the "Seal of the prophets" belongs to all times and all places. God sent him during an interval between the messengers, at a time when unbelief was manifest and Allah's true way was blotted out. Through Mohammed, the Way was restored, idolatry destroyed, and unbelievers conquered. By revealing his Divine message, Allah perfected the Quran and completed Islam.

---

16. Geoffrey Parrinder, *Jesus in the Quran*, (New York: Barnes and Noble, Inc., 1965), p.145.

17. Ibn Taymiyya, *A Muslim Theologian's Response to Christianity*, p.114.

Debate on Soteriology and Ecclesiology

The Quran does not account for Jesus' proclamation of the Kingdom of God, the Beatitudes, the meaning of the servanthood of the Son of Man, his impending sacrificial death on the cross, and the sending of the Holy Spirit. The Quran does not contain any direct quote from the Bible nor does it refer to the followers of Jesus as Christians or apostles or disciples. The Quran refers to them as Nazarenes, after the place Jesus came from. Giving any other name to the followers of Jesus, it is believed, would elevate Jesus from prophethood.

Islam states that a prophet cannot have followers. He is only a messenger and servant of Allah. The servant role of Jesus does not hold any special relationship with Allah, as Paul protrays in his epistle to the Philippians.

> Though [Jesus Christ] was in the form of God, did not count equality with God a thing to be grasped, but emptied himself taking the form of a servant, being born in the likeness of men. And being found in human form he humbled himself and became obedient unto death, even death on a cross. Therefore, God has highly exalted him and bestowed on him the name of Jesus every knee should bow, in heaven and on earth and under the earth, and every tongue confess that Jesus Christ is Lord, to the glory of God the Father (Phil. 2: 6-11).

Jesus' life and ministry, according to Islamic teachings, have no salvific effect. The Muslims charge that the Christian concept of salvation was a brain child of Paul who manufactured it in retaliation against the Jews. Muhammad Ata ur-Rahim asserts:

> Paul produced a religion which encompassed different contradictory elements. He took the unitarianism of the Jews and added to it the philosophy of the pagans. This admixture was combined with some of what Jesus had taught and some of what Paul claimed Christ had revealed to him. Paul's theology was based on his personal experience interpreted in the light of contemporary Greek thought. Jesus was deified and the words of Plato were put in his sacred mouth. The theory of redemption was the child of Paul's brain, a belief entirely unknown to Jesus and his disciples. It was based on the belief in "original sin", the "crucifixion", and the "resurrection", none of which have any validity. Thus, a synthetic religion was

produced: Christianity-mathematically absurd, historically false, yet psychologically impressive. In the magnificent temple of the religion which Paul helped so zealously to erect, he built doors on all sides. The result was that people who came across his brand of Christianity for the first time, when they entered its temple, were given the impression that they were paying homage to the same deity that they had worshipped all along, whether they were Jew or Gentile. As the basic misconception introduced by Paul evolved and became established, many a man who thought that he was following Jesus followed Paul without knowing it.[18]

The Muslims also believe that Jesus had no intention of establishing a church and leaving behind a community to worship him. It was innovated by the political and religious leaders of the fourth and subsequent centuries who corrupted the scriptures and managed to control and manipulate the minds and hearts of the adherents of the faith. For instance, the Gospels written during the first two centuries do not say that Jesus was a Messiah or a Saviour of the world. They only say he was Allah's messenger. The major conspiracy and corruption of the scriptures occurred only during the early church councils held in the fourth century, especially the Nicene Council which met in 325 C.E. Ur-Rahim asserts "the manuscripts of the New Testament which were written after the Council of Nicea are different from the manuscripts that existed before the Council".[19] The church has also been accused of being founded on false theological and biblical creed. Some enthusiastic, religious zealots who had no first-hand contact with Jesus invented intricate narrations and fancy notions about God and His commandments. The worst character of them all was Paul. Ur-Rahim contests:

> The established church is founded on the doctrine of original sin, of atonement and redemption, of the divinity of Jesus, of the divinity of the Holy Ghost and of the Trinity. None of these doctrines are to be found within the gospels. They were not taught by Jesus. They were the fruits of Paul's innovations and the influence of Greek culture and philosophy. Paul never experienced the company nor the direct transmission of

---

18. Muhammad 'Ata ur-Rahim, *Jesus Prophet of Islam*, (Diwan Press: Norfolk, England, 1977), pp. 71-72.

19. Ibid., p.196.

knowledge from Jesus... His teaching is based on an event
which never took place, the supposed death and resurrection of
Jesus.[20]

As the Christians exaggerated the teachings of Christ and corrupted
Allah's revealed message, they have become unbelievers and idolaters,
and therefore have incurred God's wrath upon them.

[The Christians] differ among themselves on all of their
innovations and they mutually curse each other. They seize upon
obscure passages in the Gospel which did not appear in any of
the earlier sacred books, and by inserting into their faith notions
which go against the nature of God, they have corrupted the
true prophetic religion. In this way the majority of their bishops
and popes discarded the religion of Christ in favor of the ideas
of the pagan philosophers against whom Abraham was sent.
Their monks invented superstitions which deceived ignorant
people, although those who were intelligent could tell that such
things were frauds. Thus, the first group, the Jews, belittled the
prophets and even killed them while the other-Christians-
exaggerated their status until they worshipped them and
worshipped even their statues. The first group claims that it is
not permitted for God to change and abrogate by a latter prophet
what He previously commanded by a previous one; the other
claims that their own leaders can permit what God forbade and
can forbid what He permitted.[21]

The Christian innovation of church has caused division,
multiplication of denominations and sects among its supporters. As a
result, they have become weak in their faith and ignorant of Allah's
teachings. A Hadith report narrates a conversation between Mohammed
and Qatada when the Najarani delegation visited the Prophet:

Qatada said that when the Jews said, "The Christians follow
nothing," he (Mohammed) said, "Yes, but the earliest Christians
followed something; then they innovated and split into sects."
When the Christians said that the Jews follow nothing, he said,
"Yes, but the early Jews followed something; they innovated
and split into sects."[22]

---

20. Ibid.

21. Ibn Taymiyya, *A Muslim Theologian's Response to Christianity*, p.75.

22. Ibid., p.102.

The worst crime the Christians have committed was not only making Jesus equal to Allah but also rejecting Mohammed, his Prophet. The Christians' rejection of the Prophet is considered far worse than the 'Jews' rejection of Jesus.

Jesus, according to Islam, was sent to uphold the demands of the Law of the Torah. When the Jews rejected him, they rejected not the Torah but only the Prophet Jesus. When the Christians rejected Mohammed, they became more unbelieving than the Jews; for, the Christians rejected the Torah, Prophet Jesus, the Seal of Prophets, and a new, independent and self-sustaining Sharia. Ibn Taymiyya charges that by rejecting Mohammed and Islam the Jews and Christians have denigrated the institution of prophecy itself.

> The Jews denigrated and cursed the prophets and mentioned faults beyond which God had elevated them. It would take too long to describe all the examples of this. Among them there was disbelief in the prophets of a kind which was vicious among their ancients. Christians, despite their exaggerated devotion to Christ and his followers, treated other prophets lightly. Sometimes they made the apostles equal or superior to Abraham and Moses. At other times they spoke like the Jews, declaring, for example, that Solomon was not a prophet but fell from the rank of prophet. Elsewhere they claimed that what God said about David and others was only intended to refer to Christ.[23]

Difference Between Inspiration and Revelation

Islam differentiates between the doctrine of inspiration and the doctrine of revelation. Inspiration (ilham), according to Muslim scholars, is accessible to all human beings. It is a secondary or indirect revelation. Divine revelation (wahy), on the contrary, is given only to a chosen few who are called to be the Prophets of God. They are given the Word of God which is sent down (tanzil) from the very presence of God to bring people back to an authentic worship of the One God. Those chosen Prophets of God are the ones who possess the incorrupt Word. Islam says Moses, David, Jesus, and Mohammed were the only human beings who received tanzil. Therefore, the difference between inspiration and revelation can be traced back to St. Paul's letters in which he often refers to that which was given to him by the Spirit (tanzil) and that which came from himself (ilham).

---

23. Ibid., p.109.

The original Gospels, except for the actual words of Jesus, are the inspired Word of God. However, the Gospels in their present form are interpolated with the disciples' narration of events and incorporation of personal comments, and hence they are not pure and authentic *wahy*. The Gospels in the present form are altered *(tahrif)* by church leaders over the centuries and they are not *tanzil*. The Bible in its present form is only the inspired word *(ilham)* as it was not the exact replica of the heavenly tablet. The Bible contains only part of God's message, which was revealed to the prophets with the help and mediation of the angels. As the message was given to human beings with God's angels, the created beings, errors and mistakes crept into the Biblical revelation. Furthermore, human beings included their own fanciful rituals and imaginative interpretations into God's revealed word. The human interpolation of unwanted rituals, mortal history, and irreligious practices have corrupted the true and authentic revelation. Hence, the Bible in the present form contains only stories and narrations about God, not messages that came directly from God.

The Quran does not talk about a self-revealing God in the way the Bible talks about YHWH of the Hebrew Scriptures or God of the Christian Scriptures. Christianity asserts that the God of the Bible is a self-revealing and a condescending God who established a covenant relationship with his people (Ex 3:13-15). He invites his people to respond to his covenant and invites them to respond to his love for them. This God knows the needs of the people, and constantly associates with human history. God coming in the form of a human being to redeem the lost humanity is an alien Islamic thought. The Quran has absolutely no room to accommodate the Christian doctrine of God who revealed himself totally in the person of Jesus as Divine Word *(khalimatuh)* (Sura 4:17).

The Christians affirm that human beings are instructed to love God and respond to him in faith by obeying his commandments and submitting to him as their heavenly Father. This Parent-Children relationship must be understood as God's covenant fellowship, not as a human relationship. As a parent, God grieves when his children rebel and sin, but, at the same time, he saves and blesses them with his abundant grace and enduring love. This loving God established his first covenant through Moses in the Sinai desert. When his chosen people failed to be faithful to the established covenant, God sent Jesus Christ into the world to establish a new covenant and God extended an invitation to all humanity to respond in submission to his call. The people who responded to such an invitation became the faith community, which is the Church.

The Muslims believe that the commandments given through Prophet Moses (the Torah) were binding until Jesus came. The Gospel of Jesus Christ superseded the Torah of Moses. Then the gospel lost its own power and authority when Mohammed arrived with the Quran. Prophet Jesus was followed by Prophet Mohammed, whose recitation replaced all the earlier revelations including the Gospel brought by Jesus. Mohammed is reported to have said, "whoever died in the faith of Jesus... died in Islam before he heard of me, his lot shall be good. But whoever hears of me today and yet does not assent to me, he shall surely perish."[24]

The Quran insists that the true People of the Book should accept Mohammed as the Prophet of God like they have accepted the Prophets of the Hebrew Scriptures.

> Strongest among men in enmity to the believers will thou find the Jews and pagans; and nearest among them in love to the believers wilt thou find those who say, "We are Christians"; because amongst these are men devoted to learning and men who have renounced the world, and they are not arrogant. And when they listen to the revelation received by the Apostle, thou wilt see their eyes overflowing with tears, for they recognize the truth: they pray: "Our Lord! we believe; write us down among the witnesses" (Sura 5:85-86).

---

24. Mahmoud M. Ayoub, *The Qur'an and Its Interpreters*, (Albany: State University of New York Press, 1984), I, p.112.

CHAPTER X
Jesus : A Messenger or a Saviour?

Jesus : The Prophet of Islam

The Quran has assigned a prominent place to Jesus among the prophets of Judaism, Christianity, and Islam. He is given supremacy among the saints who were raised from among the Arabs (Sura 19:30, 31, 4:172; 5:17, 75). He is ranked with venerated prophets, "Zechariah and John and Jesus and Elias, each one of the righteous" (Sura 6:85). Jesus is esteemed both as a prophet and a messenger to whom Allah "gave pre-eminence over others" (Sura 2:253-254). The Quran attests that Jesus was given both the Gospel (Injil) and the ability to perform miracles. Hence, the coming of Jesus was announced as "glad tidings" (Sura 3:45).

In spite of his special status, Jesus remains a mere human being like the prophets of the Hebrew Scriptures (Sura 3:59). According to the Quran, amongst those born of women, Jesus represents a special creation.

> "Every child born of the children of Adam, Satan touched with his finger, except Mary and her son, peace be upon them both." Jesus is free from the taint of evil and impurity. He is the word of God and God's messenger (Sura 3:45; 4:171).

> We gave Moses the Book and followed him with a succession of apostles; we gave Jesus the son of Mary clear (signs) and strengthened him with the holy spirit. Is that whenever there comes to you an apostle with what ye yourselves desire not, ye are puffed up with pride?- some ye called impostors, and other ye slay! (Sura 2:87).

In Jesus, the divine power of revelation was manifested in a mighty way.

> I followed up the others (prophets) with Jesus the Son of Mary, confirming the law which was before him. I gave him the gospel containing guidance (guiding men to cofess God is one) and

light (by means of this men can find the right way) verifying the law which was before it, guiding and admonishing all who fear (Sura 19:30).[1]

Jesus observed the teachings of Allah and worshipped him. Allah taught Jesus the Torah, the Wisdom, and the Gospel (3:43-48). With special mercies Allah showered upon Jesus, he was able to bring the Gospel to the world. The divine birth of Jesus, the favour he received from Allah, and the miracles he performed as a child and man are documented in the Quran and the Hadith. However, the Quran attests that the miracles Jesus performed do not prove that he contained divine essence in him. It does not give any credence that he was engaged in a redemptive mission. Rather, as a prophet of Allah, he was endowed with special honour and sent as "a sign to the people" (Sura 19:21) "a sign to· the worlds" (Sura 21:91), and a "sign from Allah" (Sura 3:44, 50), and to share the good news that Allah cared about the people of the world and he would never abandon them.

The Quran lists the names of only 28 prophets although Islamic tradition says there are a lot more. Some prophets are revered and acclaimed with special titles ascribed to them. For example: Adam is known as the Chosen of Allah *(Safiy Allah)*; Noah as the Prophet of Allah *(Nabi Allah)*; Abraham as the Friend of Allah *(Khalil Allah)*; Moses as the Converser with Allah *(Kalim Allah)*; Jesus as the Spirit of Allah *(Ruh Allah)*; and Mohammed as the Apostle of Allah *(Rasul Allah)* and the Seal *(Khatam)* of prophets.[1]

This affirmation of Jesus' humanity was necessary as Mohammed had been criticized for eating food at market places (Sura 25:7,8). Some people believed that true prophets and messengers of God, like John the Baptist, would not care for food. Hence, the Quran had to insist that all messengers of God were ordinary human beings and they had to eat, sleep, and live like any other human being (Sura 25:20-22). The human needs of Mary and Jesus are affirmed in the words of Quran: "both of them ate food" (Sura 5:75, 79).

Jesus : A Human Being

The Quran presents Jesus only as a human being who was empowered by God and "fortified with the holy Spirit". It denounces the divinity of Jesus without denying his special humanity (Sura 2:87, 253).

---

1. Some mystics like Ibn Arabi said, "Mohammed is the Seal of the Prophets and Jesus is the Seal of Saints".

Formerly God spoke to Jesus the son of Mary, saying, remember my favour toward thee and your mother. At times I helped you with the pure spirit. You spoke to men in the cradle and when grown up (Sura 5:113).

At that time I taught you the book, wisdom and law and gospel. At that time, with my permission, you made the likeness of a bird from clay and breathed upon it. With my permission you healed the blind and the leprous. At that time you brought forth the dead with my permission (Sura 5:113).

However, it is important to note that Islam is the only religion outside Christianity that talks about Jesus and his ministry.

In the first few centuries of Christianity, a number of schismatic groups denied either the humanity or divinity of Jesus Christ and failed to comprehend the mystery surrounding the incarnation of Jesus. The apocryphical literatures bear testimony to such confusion.[2] For instance, the Docetic Christians thought Jesus had not experienced mortal needs and he was a human being only in appearance *(dokein)*. That view was opposed as heresy and condemned as non-soteriological at later Christian Councils.

During the fifth century, Nestorius, the patriarch of Constantinople, refused to accept the title given to Mary as the Mother of God *(theotokos)*, the bearer of God. Instead, he called her, "mother of Christ" *(Christonokos)* and "mother of man" *(anthropotokos)*. Nestorius even denied the fundamental Christian tenets such as "God was born" and "God had suffered". He preached that Jesus was only a human being whom God used as his vessel. The early church was divided on this issue. Nestorius was vehemently opposed by the monophysites and was exiled to the desert region of Arabia. He and his followers moved eastward and established a strong missionary church known as the Nestorian church along the way until it reached China. The Muslims, to date, prefer the teachings of Nestorius over the monophysites and condemn the Christian hierarchy for persecuting and silencing Nestorius and his followers.

The ministry of Jesus plays a vital role in Islamic faith. He is considered the bridge-builder between Moses and Mohammed. A careful reader can see that the removal of Jesus from the Quran would result in

2. Edgar Henneck, *The Infancy Gospel of Thomas and the Protevangelism of James, New Testament Apocrypha*, ed. and trans. R. McL Wilson, (Philadelphia: Westminster Press, 1963).

the deification of Mohammed. He would become the central character of divine drama and Islam would revolve around Mohammed, if there were no Jesus in the Quran. Mohammed had a profound respect and great admiration for Jesus. Mohammed himself confessed that he was only a messenger of Allah who was called to warn the people of the path of Allah. Unlike Jesus, Mohammed was not called to perfrom miracles.

> They say, why does he not show us some signs from the Lord? You say, all signs are with God (only the Lord can freely show forth miracles). I am an obvious warner (Sura 29:49).

Jesus: Is His Death Vicarious?

The Muslims do not accept the Biblical account of Jesus' death and resurrection. The Christian claim of the hidden salvific and paschal mystery of God as revealed in the incarnation of Jesus, his resurrection, and his promise of parousia, which serve as the hope and foundation of Christianity are denied and set aside by Islam. Islamic affirmation is that God can neither suffer in human hands nor reveal his person to humanity as he is absolutely transcendent.

The Christians respond that the anthropomorphic narration of the God of the Bible should not be taken literally but metaphorically. For instance, when the Bible talks about God as the parent, no Christian would suppose God has a physical body like a human parent does. Neither when the Bible says God repents or thinks or watches, he acts like a human being does. The person of God is explained in a metaphorical language and in allegorical concepts for human comprehension. Keith Ward argues in his essay in *Christian Faith and Philosophical Theology*.

> The obvious reply is that God cannot transcend *all* human concepts, since then nothing at all could be said of God; not even that God exists. Some concepts must apply to God in a literal sense, or we would literally not know what we were talking about God. And it does seem that among the things we must say literally of God are such things as that God knows all things, God cares about the good of creatures and God freely gives good things to those who love him. Knowing, caring and freely giving are all things that persons do; so does it not follow immediately that God is a person?[3]

---

3. *Christian Faith and Philosophical Theology* (Essays in Honour of Vincent Brummer) ed., Gijsbert van den Brink, (The Netherlands Pharos, 1992), p.260.

The God of the Bible is ineffable and infinite yet he can reveal himself in a person. That indescribable God can come close to a person in meditation and prayer.

> Yet God is as far beyond being a person as the infinite is beyond the finite. And, in the Christian tradition, we may better say that God can be worshipped as Father, seen in the life of Jesus, and experienced as the power of the Spirit; so that the Divine being both includes and transcends these different personal forms in a reality which may best be described as supra-personal and utterly unique in kind.[4]

Ward argues, the union of the Spirit of God and a Christian believer, which the Christian Scriptures talk about, is much closer than the union or inclusion of two human beings.

> However closely persons come together, they remain distinct; each person is alone, and each must respect the 'apartness' of the other. But the relation of God and the soul is not like that. God is closer to the heart of each of us than any other person can ever be.[5]

Ward uses the affirmation of the Gospels that the believer is in Christ and Christ is in the believer with the oneness God the Father and Jesus the Son had manifested. Ward concludes his argument with the declaration that the invisible presence of God in the believers is "much closer and more intimate than that of one person relating to another".[6] The biblical writers used anthropomorphic expressions of God in a strictly allegorical sense and invited the readers of the Bible to go beyond the images expressed through faith and commitment. Therefore, Ward concludes, "Christian spirituality requires us to go beyond thinking of God as a person in relation to us, and asks us also to think of God as present and at work within us, as the true centre of our beings."[7]

The metaphorical narrative of the nearness of God can be seen in the Quran as well : Allah is nearer to us than our jugular veins and is ready to *hear* our supplications, declares the Quran (50:16). The

---

4. Ibid., p.265.

5. Ibid., p. 264.

6. Ibid.

7. Ibid.

closeness and the intimacy of a believer with Allah and his nearness to care for humanity's concerns are expressed in figurative language. The Quranic utterance about Allah who is "ready to hear our supplications", projects an image about Allah who, like human beings, has ears to hear and a mind to listen. As Allah is represented as a male, he has been given some human traits as well.

Finding peace through submission and meriting God's favour through worship are not alien concepts to the moral teachings of the Hebrew Scriptures. The Hebrew Prophets warned the people of God about the dangers of wandering away from him. Those who strayed from God were reminded of the laws and commandments of God and were summoned to return to him. Those who responded to the message of the prophets in penitence were blessed with the joys promised to God's children.

Apostle Paul wrote in his letters that the laws of the Hebrew Scriptures were like the Old School Master. The New Dispensation provided for in Christ has nullified the Law and offered a new paradigm of God's love and mercy: not by merit but by grace one finds favour in the eyes of God; and, not by deeds but by the mercies of God one obtains salvation. "We are saved through grace and by faith", declares Paul.

> Before faith came, we were confined under the law, kept under restraints until faith should be revealed. So that the law was our custodian until Christ came, that we might be justified by faith. But now that faith has come, we are no longer under a custodian; for in Christ Jesus you are all sons (and daughters) of God, through faith. For as many of you as were baptized into Christ have put on Christ. There is neither Jew nor Greek, there is neither slave nor free, there is neither male nor female; for you are all one in Christ Jesus. And if you are Christ's, then you are Abraham's offspring, heirs according to promise (Gal. 3:23-29).

Contrary to the Quranic affirmation that human beings are born sinless and Adam's sin had not alienated humanity from God, the Bible declares: "We have all become like one who is unclean, and all our righteous deeds are like a polluted garment" (Isaiah 64:6). "None is righteous, no, not one... All have turned aside, together they have gone wrong; no one does good, not even one" (Ps. 14:1-3). "All have sinned and fallen short of the glory of God" (Rom. 3:23). Human beings deserve punishment as they are rebellious and sinful. "The wages of sin is death" (Rom. 6:23). In order to save the sinful humanity, Jesus was sent to the cross to endure pain and suffer punishment. Isaiah prophesied, "He (Jesus) was wounded for our transgressions, He was bruised for our iniquities; Upon Him was the chastisement that made us whole, and with his stripes we are healed" (Isaiah 53:5). The crucifixion and death of Jesus Christ has been interpreted as the manifestation of God's love for his rebellious people and the inner mystery of the Kingdom of God which Jesus was talking about during his earthly ministry.

The Hebrew Scriptures contain commandments about sacrifices people had to offer to YHWH on different occasions, such as sin offering and thank offering. Every year, the people of Israel had to offer an animal sacrifice for the atonement of their sins in accordance with the law of Moses given at Mount Sinai. Those commandments were given at the time when YHWH established a covenant with his people. Those sacrifices had to be offered to God by the priests at the tabernacle before Solomon built the first temple in Jerusalem.

Since those sacrifices had to be repeated every year and offered at a place where the people and priests gathered together year after year, people were not able to obtain permanent remission of sins. Hence, according to the Epistle to the Hebrews, Jesus was sent as the Lamb of God to die on the cross as a vicarious sacrifice and to bear all the punishment and sin upon himself once and for all. The Epistle to the Hebrews says that Jesus offered himself as the perfect and complete sacrifice for the sins of the whole world for eternity. By doing so, Jesus abolished the yearly animal sacrifices forever (Heb. 5-7).

The Quran, however, does not accept the salvific death of Christ on the cross. The Sovereign Lord would not have allowed his Prophet Jesus to suffer such a low kind of death. Ibn Taymiyya says:

> In the Quran, Adam repents and is pardoned; although this is not explicitly stated in the Bible, there is nothing which contradicts that. How...could God imprison in hell prophets like Abraham and Moses for the sin of Adam, when God forgave them their own sins and those of their parents? The Christian teaching is opposed to the justice of God and would allow Satan to imprison upright individuals for the sin of another. Moreover, what is the connection in justice or logic between Christ's presumed death on the cross and the redemption of individuals

from the power of Satan? If Satan was acting wrongly in this, God would not have needed a crucifixion to rectify their situation; if Satan was acting properly in imprisoning them, the crucifixion of Jesus would not make his action improper.[8]

Jesus : His Second Coming

Both Christianity and Islam believe that Jesus will come again to judge the world. Contrary to the teachings of the Christain Scriptures, Islam denies the death of Jesus Christ on the cross and believes that Jesus was taken up to heaven alive. Some Muslim commentators believe that Allah has shown a special favour for Jesus and he has been accorded a special place in heaven to intercede for true Muslims. Zamakshari says that Jesus has been given "the office of prophet and supremacy over men in this world, and in the next world, the office of intercessor and loftiness of rank in paradise".[9]

When Jesus comes back, the Jews and Christians will believe in him as God's messenger. The Jews would not reject him as they did 2000 years ago; the Christians will not exalt him as the Son of God as they did during his first coming. When Jesus returns from heaven, the hadith reports, he will fight with *Al-Dajjal* (the anti-Christ), the personification of all evil, who kept all people from doing Allah's will. This Jesus is expected to return upon the white tower in Damascus to break "the cross, kill the pig, impose the *Jizya*", inaugurate millennial righteousness and bring the people of the world to worship Allah. Ultimately, he would suffer a natural death and occupy the tomb prepared for him beside Mohammed and the first two caliphs in Medina.

In some countries like India, the closed "door" inside the mosque which the Muslims inevitably see when facing Mecca in worship has reference to Jesus. The closed door represents Christ's descent to earth as he was raised up to God. When he comes back he will gather up the believers and lead them to the Garden of Bliss. "I am gathering you and causing you to ascend to me", says Jesus in the Quran (Sura 3:55).

When he descends, the closed doors in mosques will be opened as proof of his return, and he will judge the people of the world. "There is no doubt that the Son of Mary, on whom be blessing and peace, shall

---

8. Ibn Taymiyya, *Muslim Theologian's Response to Christianity*, p.120.

9. Quote taken from Rolf A. Syrdal, "Christ in the Chinese Koran", *The Muslim World*, Vol. xxvii No.1, Jan. 1935, p.81.

descend in the midst of you as a righteous judge" (3:55). Commenting on the manner and the result of Jesus' return Zamakhshari quotes the Hadith:

> Jesus (on him be peace) will descend on a narrow pass in the holy land called Afiq wearing two light yellow garments, the hair of his head lank, in his hand a lance with which he will kill the Antichrist. Then he will go to Jerusalem when the people are at dawn prayer led by the imam. The imam will move back but Jesus will give him precedence and pray behind him in accordance with the sharia of Mohammed (the peace and blessings of God be upon him). Then he will kill the pigs, break the cross, demolish oratories and churches and kill Christians except those who believe in him.[10]

In contrast to Christian proclamation, Jesus will return not to judge the world but to establish Islam and uphold Mohammed's teachings of Allah. In his article "Christology in Islam" a contemporary Muslim scholar Mohammed M. Ayoub writes:

> We see Jesus in Islam, as in the Gospels, as the messenger of forgiveness and love...the poverty, austerity and detachment from this world of the Christ of the Gospels receives, in Islamic piety, a far greater emphasis. Hence, Jesus becomes the example of piety, renunciation of worldly pleasures, and poverty...the one after whom they (the Muslims) sought to pattern their lives and conduct.[11]

Jesus and Crucifixion

In the Quran, the crucifixion of Jesus is presented as a challenge and judgment.

> They devised and God devised, and God is the best of devisers. (Sura 3:54).

> "And whosoever disputes with you concerning him (Jesus) after the knowledge which has come to you, say: 'Come! Let us summon our sons and your sons, our women and your women,

---

10. Quoted by Neal Robinson, *Christ in Islam and Christianity: The Representation of Jesus in the Quran and the Classical Muslim Commentaries*, (London: Macmillan Press Ltd., 1991), pp. 91-92.

11. Mohammed M. Ayoub, *Muslim World*, Towards an Islamic Christology, vol.=XVI, July 1976, No.3, p.167.

ourselves and yourselves, then we will pray humbly and invoke the curse of God upon those who lie'" (Sura 3:61).

The Quran attests that Jesus was raised up alive and was saved from death so that people might believe in him before his death. When he is in Allah's presence, God purifies Jesus to be a righteous judge and righteous Imam. Allah prepares the people of the world for his coming again, for the Quran itself witnesses "I am purifying you (Jesus) from those who disbelieved" (Sura 3:55).

Although, the Quran robs Jesus Christ of his earthly mission as the Messiah, denies his shameful death on the cross for the salvation of humankind, and omits his victorious resurrection from the dead on the third day, Islam has assigned the highest place for the man Jesus in its religious realm. Islam continues to honour the teachings of Jesus as they are found in the Gospels, and venerates the Hebrew Prophets.

It is hard for a Muslim to comprehend how and why a Prophet of the Sovereign God could endure pain in the hands of the mortals. The presumptuous teaching of a "suffering servant" is a grand betrayal of the dynamics of Allah's revelation and a humiliating dishonour brought upon the office of the messenger of God. After all, Islam does not share the Christian view of sin and salvation and the pouring of blood on the altar of God for the redemption of human beings. The Quranic belief is that every child born in this world is sinless. One does not inherit sin but acquires sin as he or she grows old. Besides, human beings are given freedom and endowed with knowledge to choose between right and wrong. Those who choose Allah's path will enjoy his blessings in Paradise and those who refuse will reap evil and condemnation.

The Quran overflows with realistic descriptions of both the pangs of hell and the pleasures of heaven. The subject matter of the Quran is mainly a mixture of warnings, protests and pronouncement in favour of certain doctrines. The narrative structure demands moral response. The stories chronicled in the Quran are mostly of events in the distant past, although references to modern incidents and Mohammed's own personal experiences are documented. The narration, the admonition, and the declarations are made mainly to evoke positive response from the listeners.

Heaven is described as the Garden of Paradise from which Adam was sent. The Garden of Eden is not on earth, as the Bible portrays, but in heaven. A true believer in Islam or those who die in martyrdom will experience the blessings of heaven. The blessings are described in material and existential terms: the presence of flowing rivers, beautiful gardens, dark-eyed female companions, and physical enjoyment with spouses. Life in heaven will be full of delights (Sura 56:12-37). Hell is not only an everlasting separation from God, but also a place of despair and torment. Punishment in hell is also vividly described.

> For the wrong-doers We have prepared a fire whose (smoke and flames), like the walls and roof of a tent, will hem them in: if they implore relief they will be granted water like melted brass, that will scald their faces. How dreadful the drink! How uncomfortable a couch to recline on! (Sura 18.29).

As discussed earlier, one unwavering message of the Quran about the person of Jesus is that he was a human being and sent out to be a servant of Allah. Jesus' mission as a messenger of Allah is emphasized in the Quran. When he asked his disciples, "Who shall be my supporters to Allah?", and when they were vacillating with doubt and unbelief, they pledged their allegiance to Allah and replied, "We shall be God's supporters; We believe in God, so bear witness that we are Muslims" (Sura 3:52). Again, when Jesus was asked if he had said to his listeners, "Take me and my mother as two gods beside God", he answered:

> I did not say to them save that which you command me, "Worship God, my Lord and Your Lord! I was a witness over them, as long as I was among them, but when you took me "You were the Watcher over them, and You are a witness over all things" (Sura 5:120).

The Quran testifies that Jesus was sinless and pure. At the end of his mission he was taken to heaven to be with Allah (Sura 19.33, 3.55). His disciples would rule over the unbelievers until the day of resurrection. "Behold! Allah said : O Jesus, I will take thee and raise thee to Myself and clear thee (of the falsehoods) of those who blaspheme; I will make those who follow thee superior to those who reject faith, to the Day of Resurrection: Then shall ye all return unto me, and I will judge between you of the matters wherein you dispute" (Sura 3.55). The Quran says Jesus was exalted to the presence of Allah without having been killed at the hands of the Jews. Mahmud Ayoub argues that Jesus was not saved from death but saved through death by Allah by raising (rafa'a) Jesus up to Himself as he did with the earlier prophets as mentioned in the Quran (Sura 2.253, 6.165, 6.83, 12.76, 4.158, 3.55). To many Muslims, the phrase "raising up" means "letting him die" as Allah's favoured prophet. All the prophets will join Allah on the last day for judgment.

The Quran accuses the children of Israel for killing prophets unjustly and attempting to kill Jesus unfairly. Jesus was sent to the children of Israel but they ventured to slay the Messenger in vain. The following verses constitute Allah's challenge to the enemies of His Prophet Jesus:

> And for their saying: "We have surely killed the Christ, Jesus son of Mary, the messenger of God". They did not kill him, nor did they crucify him; rather it was made only to appear so to them. And those who have differed concerning him are in doubt regarding him; they have no knowledge of him, except the following of conjuncture. They did not kill him with certainty. Rather God took him up to himself, for God is mighty and wise (Sura 4:157-158).

The Meaning of *Shubiha Lahum*

The interpretation of the phrase "rather it was made only to appear so to them" *(Shubiha Lahum)* has generated a heated debate among Islamic scholars. Islam has some interesting theories about the death of Jesus Christ on the cross and his last days on earth. Although the Quran refers to crucifixion, Muslim scholars deny Jesus as the one who died on the cross (Sura 3.55, 5:117, 19:33).

Ibn Taymiyya, alongwith several other Muslim scholars argues that Jesus had never been crucified. Since Jesus had neither been crucified nor buried, it is highly impossible to accommodate the notion that he appeared to the apostles as resurrected Christ. Commenting on John 20:19-29, which narrates the death, burial and resurrection of Jesus, Taymiyya argues that one of the Jinns (angels) personified himself as Jesus and appeared to the apostles in order to mislead them. Commenting on Shubiha Lahum, Michael Hayek, a Lebanese theologian writes:

> This opinion may be related to a Christian heresy which had many supporters in Najran just before the rise of Islam. This was the heresy of the docetics who had denied the sufferings of Christ. Some of them claimed that Simon the Cyrene was the man who bore the likeness of Christ.[12]

---

12. Michael Hayek, *Messiah*, (Beirut: Catholic Press, 1961), p.21.

However, it is highly unlikely that Islam borrowed docetic philosophy from early Christians. The Quran consistently narrates the birth of Jesus to Virgin Mary, and his earthly activities as a Prophet of Allah (Sura 19:22, 23). He was clearly a man and a messenger. Islam has no room for phantoms. About the last days of Jesus, the Quran says that he must die like all the rest of the Muslims and rise again for the final reckoning.

Although the Quran acknowledges the biblical narration of crucifixion as a historical fact, it is not too specific about the death of Christ. One Islamic tradition says that at the end of his ministry on earth Jesus asked for a volunteer to take his likeness and be killed in his place. One of his disciples willingly took his place by responding, "I would, O prophet of God." Thus that disciple was crucified and God's Prophet Jesus was protected. Later on Jesus was taken up to heaven.[13]

Another legend comes very close to the biblical account of the last hours of Jesus with his disciples in the Garden of Gethsemane. This legend portrays Jesus as being afraid of his impending death, and prayed, "O God, if Thou wouldst take away this cup from any of thine creatures, then take it away from me." Jesus was filled with grief and fear, and was drenched with blood. Then he entered a house with his disciples and asked for a volunteer to take his place in exchange for a place in Paradise. The owner of the house, Sergus, came forward and died in the place of Jesus on the cross. Later, Jesus raptured to Allah's presence.

Yet another legend says that when Yudas Zechariah (Judas Iscariot) led the enemies of Jesus to where he was, Yudas Zechariah's face was altered, and he was made to bear the likeness of Jesus. Judas was seized and crucified. All the while he cried out, "I am not the one you want! I am the one who led you to him."[14]

One tradition says that the Jews were looking for Jesus but were not able to find him as he was hiding in a niche in a wall. The Jews were frustrated at not being able to find him. Hence, in his place, one of his disciples was captured and killed. This story comes nearer to the Gospel accounts which say that Jesus "escaped" from his enemies (Luke 4:30 and John 8:59). A similar tradition says Simon of Cyrene was the one who was actually crucified on the cross. According to this tradition,

---

13. Ali Tabari IX, 370.

14. Tabari IX, 370-71.

a little before the crucifixion Jesus changed form with Simon of Cyrene who was asked to carry the cross by the Roman soldiers. When both Simon and Jesus reached the place of crucifixion, Jesus disappeared and Simon was taken and nailed on the cross. The theory of substitution has been accepted by many Muslim authors. There is a wide range of substitutes, their names, and their origins have been suggested: Simon of Cyrene, a volunteer, Judas, Pilate, a disciple, and the devil himself.

Another tradition reports that when the Jews sought to kill Jesus, Allah took him up to Paradise. In order to conceal his ascension into Allah's presence, the Jews took another person and crucified him on a high and isolated hill. The mob was allowed to see only when his features had changed beyond recognition. And thus they were able to spread reports of his crucifixion and death.

Some Muslim commentators support the theory of substitution based on the account described in the Gospel of Barnabas. The Gospel of Barnabas, which is widely believed by the Muslims to be written in the first century, tells us that Judas Iscariot led the Jewish and Roman soldiers to arrest Jesus at night in a house where Jesus and the disciples were sleeping. As Judas entered the house, Jesus was taken away by the angels, and carried up to heaven. As he was taken up, his likeness and voice were cast upon Judas who woke up the other disciples when the master had gone. They, however, hailed him as the master and thought he was distraught by the fear of death. In Jesus' place, Judas was taken and crucified. After three days, Jesus appeared to his mother and the rest of the disciples to comfort and reassure them. He announced them of the coming of the Prophet Mohammed, who would fulfill all the things Jesus had taught.[15]

However, the authorship and the chronology of the Gospel of Barnabas have been seriously challenged by Christian scholars. The document came to light only in the early nineteenth century. It was translated into Arabic in the early decades of the twentieth century. It is most probably a late work and written under Islamic influence as it agrees with Islam on several crucial points.[16] The Gospel of Barnabas addresses Mohammed as the Messiah *(Al-Masih)* which the Quran reserves only for Jesus. The birth narrative of Jesus also disputes the

---

15. *Gospel of Barnabas*, pp. 481 ff.

16. *Gospel of Barnabas*, ed. and trans. Lonsdale and Laura Ragg (Oxford: Clarendon, 1907).

Quranic accounts. The oldest manuscripts are in Italian and Spanish. Hence, many believe that the Gospel of Barnabas was written in late medieval time in Europe by a renegade monk.[17]

The Ahmadiyyahs, a heterodox sect founded by Mirza Ghulam Ahmad, a Punjabi, however, have a different theory about the crucifixion of Jesus. They believe that Jesus was indeed crucified on the cross. After hanging on the cross for several hours, the enemies of Jesus thought Jesus had been dead and hence removed his body from the cross while life was still in him. His disciples put the corpse in a cool, dark tomb where Jesus' body came alive and drew vitality by the anointing of oil by his friends. After he regained strength to travel, he was carried away eastward by his disciples. Jesus lived until he had attained the age of 120 before dying and being buried in Srinagar, Kashmir. This theory, however, denies the Quran's affirmation which says "... on the contrary, God raised him to Himself."

The Sufi Muslims believe that Jesus was taken to heaven because his entrance to wordly existence was not through the gate of lust, therefore, his departure from it was not through the gate of death. He rather entered through the gate of power and departed through the gate of majesty. In heaven, God gave him wings and clothed him with light and removed from him the desires for food and drink. And thus he flies with the angels, and is with them around the throne. For he is human and angelic, heavenly and earthly.

Some Muslim scholars believe that Jesus was killed on the cross but his death was only of the body not of the soul. This argument has a biblical foundation as well. Kamal Hussein argues that Jesus was indeed condemned and taken to be crucified. However, God caused darkness to cover the land for three hours and when the darkness was lifted Christ was nowhere to be seen.[18]

Islam is not the only religion which denies the crucifixion and death of Jesus Christ. A dissenting group within early Christianity also denied the violence and death of Christ on the cross. The Apocryphal Acts of John, written about the middle of the second century, says that Jesus is

---

17. See J. Slomp, *Pseudo-Barnabas in the Context of Muslim-Christian Apologetic*, (Rawalpandi: Christian Study Centre, 1974).

18. Kamal Hussein, *City of Wrong*, Trans. E.T. Amsterdam, (London: Geoffrey Bles, 1959), pp. IX, 183.

said to have appeared to John on the Mount of the Olives at the precise moment of crucifixion, and told him that the crucifixion was unreal. Jesus said to John, "John, unto the multitude below in Jerusalem I am being crucified and pierced with lances and reeds, and gall and vinegar is given to me to drink. But unto thee I speak."[19]

This theory mixes up Islamic existential argument with Hindu metaphysical concept of maya (illusion). This story denies the Quranic narration of God's intervention and Jesus' ascension to heaven. The apocryphal Gospel of Peter written in the second century said that Jesus was silent and painless on the cross. In the end, unlike what the Gospel says in Mark 15:34, Jesus cried out, "My power, my power, you have left me." When he spoke, his power left him and then he was taken up.

The Docetics in the early church believed that Jesus was not a human being. He only appeared to be human. Some of the Epistles may have contributed to such a confusion. They must have misunderstood Paul's letter to the Philippians which mentions that Jesus was "made in the likeness of men" (2:7) and the writer to the Hebrews who says that Jesus was "made like his brethren" (2:17). Nonetheless, one needs to be aware that there is a vast difference between likeness and personality. Neither the Christian Scriptures nor the Quran had any intention of presenting a docetic doctrinal view of Jesus.

One must bear in mind that the Quran does not deny the death of Christ. It only challenges the enemies of Allah who thought they had power over Jesus Christ the Prophet. The Quran attests:

> That they [the Jews] said (in boast), "We killed Christ Jesus the son of Mary, the apostle of God"; - but they killed him not, nor crucified him, but so it was made to appear to them, and those who differ therein are full of doubts, with no (certain) knowledge, but only conjecture to follow, for a surety they killed him not (Sura 4:157).

The Quran firmly denies that the Jews were responsible for the death of Jesus, when it stresses "they (the Jews) said" (Wa Qawlihim) that they killed Jesus. In another place, the Quran says God had withdrawn his overflowing grace from the Jews as they breached God's covenant. Consequently, they "were no longer protected from the assaults of evil,

---

19. Joseph Barber Lightfoot (New York: Macmillan, 1890), p.156.

and they became impervious even to the message of forgiveness and mercy which is open to all God's creatures."[20] The Quran also accuses the Jews of falsifying the scriptures and by keeping back knowledge of God by either adding to them or by deleting from them. The Quran also accuses the Jews of twisting their tongues to sound the sacred message of Allah to mean an entirely different and heretical message.

> Of the Jews there are those who displace words from their (right) places, and say: "We hear and we disobey"; and "Hear what is not hear"; and *Ra'ina* with a twist of their tongues and a slander to faith. If only they had said: "We hear and we obey"; and "Do hear"; and "Do look at us"; it would have been better for them, and more proper; but God hath cursed them for their unbelief; and but few of them will believe (Sura 4:46).

Ali says that the Jews twisted words and expressions so that the most solemn words of Allah could be made fun of and ridiculed.

> Where they should have said, "We hear and we obey", they said aloud, "We hear," and whispered "We disobey". Where they should have said respectfully, "We hear", they added in a whisper, "What is not heard", by way of ridicule. Where they claimed the attention of the Teacher, they used an ambiguous word apparently harmless, but in their intention disrespectful.[21]

---

20. Yusuf Ali, *The Holy Quran: Text, Translation, and Commentary*, p.245.
21. Ibid., p.194.

CHAPTER XI
Islam and Christianity

Islam and Christianity embrace the same themes: monotheism, belief in the Lord God who is the Creator and Sustainer of the world, divine revelation offered through prophets, Abraham the father of faith and a friend of God, the way of worship (fast and prayer), life after death, bodily resurrection, God's judgment of humanity, and human responsibility to God and his creation. However, the two religions differ about the means that God has used to reveal his message and humanity's response to God's revelation.

Muslims believe that God can be known only through the message revealed by his prophets. God has revealed his final message in Mohammed by making him copy from the heavenly tablet which contained all of God's message. Mohammed read the message of God with the help of angel Gabriel, committed it to his memory, and recited it to the people who listened to him. His listeners wrote the revealed message down and compiled the Quran. The message of the Quran is about Allah, the One God, who calls people out of idolatry and disbelief so that human beings may submit to his will and do what is commanded in the Holy Book.

Conversely, the Christians believe in a God who has redemptively revealed himself in the person of Jesus Christ who suffered on the cross to save a sinful humanity. "God was in Christ, reconciling the world to himself," writes Apostle Paul in II Corinthians 5:19. By knowing Jesus, one can know God himself, writes Apostle John. This Jesus is still revealed in the world as the indwelling Spirit of the Church, a believers' community. In 1 Corinthians 15, Paul portrays Jesus as the new, flawless and obedient second Adam who overcame the rebellion and disobedience of the old Adam through whom death was brought into this world.

The Christian Scriptures acknowledge Jesus as the Eternal Son of God, the Supreme Revelation of the Father, and the Reviving Spirit of Life. And so, the early Christians described God as the One Supreme

Lord who revealed himself in a threefold way. The triune revelation was soon used as a formula to baptize: "In the name of the Father, and of the Son, and of the Holy Spirit," (Mt. 28:19) and bless believers: "the grace of the Lord Jesus Christ, and the love of God, and the communion of the Holy Spirit" (2 Cor. 13:14).

The concept of Jesus as the Son of God was not invented by Christians. The titles "Messiah," "King of Israel," "Son of David", and "Son of God" are synonymous in the Gospels and they trace their origins back to the Old Testament Jewish imagery. Jesus fulfilled the conditions for Israel's king by being born in the lineage of David, attested to be God's Son on the three occasions of his birth, baptism, and resurrection, and affirmed by the witness of the title Messiah by the disciples and by those who believed in his teachings. W. Malcom Clark observes that the three attestations by God himself are to prove the "three moments" in the life of the King: the decree by God before birth (I Chr. 22:9), the formal disclosure of the choice (I Sam.16), and the initiation into office (Ps.2:7).[1] God himself confirmed Jesus as the Son of God at his baptism and transfiguration. James R. Brady concludes that Jesus himself acknowledged his office as Messiah and Son of God.

> The titles "Son of God" and "Messiah" were seen to be practically synonymous is evident from Peter's confession (Matt. 16:16), Caiaphas' question (Matt. 26:63), the demoniac's confession (Lk. 4:41), Martha's affirmation (Jn. 11:27), John's statement of purpose for his Gospel (Jn. 20:31), and Paul's initial preaching of Jesus (Acts 9:20-22).[2]

The Christian scholars argue that Jesus was greater than King David and superior to all the prophets. The Greek translation of the Hebrew Scriptures refers Kurios (LORD) to YHWH as the Gospels and Epistles refer it to Jesus. The attestation of Kurios to both YHWH and Jesus becomes more evident in Zechariah 14:5 and I Thessalonians 3:13.[3] Brady argues that Jesus was God himself who was "given" as a sacrifice to redeem the lost humanity.

---

1. Quoted by James R. Brady *Jesus Christ; Divine Man or Son of God*, (Lanham, Maryland: University Press of America, 1992), p.76

2. Ibid.,p.67.

3. Ibid., p.87.

There are implications within the Old Testament for the "son" being equal to Yahweh. Proverbs 30:4 asks a series of rhetorical questions with obvious reference to Yahweh: "Who has ascended into heaven and descended? Who has gathered the wind in his fists? Who has wrapped the waters in his garment? Who has established all the ends of the earth?" The next question asks, "What is his name or his *son's* name?" ...The Messiah is *Immanu-El*, the "son" who will be the "mighty God" and "Father of Eternity" (9:6). There is thus a distinction to be made in the terminology of the passage. A "child" is born, but a "son" is *given*. This son has no beginning.[4]

If one has to understand God, Christians argue, it is absolutely essential to know the sacrificial death of Jesus Christ on the cross. God chose to communicate himself in and through the person of Jesus Christ and the activity of the Holy Spirit. Through the vicarious suffering of Jesus Christ and the inner renewing of the Holy Spirit, the Christians are made intimate partakers of the Creator God. For Christians, Jesus is the paradigm of God's caring love and redeeming virtue; soteriology cannot be separated from Christology, and vice versa. This Jesus Christ, consequently, is central to the existence of the Church and pivotal to the life of the Christian. This encounter between the divine and human which occupies the central theme of the Christian faith has been denied by Islam.

The origin of the Church, a charismatic institution, can be traced back to Jesus Christ in whom God has come to dwell among humanity. This also brings with it an imminent judgment. The Church calls for the continuation of Word and the gifts of God as brought by Jesus Christ. This Word which calls for a decision for God is also a call which reflects the imminent presence of judgment. The Holy Spirit was sent in order to maintain the vitality of the Church, to retain the gifts of God, and to strengthen the believers. The Holy Spirit is the intimate and physical presence of Jesus Christ in his Church.

By comparing the local church with the Islamic umma, the Muslims challenge Christian leaders for not being able to provide a cohesive force to fasten the entire Christian community together. The Christians response is that the local church may represent the universal Church and may bear the blame for the divisions and bickering within, yet the "real

---

4. Ibid., p.88.

Church" is made up of two or three (or more) believers when they gather together in the name of Jesus to worship in any place and at any time (Matt. 18:20). The Church is a pilgrim community, *en route*. The Church is the contemplating sign of the coming of God. The Church is the body of Christ and the people of God.

The Church is a mystery revealed in Jesus Christ which the Christian believers in every part of the world practice in diverse forms and in different places. The mystery of Christ can be understood, the grace of God can be experienced, and the oneness of the believers can be achieved not by the visible gathering of the Christians but in the participation of the believers in the Eucharist. When the believers gather together to celebrate the Eucharist, the power and presence of Christ are experienced. Since the Eucharist is practiced in the gathering of believers, which the Christian Scriptures call Church, and a place to assemble is necessary. The place of gathering may be a thatched roof shed or a spiral cathedral. The make-up of gatherings may be illiterate peasants or sophisticated city folks. It is the sacramental unity that binds together Christians of all ages and in all places whom the Bible calls "clouds of witnesses" (Heb. 12:1).

Christian-Muslim Relationship : A Historical Perspective

Very often Christians have not had a significant relationship with the adherents of Islam. From the Middle Ages to the modern times, Islam has been considered by several Christian groups as a distorted Judeo-Christian religion. Mohammed's treatment of the People of the Book and his polygamous marriages have drawn a lot of criticism from Western Christian scholars. A substantial amount of early Christian writings about Islam have been polemical. They allege that Mohammed was an imposter who gave a warped account of the Bible and Jesus. Mohammed was accused of deriving his information about Jesus from heretics, particularly from Sergius a heretical monk, who was forced to flee Christendom and had met with Mohammed in Arabia.

Mohammed's mystical experiences were explained away by the claim that he was an epileptic, which during the Middle Ages was analogous to saying that he was demon possessed. He was identified with anti-Christ, and considered a power and sex hungry infidel as he was married to several wives. The thriving expansion of Islam was attributed to the sword. Even the teachings of Islam were misrepresented. Muslims were reported to have believed that women had no soul, although the Quran places men and women in the same place in Paradise and both of them have equal standing in the sight of God. The anger against Islam and Mohammed was well-reflected in several Western literary works as well.

Dante Alighieri, in his *Divine Comedy*, presents Mohammed as the worst enemy of Christianity. This late medieval poem is Dante's journey through hell, purgatory, and paradiso. He depicts the dominant theology of his day in his journey which begins with him being lost in a dark wood and ends in his vision of the Biblical God, who is Trinitarian in nature. He also sees several spheres of the heavens and the pit of hell. In the poem, Dante assigns specific destinations for different people: either into heaven or into hell. The bishops, the monks, the theologians, and the Christian philosophers are assigned to the fourth heaven of the Paradiso, as they all have a common cause. The virtuous pagans like Euclid, Ptolemy, Socrates, Plato, and Aristotle are in Limbo. Included, are also Avicenna and Averroes (the two notable intellectual Muslim philosophers whose original names are Ibn Sina and Ibn Rushd). The heretics and the rebels of Christianity are assigned the Eighth Circle of Hell, which is the lowest pit of hell, where they suffer severe punishment.

> Truly a cask by losing mid-board or stave is not so split open, as one I saw who was cleft from the chin to where th wind is broken; his entrails were hanging between his legs, his pluck was visible, and the dismal sack which makes ordure of what is swallowed. While I fit myself all on seeing him, he looked at me, and with his hands opened his breast, saying: 'Now see how I rend myself; see how mangled is Mahomet. In front of me goes Ali (cousin and son-in-law of Mahomet, and himself the head of schism) weeping, cleft in the face from chin to forelock; and all the others whom thou seest here were, when living, sowers of scandal and of schism, and therefore as they cleft.[5]

Dante portrays Muslims with offensive severity, warped teaching, and with an foreboding characterization. In the same canticle, Mohammed is presented as a penitent sinner sending a message of warning to a contemporary priest, Fra Dolcino, about the impending punishment.[6]

---

5. *The Comedy of Dante Alighieri*, Cantica i: Hell, trans. Charles Eliot Norton (Chicago : The University of Chicago, 1977), p.41.

6. Fra Dolcino, was a heretic and reformer, who for two years maintained himself in Lombardy against the forces of the Pope. Finally being reduced by famine in time of snow, in 1307, he was taken and burnt at Vercelli. Ibid., p.41.

"Now say then to Fra Dolcino, thou who perhaps wilt shortly
see the sun, if he wish not speedily to follow me hither, so to
arm himself with provisions that stress of snow may not bring
the victory to the Novarese, which to gain otherwise would not
be easy." Mahomet said to me this word, after he had lifted one
foot to go on, then to depart he stretched it on the ground.[7]

Little has changed in the West about the general misconception about
the people in the East and their religious practices. In his book
Orientalism, Edward Said laments how the media and the orientalists in
the West perpetuate the myth about the malignity of Islam and its
adherents. A study published in 1975 of Arabs and Islam which was
published in an American textbook says:

The Moslem religion, called Islam, began in seventh century.
It was started by a wealthy businessman of Arabia, called
Muhammed. He claimed that he was a prophet. He found
followers among the other Arabs. He told them they were picked
to rule the world.[8]

Over the centuries, Christian polemicists questioned the authenticity
of the Quran by citing the factual errors and inconsistencies found in
the book. For instance, the Quran says in Sura 19.7 that nobody had been
called John before Zechariah's son. "O Zakariya! We give thee Good
News of a son: His name shall be Yahya (John): On none by that name
have We conferred distinction before." In fact, the name John does occur
in the Hebrew Scriptures in II Kings 25:23. The Quranic reference to
John the Baptist, the Christians argued during al-Jihaz's time, was a
misunderstanding of Luke 1:61 where it says that there was nobody in
Zechariah's family who bore that name. Nicetas of Byzantium, a ninth
century Christian theologian, questioned the Quran's reference to Mary
as the "Sister of Aaron" (Sura 19:28). The confusion of associating Mary
as Miriam, the sister of Aaron and Moses, could have come out of the
Greek and Arabic translations which call Mary as Maryamm, Nicetas
concluded.

In the seventeenth century, Maracci accused Mohammed of calling
Jesus "Isa" because Mohammed was confusing Jesus with Esau, son of
Isaac. Maracci argued that the early Jewish converts to Islam, in hatred

---

7. Ibid., pp.41-42.

8. Edward Said, *Orientalism*, (New York: Vintage Books, 1979), p.287.

for Christianity, who used Mohammed to corrupt Jesus and his followers, called Jesus as Esau, and consequently, Mohammed took the name from them out of ignorance. John of Damascus said that Mohammed conceived a heretical teaching of his own because of his limited understanding of the Bible and brief association with an Arian monk, possibly Bahira whose name is mentioned by Mohammed's biographer. Furthermore, there are no historic evidences to prove the claim that Mohammed was indeed used as a tool to spite the Christians. Mohammed's personal contact with Christian leaders and monks has been unsubstantiated. A Muslim legend lends its support to ascertain how Mohammed was considered a prophet even by Bahira, an Arian monk, who was well-versed in Christianity. A few others believe that Mohammed gained knowledge about Christianity from his wife's cousin Waraqa and other Christians during his exile.

During the Middle Ages, Mohammed was scoffed at because of his limited knowledge about the Bible and obscure understanding of Christian history. He was accused of being confused about the deeper salvific message of the Bible. Christian scholars argued that Mohammed was in close contact with Christians during his flight to Mecca, as he felt safer in the Monophysite Christian community than in an idolatrous Mecca. During that time he learned bits and pieces of Christian teachings from the oral Christain tradition, and, once he became an established leader of the bedouin community, he gave his own version of Biblical history. Since the Bible had not been translated into vernacular languages, the Islamic version of biblical history was perpetuated by the Muslims.

In the twentieth century, several Christian scholars challenged the originality and the veracity of the Quran. They accused Mohammed of his narrow understanding of the Christian faith and condemned the Quran as it presented a distorted image of basic biblical truths. Thomas O'Shaughnessy writes:

> Mohammed's Koran displays a cross-section of the religious ideas that prevailed in the Arabia of his day; Orthodox, Nestorian and Monophysite - all set against a backdrop of biblical plagiarism and Jewish legend culled from the Talmud and Midrash.[9]

---

9. Thomas O'Shaughnessy, *The Koranic Concept of the Word of God*, (Rome: Pontificio Instituto Biblico, 1948), p.33.

It has been widely reported that Mohammed's attitude toward Orthodox Christianity turned sour after Zayd, Mohammed's adoptive son, was killed in a battle with Byzantine soldiers when he led an expedition to Mu'ta in Palestine. When the Byzantines were expanding their power over the Arab territories, Mohammed felt that he should prove to the Arabs that he could stand up to an alien power. When the Emperor Heraclius defeated the Persians and restored Christianity in Jerusalem, Mohammed thought his time had come. He organized a massive army consisting of over thirty thousand soldiers and marched north subduing both Christian and Jewish groups.

Mohammed was hard on the Christian communities in the north because of their association with the Byzantium. He made treaties with them, but imposed poll-tax on them as well. He also gave the Christians and Jews a special status as People of the Book. Nonetheless, he was not as hard on the Christians in the south because of hospitality shown to him and to his followers during their time of exile and the southern Christians' lack of contact with Byzantine. On one occasion, the ruler of Najran in southern Arabia sent emissaries to Mohammed consisting of Christian scholars who were permitted to use the mosque in Medina for prayers. However, the Christians never became Muslims and chose instead to pay the poll tax which was imposed by Mohammed.[10]

Some Christian scholars believe that Mohammed was actually a convert to Judaism and was used by the Jews to distort the fundamentals of Christian doctrine. Although this argument is baseless and has no substantial evidence to prove that Mohammed ever came close to becoming a Jew, supporters of this theory still exist. J. Windrow Sweetman wrote in his influential book *Islam and Christianity*, that Mohammed was deeply influenced by Judaism and its teachings and that he might have been either a convert or a would-be convert to know enough about the Hebrew Scriptures and to oppose major Christian doctrines. Sweetman wrote:

> There seem to have been several Jewish tribes in Arabia, and in Medina they constituted an influential trading caste. The *Kitab ul Aghani* contains some fanciful legends to account for the existence of the Jewish tribes of Yathrib and mentions the

---

10. Poll tax was not something that was newly introduced by the Muslims. The citizens of the Middle East always had to pay tax to the conquerors even before Islam arrived on the scene in exchange for protection from maribaunds and invaders.

two tribes Nadir and Quraiza by name. Philostorgius says that when Theolphilus, the Indo-Syrian missionary to South Arabia (A.D. 557-561) preached in the Himyarite Kingdom, there were many Jews there. *Dhu* Nuwas (c.521) a Himyarite king, probably embraced the Jewish religion from a political motive, because he was dominant for some time in South Arabia. It is thought by some that Sura lxxxv 5ff refers to a persecution of Christians in Najran for which *Dhu* Nuwas was responsible. Bishop Jacob describes such a persecution occurring in A.D.524. Some old Muslim writers say that a king called Abu Qarib (c. A.D.450) was converted to Judaism. Inscriptions, however, would seem to indicate that he was a pagan. We find many Jews spoken of by early Muslim historians and all of them have Arab names. It is suggested that these may have been adopted or that their bearers were Jews by religion and Arabs by race, for proselytization was not uncommon. Muhammad himself may have been a proselyte or a would-be proselyte. Bearing in mind that Christianity was identified with Rome on the one hand and with the Abyssinian enemy on the other, it should not be deemed surprising if resistance of a political and patriotic character to the missionaries who preached in pre-Islamic Arabia, may have encouraged the employment of Jews to refute the main tenets of Christianity and particularly the doctrines of the Holy Trinity and the Incarnation. When such ideas are opposed in the Quran, it is not wildly improbable to think one hears the popular echoing the Jews.[11]

Sweetman's speculation is based on conjectures and far-fetched theoretical assumptions. Mohammed may have had a close association with the Jewish community on account of commerce and trade. He may have known their religious practices and listened to their monotheistic confessions. Nevertheless, there is no conclusive documented evidence to ascertain that Mohammed was indeed a "proselyte or a would-be proselyte."

Furthermore, Sweetman's supposition that Mohammed took sides with Jews to oppose Christian doctrines is unjustified. Jews were not the only ones who opposed the fundamental doctrines of Christianity during Mohammed's time. There were several "Christian" groups in Arabia who

---

11. J. Windrow Sweetman, *Islam and Christian Theology: A Study in the Interpretation of Theological Ideas in the Two Religions*, (London and Redhill: Lutterworth Press, 1945), pp.1-2.

refused to accept the divinity of Jesus. The novel idea of God coming in the form of a human being in whom both the divine and the human could combine generated a host of speculations about the nature of this special person and triggered theological and soteriological debates. Arius preached that Jesus was not identical with God. Jesus was begotten by God and thus only similar to him. The Pauliciano or the Adoptionists said that Jesus was not born of God to Mary in a special way, but that God adopted Jesus as his Son in baptism by John the Baptist.

Virgin birth was not accepted by some early Christian groups like the Ebionites (a Jewish-Christian sect) which said that Jesus was born of a man but chosen of God to be his Christ. He was not begotten of God but created as one of the archangels. The apocryphal Gospel according to the Hebrews says that Jesus spoke of "my mother Holy Spirit". Some of the apocryphal literatures give a much more detailed narrative about Mary, nativity, and the life of infant Jesus than the Gospel accounts. The Book of James presents Joseph as an old man who sought out and found a cave for Mary at the time of delivery. He brought a midwife by the name of Salome who helped Mary with the child and proved that Mary was still a virgin even after she delivered the child Jesus.

The Dyophysites who are known as Nestorians (the School of Antioch), who had a strong missionary church in Arabia which stretched as far as India, said that the Word of God had two natures, human and divine which were separate.[12] The Nestorians were nurtured by the Mesopotamian traditions to whom the idea of the incarnation was alien. The Monophysites (who came to be known as the Alexandrians or the Oriental Orthodox Churches: the five ancient churches of Egypt, Syria, Armenia, Indian and Ethiopia), said that Jesus had only one nature, a divine one. This view placed Mary, as the mother of a god, in a higher position within the realm of God's creation. Yet another group called the Monotheletes, claimed that Jesus had only one will and it was divine.

Christian Response to the Divinity of Jesus

The Council of Chalcedon held in A.D. 451 tried to resolve the whole question of Christology and affirmed that Jesus had both a divine and a human nature bound together in a natural unity (union without fusion

---

12. This church nearly came to extinction by the Mongolian invasion in the Middle Ages. A few congregations still exist in Iran. See Williston Walker, Richard A. Norris, David W. Lotz, and Robert Handy, *A History of the Christian Church*, (New York: Charles Scribner's Sons, 1985), p.172.

and distinct without separation). After 125 years of conflict and bitter debates at several ecumenical councils, the final formula was drawn out. The Greek Orthodox and the Roman Catholic churches accepted the Chalcedonian affirmation as the formula which amalgamated the divine and human mystery in the person of Jesus Christ. Chalcedonian affirmation reiterated this divine unity in clear terms: "One and the same Christ, Son, Lord, Only-begotten, to be acknowledged in two natures, inconfusedly, indivisibly, inseparably; the distinction of natures by no means taken away by the union." J.N.D. Kelly gives an elaborate account of the Chalcedonian formula:

> Wherefore, following the Holy Fathers, we all with one voice confess our Lord Jesus Christ one and the same Son, the same perfect in Godhead, the same perfect in manhood, truly God and truly man, the same consisting of a reasonable soul and a body, of one substance with the Father as touching the Godhead, the same of one substance with us as touching the manhood, like us in all things apart from sin; begotten of the Father before the ages as touching the Godhead, the same in the last days, for us and for our salvation, born from the Virgin Mary, the Theotocos, as touching the manhood, one and the same Christ, Son, Lord, Only-begotten, to be acknowledged in two natures, without confusion, without change, without division, without separation; the distinction of natures being in no way abolished because of the union, but rather the characteristic property of each nature being (hypostasis), not as if Christ were parted or divided into two persons, but one and the same son and only-begotten God, Word, Lord, Jesus Christ; even as the Prophets from the beginning spoke concerning him, and our Lord Jesus Christ instructed us, and the Creed of the Fathers was handed down to us.[13]

The Christians affirm the authority of the Bible and claim that "salvation is found in no one else" except in Jesus Christ (Acts 4:12). Jesus Christ is the final and complete revelation from God. The Incarnation, life, death, and resurrection have a redemptive theme. He sent his Holy Spirit to strengthen those who believe in him. He was taken up to heaven to be seated at the right hand of God the Father only to come again as a Judge. The Lord of history will come again as the Judge of humanity.

Therefore, they witness to Jesus Christ as redemptive hope, coming Saviour, and Eternal Lord.

---

13. Kelly, *Early Christian Doctrines*, p.12.

Islam's inadequate understanding of the biblical concept of personal sin, its denial to acknowledge the need for redemption, its compelling affirmation as a post-Christian religion and the symbiotic association of legalism and ritualism have led some Christians to denounce Islam as the religion of the Antichrist. The apocalyptic narration about the last enemy of the end times as disclosed in the Book of Revelation has often been associated with Mohammed and his religion.

Since Islam, being a monotheistic religion, traces its origin and belief back to Adam and Abraham, questions the integrity of the Bible, denies the validity of Christ's incarnation and death, and challenges the practice of Christianity in the West, it was taken as a threat to the West's political and religious stability. Islam was reduced to a religion of the sword and faith persuasion of desert-dwelling Arab bedouins. Muslims were subjected to persecution and punishment by the Western traders, colonizers and religious zealots. The Lateran Councils of 1179 and 1215 condemned both Judaism and Islam as opponents of Christianity. In 1227, Pope Gregory IX insisted that the Jews and Muslims wear special clothing. Their religious practices were curbed; their faith traditions were restricted, and their movements were confined to limited geographical areas.

The Word of God

For Muslims, the Quran is the Word of God just as Jesus Christ is the "Word of God made flesh" for the Christians. Just as Mary conceived and brought Jesus into the world in a miraculous way, Mohammed received and delivered the Quran in a miraculous way. The Muslims, therefore, believe that they owe a great deal to the prophetic ministry of Mohammed who was instrumental in bringing the revelation which enables them to confess their belief in Allah and provides a chartered way for all walks of life.

Islam does not present Mohammed as one who claimed to be more than a messenger, but it clearly conveys that Mohammed was a chosen instrument of God who was faithful in his call to receive the way to salvation from Allah. As such,there is no comparison between Jesus the Messiah and Mohammed the prophet. Christians, who in their false enthusiasm compare Jesus as someone greater than Mohammed, have woefully misunderstood the very foundation of Islamic faith. After all, the Quran portrays Jesus as Allah's word and spirit (4:171). Jesus was Allah's special creation like Adam and hence Jesus was able to perform miracles. Often Mohammed himself confessed, he was only a warner not a performer of miracles. The honour attributed to Jesus by the Quran has not been ascribed to Mohammed.

The centre of debate between Christianity and Islam has been a question about Christology. Since Islam came after Jesus Christ, the Muslims claim superiority over Christian revelation and call for the Jews and the Christians to submit to Allah's will and the Quran's teachings. The People of the Book must renounce their corrupt religions and join the Islamic Umma. They should serve as agents of Allah to bring the whole world under the One, Sovereign God. Christians must abandon their spiritual arrogance and religious confidence in Jesus, who has liberated humanity from the bondage of sin. The Quran admonishes: "The Jews and Christians say: We are sons of God and His beloved. Say: why then doth He punish you for your sins? Nay, ye are but men" (Sura 5:20, also 3:59-64).

The Muslims say that the early Christian and political leaders, in order to take part in the control over the world which God allegedly gave to Jesus, exalted him as God, organized an ecclesiastical hierarchy in his name, and made a mere human being, the Pope, as God's representative. The introduction of Jesus, the messenger of God, as mediator and reconciler breaks the first of ten commandments. The alleged death of Jesus on the cross is the supreme folly of the Christian faith.

The cross of Jesus Christ has not only been a stumbling block to the Muslims, but also to the Romans, the Greeks, and the Jews. A Christian writer from the second century wrote: "They proclaim our madness to consist in this, that we give to a crucified man a place second to the unchangeable and eternal God, Creator of all." [14] Understanding the mystery surrounding the cross of Christ has been a major problem of both the intellectuals and uninformed from the time of Jesus to the modern period. When the cross of Christ is denied, the atoning death of Christ is also disclaimed. When the atonement of Christ is denounced, the very foundation of Christianity, which is the Christian hope of resurrection in the model of Christ is also disavowed. [15]

---

14. Justin Martyr, *Apology* (New York: Christian Heritage, 1949), I, 13.4.

15. We have already explained in the last chapter about the legends and fables surrounding the crucifixion of Jesus on the cross. The Quran's reference to crucifixion of Jesus is in the context of specific criticism of the Jews of Medina who did not acknowledge Mohammed as a prophet. The Jewish claim that Jesus had been crucified by their ancestors has been refuted by the Quran. It claims that Jesus's death on the cross never occurred but it "was made to appear to them." Perhaps, Mohammed himself thought that the crucifixion of Jesus was a Jewish fantasy.

The Crusades and Western Domination

The origin of the deterioration of Christian-Muslim relationship could be traced back to seventh century, when the Arab armies under Omar in 638 conquered Jerusalem, a pilgrim centre for Christians. The Muslims claimed that Jerusalem was the third holy site for them. They believed that Mohammed was taken to heaven from Jerusalem, and he was given a tour around paradise where he led all the prophets in worshipping Allah before he was returned to earth to teach human beings about the true way to Allah.

When Omar conquered Jerusalem, he assured the Christians living in the city that he would neither interfere with their religious faith nor disturb their churches. He gave a special quarter to the patriarch and his adherents to live, and committed all the sacred places to his care. The Jews who were expelled from Jerusalem by Christian rulers were permitted to return. Then Omar built a shrine inside the city wall from where Mohammed was taken to heaven and a mosque (Al-Aqsa) to worship near the area where Herod's Temple used to stand and right behind the Wailing Wall, the only remaining part of Solomon's Temple.

The relationship between Muslims and Christians turned sour and they became bitter enemies only after the Crusades. When the Seljuk army of Malik Shah defeated the Byzantine army in 1071, the Byzantine emperor Alexius Comnenus sought the help of fellow Christians in Europe and the Pope in Rome. The emperor asked the Christian West to help him put an end to the expansion of Islamic rulers in the East, but his plea went unheeded. At the Council of Placentia held in March 1095, a delegation was sent from Alexius to explain the precarious plight of Constantinople and it asked for the help of Western Christians. Pope Urban II would not consent to the appeal, and Alexius had to wait until after a second council at Clermont in November 1095. Having assessed the situation of the Muslim world and being driven by his own ambition to establish political and ecclesiastical supremacy over the Eastern Church, Urban II conceived a plan to deliver Eastern Christians from Muslim rulers and to deliver Jerusalem from Islamic control.

Urban II saw that the Seljuk empire was not as strong as it had previously been. The empire was broken into four warring groups after Malik Shah's death in 1092. Egypt had recovered its lost possessions and the Fatimid vizier Aphdal conquered Jerusalem from Ortuk in 1096. Urban II decided to take advantage of the divided empire and the volatile political climate. Being an energetic reformer who had become the pope during a time of controversy and divisiveness in the Church, his major challenge was to bring unity and solidarity. He seized an opportunity to direct the minds of the people to a common, external enemy, and preached on liberating Jerusalem, the Holy City. He warned the Christian public that the Muslim infidels had occupied the Holy Sepulchre, and he promised spiritual and eternal blessings on those who would take up the cross and join the liberating army.

Urban II told his listeners of the peril which had descended upon the Eastern churches. This heightened the fear of the expansion of Islamic rule. His favourite text was Mt. 19:29, in which Jesus says: "Every one who has left houses, brothers, sisters or father or mother or children or farms for my name's sake, shall receive many times as much, and shall inherit eternal life." He incited the soldiers to bear arms and be ready to die for Christ's sake.

Urban II was a dynamic speaker. He intermingled politics with religion in his preaching. Soon motives of commerce, pilgrimage to Jerusalem, and protection of Christianity were also combined with the cause of conquering the East. With that aspiration of establishing Papal supremacy, he introduced a plenary indulgence which induced people from all walks of life to join the army.

Urban II reunited politics and religion under one banner, the secular and sacred under a single flag. By doing so, Urban II returned the political and religious trends of his day to the original days of the Holy Roman Empire. Lamin Sanneh maintains that the church during the Holy Roman Empire was actively involved in politics and it combined both the sacred and secular in carrying out its duties. Sanneh observes:

> Under the empire, Christianity became Christendom, and the political ruler was seen as God's appointed agent, the earthly counterpart to the heavenly sovereign. In that scheme political affairs and religious matters were two aspects of one and the same reality. It followed from this that church and state were united for the same purpose, even though as institutions they represented different functions. While the church reserved to itself custody of the moral law, the state was concerned with enforcing the rules of conformity that gave practical expression to the higher spiritual law. Conformity rather than personal

persuasion was the chief end of religious activity under this corporate arrangement.[16]

Urban II asserted that the Seljuk Turks were, "a barbarian race from Central Asia," who had become Muslims and had conquered a Christian Byzantine empire. The Turks, he said, were "an accursed race, a race utterly alienated from God, a generation, forsooth, which has neither directed its heart nor entrusted its spirit to God."[17]

When the Turks invaded Constantinople in 1071 and in 1074, Pope Gregory II had also called the Knights of St. Peter to liberate the Christians of Constantinople from Muslim infidels. He preached that the martyrs of this liberation move would inherit "eternal reward." Gregory assured the Knights that he would lead the army himself. He told them that they would first conquer the Turks in Asia Minor and then move on to Palestine to liberate Jerusalem, the Holy City.[18] But the response of the warriors and the general public was anything but enthusiastic, and the plan to invade was eventually dropped.[19]

When Urban II offered the eloquent appeal to the people intermingling spirituality, commerce and race, the general response was overwhelmingly good. In the meantime, travel to Jerusalem was made a

16. Lamin Sanneh, *International Bulletin of Missionary Research*, "Can a House Divided Stand? Reflections on Christian-Muslim Encounter in the West", October 1993, p.164.

17. Quote taken from August C. Krey, *The First Crusade: The Accounts of Eye-Witnesses and Participants*, (Princeton and London, 1921), p.30

18. Jonathan Riley-Smith, *The Knights of St. John in Jerusalem and Cyprus, 1050-1310*, (London: 1967), pp. 5-8, 16-17.

19. By the end of the eleventh century, Europe awoke from its slumber with religious chivalry and spiritual unity. Pope Gregory II had already united the Christian armies in the West to stop the invading Muslim "infidels" into Spain. A new concept of holy war was introduced into Western Christianity. Earlier, St. Augustine had written about just war in *Civitate Dei* centuries before. However, what exactly Augustine was talking about a justifiable war which would fulfill the commandments of God is still debated to date. The Eastern Church considered all war as evil and hence it dealt with its enemies with diplomacy. The Byzantine Empire for centuries traded with their enemies, accepted their cultural and religious differences and lived in harmony with them. The Eastern churches (Antioch, Alexandria, Jerusalem, and Byzantine) were considered rivals to Rome. Constantinople, because of its long history, stood on par with Rome. The two churches did not agree on matters of church liturgy, ritual and polity, The Greek church from Constantinople refused to acknowledge papal supremacy and would not take the Son as equal to the Father and Spirit in the Creed. Besides, there were cultural and social differences which separated the Latins from the Greeks.

popular Christian pilgrimage. A visit to Palestine was considered a religious undertaking. Amid the cries of *Deus Hoc Vult* (God wills this), the crusade to liberate the Holy City was undertaken. A red cross, from which the title "Crusade" was arrived, was sown on the breast of the soldiers. Armies from all over Europe, mostly from Rhine districts, soon joined together from different directions and converged on Constantinople. From there, they marched on and captured Nicaea, the capital of Rum in 1097, defeated the Turks, crossed the desert and conquered Antioch in 1098, and finally reached Jerusalem in May 1099.

In the battle over Jerusalem, 70,000 Muslims, including women and children, were killed. Eight days after the conquest, Godfrey of Bouillon was elected king of Jerusalem.[20] Soon the Dome of the Rock which Omar built was converted into a Christian church and the al-Aqsa mosque was made into a residence for the king.

Thus, the concept of Holy War was introduced into human history not by the Muslims but by the Christians. The vestiges of Holy War can be traced back to the Hebrew Scriptures. The Crusades caused so much devastation to the Muslim culture and families that the Muslim historians consider the Middle Ages the darkest chapters of Islamic history. Harvey Cox aptly summarizes the Muslims' feelings: "For many Muslims the Crusades -the Christian Jihads- remain the most graphic expression of what the cross means."[21]

The political reign established by the crusaders did not last too long. After several invasions, in 1168, the Turkish amir Assad al-Din conquered the Fatimids of Egypt and their French allies. He burnt Cairo, destroyed the Fatimid dynasty, and restored Egypt to the allegiance of the Abbasid Khalifs of Bhagdad. When the Turkish amir Assaid al-Din died in 1169, his nephew, Kurd Salam al-Din (Saladin) became his successor and vizier of Egypt. Saladin began to expand his territory and consolidated his kingdom. The Kingdom of Jerusalem was beginning to decay through dissensions. Latins were beginning to lose popularity. In the meantime, Saladin was training his army in French methods of warfare and becoming more and more powerful. In July 1187, he invaded Tiberian (Hattin) and moved toward Jerusalem which was finally conquered in October of 1187.

---

20. The real title: "Advocate of the Holy Sepulchre of Jerusalem".

21. Cox, *Many Mansions*, p.36.

Soon the European crusaders were divided into rival groups and they developed hatred for one another. The Latin rites imposed upon the Christians in Jerusalem and all over the Middle East were abandoned. The Greek and Latin churches denounced each other as heretics; smaller Christian groups were accused as schismatics. To make it worse, there arose national and political rivalries between Germans and French which sealed the doom of European conquest of Jerusalem.

Only a battered and divided Christendom existed in the thirteenth century. The frayed Christianity and a weakened European power in an alien land became a vulnerable and weak force before the unified and powerful Islamic empire.

In 1453, Constantinople was conquered by the Turkish Muslims and, soon, Islam was beginning to spread toward the East and the West again. The Muslim rulers were more benevolent to the Arab Christians than the Latin rulers had been. As a result, a large number of Nestorian and Monophysite Christians abandoned their faith and took refuge in Islam as a safe political and religious haven. In his article, "Christendom Vs Islam: Interaction and Co-Existence," Roger Savory summarizes the incongruity of the time. He says:

> An ironical but undeniable result of the Crusades was the deterioration of the position of Christian minorities in the Holy Land. Formerly these minorities had been accorded rights and privileges under Muslim rule, but, after the establishment of the Latin Kingdom, they found themselves treated as "Loathsome schismatics". In an effort to obtain relief from persecution by their fellow Christians, many abandoned their Nestorian or Monophysite beliefs, and adopted either Roman Catholicism, or-the supreme irony-Islam.[22]

The middle of twelfth century generated interest among some Christian leaders to understand Islam. In 1141, Peter the Venerable, the Abbot of Cluny, appointed a team of Muslim and Christian scholars to translate the Quran and other Islamic texts to Latin. It was a massive undertaking. The project was completed in 1143 with the translation of the Quran, a collection of Muslim legends, teachings of Islam and the *Apology of al-Kindi*. The translation of the text achieved little with regard

22. Roger Savory, "Christendom Vs Islam: Interaction and Co-Existence" *Introduction to Islamic Civilization* ed., Roger Savory (Cambridge: Cambridge University Press, 1976), p.133

to Muslim-Christian relationship in Europe. In 1147, King Louis VII of France, undertook the Second Crusade against the Muslims. Peter the Venerable sent the king to fight the Muslims with his blessings.[23]

The Reformers had a limited understanding of Islam and compared the evils of Christianity with the teachings of Islam. John Wycliffe compared Western Christianity's lust for power, religious pride, and disrespect for the teachings of the Bible to the person of Mohammed and called the Christians "Western Mahomets".[24] Luther, Zwingli and other later reformers also compared their religious adversaries, particularly Rome, with "Muhammadanism".

Even during the Renaissance, the European understanding of Islam as a religious faith was narrow and limited. The scholars who had studied the Quran and Islamic literatures reveal the prevalent opinion of the day. Barthelmy d'Herbelot published a massive book entitled *Bibliotheque Orientale* in 1697 which became an influential source of reference on Eastern studies in Europe until the beginning of the nineteenth century. During the same period, Humphry Prideaux published an equally important book entitled *Mahomet: The True Nature of Imposture*. In spite of their massive work and extensive research, their approach to Islam was polemic. D'Herbelot presents Mohammed as an impostor and a heretic. Prideaux pictures Islam as a distorted Christian religion with no logic or reason.

In the nineteenth century, Prideaux's theory of Islam as a primitive religion was repeated. Europeans began to look at the East with a new pair of eyes, especially with European racial, cultural and religious superiority. Eastern religions and oriental civilizations were considered backward and primitive and assigned to the lower scale of global civilization. Eastern religions and cultures were compared to the advanced European industrial society and western scientific achievements and it was believed that the Asian, non-Christian societies needed Western intervention. In *Itineraire de Paris a Jerusalem, et de Jerusalem a Paris (1810-1811)* [Journey from Paris to Jerusalem and from Jerusalem to Paris (1810-11)], Chateaubriand wrote that Islamic society had fallen into disrepute with no cohesive purpose. Only the Christian

---

23. See Benjamin Kedar, *Crusade and Mission: European Approaches to the Muslims* (Princeton, 1984), pp.99ff.

24. Quoted in Richard William Southern, *Western Views of Islam in the Middle Ages,* (Cambridge, Mass: Harvard University Press, 1978), p.79.

West, with its political and religious principles, could liberate the Muslims from their cultural and civilizational pathos. He wrote that the Quran "preaches neither hatred of tyranny nor love of liberty". It contains *ni principe de civilisation, ni precepte qui puisse elever le caractere* (neither a principle for civilization nor a code that can elevate character).[25]

The nineteenth century colonial ideologies have been carried over to the twentieth century as well. Non-Western culture, particularly, the Oriental culture was looked down upon. Eastern religions and cultures were reduced to a simple and primitive social status so that only Western civilization and religion could enlighten them. At the turn of the twentieth century Evelyn Baring, Lord Cromer wrote in *Modern Egypt*:

> Sir Alfred Lyall once said to me: "Accuracy is abhorrent to the Oriental mind. Every Anglo-Indian should always remember that maxim." Want of accuracy, which easily degenerates into untruthfulness, is in fact the main characteristic of the Oriental mind.
>
> The European is a close reasoner; his statements of fact are devoid of any ambiguity; he is a natural logician, albeit he may not have studied logic; he is by nature skeptical and requires proof before he can accept the truth of any proposition; his trained intelligence works like a piece of mechanism. The mind of the Oriental, on the other hand, like his picturesque streets, is eminently wanting in symmetry. His reasoning is of the most slipshod description. Although the ancient Arabs acquired in a somewhat higher degree the science of dialectics, their descendants are singularly deficient in the logical faculty. They are often incapable of drawing the most obvious conclusions from any simple premises of which they may admit the truth. Endeavor to elicit a plain statement of facts from any ordinary Egyptian. His explanation will generally be lengthy, and wanting in lucidity. He will probably contradict himself half-a-dozen times before he has finished his story. He will often break down under the mildest process of cross-examination.[26]

---

25. Said, *Orientalism*, p.171-175.

26. Quoted in Said, *Orientalism*, p.38.

CHAPTER-XII
Christian-Muslim Relationship
A Debate Over Prophethood and Scriptures

Christians focus their faith on the person of Jesus whose message was centred on the coming of the Kingdom of God and the invitation extended to men and women to respond to God's rule. The Christian Church has historically laid emphasis on the titles of Jesus and the confession of his disciples that Jesus was indeed the Messiah. The Church gives emphasis to the "I am" sayings of Jesus in John's Gospel in which he makes explicit claims for himself and presents himself as the means of entry into a loving and personal relationship with God.

Islam's contention is that the early Church lived in anticipation of Christ's second coming. When Christ did not come, the church accepted its lot and found its place in society. The early church, in its search for God's revelation, acknowledged the presence of Jesus even in pagan philosophical systems, and thus compromised the revealed divine message. For instance, when Paul preached to the Greeks, he confessed that "God never left Himself without a witness," (Acts 14:17) and in his public addresses Paul often quoted from their sacred texts. In the Epistle to the Hebrews, the writer says that God spoke to men and women at various times, in numerous ways, and, finally, in the fullness of time He spoke through His Son Jesus Christ. Therefore, the Muslims argue that the Bible itself talks about the universality of truth and the presence of God in other religious traditions. This universalist view of God's revelation was lost only when divisions occurred within the church.[1]

Islam, however, teaches that prophecy is sealed in Mohammed and, after him, no other Prophet will arise. Mohammed is said to have announced, "Whoever died in the faith of Jesus, and died in Islam before

---

1. However, in the Synoptic gospels Jesus does not make explicit claims for himself, although, often speaks with authority of the ways of God and his Kingdom.

he heard of me, his lot shall be good. But whoever hears of me today and yet does not assent to me, he shall surely perish."[2] Islam avows that any given religious dispensation or divine revelation would remain valid until the coming of the next prophet. The new revelation shall take effect and supersede all the earlier dispensations from the moment the newest and ultimate message is revealed to the next prophet.

The prophets who came before Mohammed had a specific mission and they were all confined to their time, people, and geographical location. When their task was completed another prophet was raised with a specific mission. In the same prophetic tradition, Jesus, a special Messenger, the created word and the spirit of God, was sent to the Israelites with Allah's Gospel. Jesus himself had confessed about his mission: "I was not sent except to the sons of Israel". In contrast, Mohammed was sent to the whole world by originating his mission from Arabia. He began his ministry first among his own relatives, then to the Qurayish and to the Arabs, and finally to the Jews, the Christians and to people everywhere.

One of the major accusations brought against Christianity is that the Gospel and earlier revelations have been corrupted by the Christian leaders. The Christian Scriptures were composed by some men who put their messages together by obtaining bits and pieces from different sources. Many writers of the Gospels were not eye-witnesses of Jesus's teachings and actions. Ur-Rahim contends:

> The metaphysics of Christianity today is totally opposed to the metaphysics which Jesus brought. The physical aspect of what Jesus brought, his code of behaviour, is today irrecoverably lost. To live as Jesus lived is to understand his message, yet there is virtually no existing record of how Jesus behaved... The most fundamental act of Jesus was that of worship of the Creator... Yet it is evident that no Christian today makes the same acts of worship which Jesus made. Jesus usually prayed in the synagogue. He prayed at appointed times each day, in the morning, at mid-day, and in the evening. The exact form of his prayer is no longer extant, but it is known that it was based on the prayer which Moses was given. Jesus said that he had come to uphold the law and not to destroy it one jot or one tithe. Jesus

---

2. Mahmoud M. Ayoub, *The Quran and Its Interpreters*, I, p.112.

was educated in the synagogue in Jerusalem from the age of twelve. He preached in the synagogue. He used to keep the synagogue clean. No Christian today can be found performing these actions. How many Christians have even been circumcised in the manner that Jesus was? The services now held in today's churches...come directly from the pagan Graeco-Roman mythological rites. The prayers they use are not the praises which Jesus sung. Due to the innovations of Paul and his followers, there is no revealed teaching left as to what to eat and what not to eat.[3]

The Christians dispute this indictment and hold that the Hebrew and Christian Scriptures which have been handed over to the believing community from the early Christian era have been translated and preserved in several languages around the world. It is highly improbable that people of many different languages, several cultures and various regions could have consented to or tolerated letting a handful of religious and political leaders alter the divine revelation, and thus allow themselves to be deceived. Beside, it would have been impossible for Jews and Christians, between whom existed ancient rivalry, to come to an agreement and to alter their own sacred texts. A grand scale, universal forgery would be an impossible task. The recent discovery of the Dead Sea Scrolls and archaeological excavations prove that certain books of the Hebrew Scriptures match the books that existed before Jesus word by word. Michael Nazir Ali maintains:

> All manuscript evidence strengthens the case for the integrity of the sacred texts. The continued agreement of the Jewish Bible with the Christian Old Testament, despite the historical mutual hostility of the Jews and Christians, is an argument favouring the integrity of the Old and New Testaments. The discovery of certain biblical books among the Dead Sea Scrolls has shown us that we have the abundance of New Testament manuscripts, the diversity of their provenance and language, their great antiquity compared to other manuscripts of ancient literature, are all powerful arguments for the integrity of the New Testament.[4]

---

3. Muhammad 'Ata ur-Rahim, *Jesus Prophet of Islam*, p.199.

4. Michael Nazir Ali, *Frontiers in Muslim-Christian Encounter*, (Oxford: Regnum Books, 1987), p.47.

Islam denounces the Christians for not having one standardized version of the Bible. The availability of many translations and several original manuscripts are cited, as an example to prove there is no consensus about the Word among Christians. In response to this incrimination, Ali, himself a Christian, claims:

> The survival of variant manuscripts is regarded as a strength by Christian scholars in establishing a critical text of the New Testament. The variations do not appear to compromise either the historical integrity of the New Testament or its reliability as a canon of Christian doctrine in any substantive way. The existence of a large number of manuscripts in different ancient languages, with their origins in widely separated churches yet in substantial agreement with each other, is an argument in favour of the integrity of the Scriptures.[5]

Another arraignment brought upon Christian faith is about the doctrine of the Holy Spirit. The Christian concept of the Holy Spirit is nothing but a mere theological and ecclesiastical invention of the early Christian political leaders. Actually, Islam contends, Jesus foretold in the Gospel about the coming of Mohammed which the Christians have suppressed and translated as the Holy Spirit or the Spirit of Jesus. Mohammed is presented as God's ultimate messenger who had a prophetic mission to Jews, Christians, and all others. Ibn Taymiyya says:

> He (Mohammed) stated even that he was sent to all the children of Adam, to Arabs and to Byzantine, Persian, Turkish, Indian, Berber, and Ethiopian non-Arabs, and to all other nations. He even stated that he was sent to both the races—the human race and that of the jinn. All these are clear issues successively handed down from him, upon whose transmission from him his companions are agreed. This is despite their great number and their dispersal into various regions and situations—those who accompanied him were in the tens of thousands and their actual number cannot be counted and is known to God alone.[6]

The Christian church leaders are reproved for replacing the Law and the Gospel with new ritualistic practices and fancy doctrines about God and worship. Ibn Taymiya directs this charge against the Christians:

---

5. Ibid., p.48.

6. Ibn Taymiyya, *A Muslim Theologian's Response to Christianity*, p.106.

Christ did not ordain for you the Trinity, nor your thinking on the divine persons, nor your doctrine that he is the Lord of the Universe. He did not prescribe for you that you make pork and other forbidden things permissible. He never commanded you to omit circumcision, or that you should pray to the east; nor that you should take your greatmen and monks as masters beside God. He did not tell you to commit *shirk* by using statues and the cross, or by praying to the absent or dead prophets and holy men and telling them your needs. He did not prescribe monasticism or the other reprehensible practices which you innovated. Christ never ordained such things for you, nor is that which you follow the Law which you received from the messengers of Christ.[7]

It is also said that Christians often rely on ambiguous and untrustworthy human resources to build their faith. Christianity is founded on the personal experiences of men like Paul, Peter, and Constantine. Paul claimed to have met Jesus on his way to Damascus, and Peter is said to have dreamt of a mantle coming from heaven, and Constantine is believed to have seen the sign of cross in the sky with the inscription "with this sign, you will conquer".

The Muslims surmise that the early church leaders were responsible for the corruption of the Gospel and the teachings of Jesus in order to shed Christianity of its Jewish moorings. In order to create anti-Jewish feelings, the Christians concocted the story of crucifixion and innovated a religion of their own fantasy.

The Christians constructed a religion from two religions—from the religion of the monotheist prophets and from that of the idolaters. In their religion, it developed that there was a portion containing that which was brought by the prophets and a portion which they innovated from the idolaters by way of opinions and deeds. Thus, they innovated terms of the hypostases, although these terms were not found anywhere in the message of the prophets. Similarly, they introduced printed idols in place of bodily idols (icons in place of statues), prayers to them in place of praying to the sun, moon, and stars, and fasting in the spring in order to combine revealed religion and the cycle of nature.[8]

---

7. Ibid., p.118.

8. Ibid., p.118.

The Muslims are convinced that the Christian church in its present form is far from what Jesus and his apostles ever intended it to be. The Christian food habits (eating of pork, sausage), the establishment of "single-sex communities", the formation of convents and monasteries, the failure to observe the Passover meal, the refusal to practise fast, circumcision, and the breakdown of the family structure in the "Christian West" are indication as evidences that the Church is not a true agent of God. Papal authority and ecclesiastical hierarchy are mentioned as human institutions, which are established to manipulate and control the spiritually hungry people. Ur-Rahim states:

> The Church was instituted by Jesus. He did not establish a hierarchy of priests to act as mediators between God and man. Yet the established Pauline church, from very early on, always taught Christians to believe that their salvation was assured if they acted and believed as the Church told them. From where did the Church derive its authority? This claim for authority, in its most extreme form, is to be found in the Roman Catholic Church's doctrine of papal infallibility.[9]

Major Christian Doctrines of Islam and the Teachings of the Quran

Islam contends that Jesus never intended to establish a community to worship him. The origin of the Church, as the Christian Scriptures portray, is a fabricated myth. The Christian Church has been divided into several rival denominations because its origin was not from God. Christianity does not have the inner cohesive force like the Islamic umma does in bringing together people of all races and backgrounds together. The umma and the Church have fundamental differences. In his book *Islam and Western Civilization*, F. R. Ansari compares the functions of the Christian Church and the performance of Islamic umma, and attempts to present Islam as a superior religion as it treats all its adherents equally, He writes:

> According to Islam, all human beings, whether white or black, red or yellow, Europeans or Africans, Westerners or Orientals, form one family. And here Islam has laid the foundations of the Fundamental Human Rights which is Islam's major contribution in the field of social relations. We might, by way

---

9. Ibid., p.201.

of contrast, refer here to the racial superiority - complex which has been - perpetrated by the Christians, the Jews and the Hindus.[10]

The Islamic umma transcends social, political, cultural, economic and racial barriers. Unlike the Church, which claims the presence of the Spirit of Christ when the believers gather together to worship, the umma is bound together by the Quran, the very word of God which came from Allah himself. Umma is governed not by human power but by the Quran which was sent from heaven. The members of the umma do not submit to human wisdom or earthly innovations but the Word which was sent by God. Umma does not have to preach that there is no difference between "Greek and Jew, circumcised and uncircumcised, barbarian, Scythian, slave, free man, but Christ is all, and in all", (Col. 3:11) as all are created equally in the image of God and whose only duty on this earth is to worship Allah. Islamic scholars like Yusuf Ali, Muhammed Ur-Rahim, Abul A'la Maududi, and Badru D. Kateregga argue that the very origin of the Christian Church is different from the origin of the Islamic umma.

> The *umma* is different from any other community. It is not centered on tribe, nationality, race, or linguistic grouping. The *umma* does not take its name from the founder or an event. The *umma* is the community of Allah. He is the Absolute Truth to which the Muslim community owes its life and existence. The life and activities of the *umma* are all under His legislative direction. Equally, the life of the individual member of the *umma*, both private and public, is under God's legal command. It is Allah's Law which must be supreme within the *umma*. What God has recommended as good for the community, shall always remain good, and what He has forbidden shall always be denied. The *umma* cannot authorize negation, deletion, or abrogation of Allah's supreme Law and scheme of values.[11]

Maududi goes one step further. He asserts that all of humanity is one umma and hence there should be no human-made division. This universal umma should worship Allah.

---

10. F.R. Ansari, *Islam and Western Civilization* (Karachi: World Federation of Islamic Missions, 1975), p.14.

11. Badru D. Kateregga and David W. Shenk, *Islam and Christianity: A Muslim and a Christian in Dialogue,* p.48.

There is no religion apart from Islam that has succeeded in obliterating distinctions of race, colour, language, place of origin and nationality in the establishing of a universal brotherhood of men... as far as Muslim society is concerned the entire human race has in fact become one *ummah*.[12]

Maududi presents Islam as the only religion in the world which considers all of humanity to be one family and proclaims that all human beings have descended from the same parents: "O Mankind, We created you from a single male and a female", declares the Quran (49:13). Islam asserts God has grouped them into nations and tribes not that they may fight with each other but that they may identify each other more easily for promoting co-operation among themselves. This so-called division into groups is to facilitate reference or identification rather than to set one against the other: "And We made you into nations and tribes that ye may know each other. Not that ye may despise each other!"[13]

The Trinity and Tawhid

In referring to the doctrine of Trinity, the Quran denies emphatically that Godhead is divided. God is One.

"O people of the Book! Do not exaggerate in your religion nor utter anything concerning Allah except the Truth. The Messiah, Jesus, son of Mary, was only a messenger of Allah, and His word which He conveyed to Mary and a spirit from Him. So believe in Allah and His messengers, and do not say "Three"- stop! It is better for you! Allah is only one God. It is far removed from His transcendent majesty that He should have a son. He is all that is on the earth. And Allah is enough as Defender. The Messiah will never scorn to be a slave to Allah nor will the favoured angels. Whoever scorns His service and is proud, all such will He assemble to Him; then as for those who believed and did good works, to them He will pay their wages in full, adding to them of His bounty; and as for those who were scornful and proud, them He will punish with a painful doom; and they will not find for them, against Allah, any protecting friend or helper". (Sura 4:168-73).

---

12. Abul A'la Maududi, *Unity of the Muslim World,* (Lahore: Islamic Publications, 1967), p.13.

13. Ibid., p.11.

For the Christians, the trinitarian theology that God redeems through Christ in the power of the Holy Spirit defines the relationship between the salvation offered through Christ and the being and mystery of God revealed to humankind in the divine drama of redemption. This God who reveals himself is *deus revelatis, deus absconditas* (God is revealed and God is hidden). God exists eternally as Father, Son and Holy Spirit, and this eternal trinitarian life is what is communicated in the economy of redemption. God's self-revelation and his self-communication would not make him a lesser God, rather by his self-disclosure, human beings could better understand God's creation, redemption and consummation which are thus rooted and secured in God's eternity.

The Quranic reference to Jesus as, "(Allah's) word which He conveyed to Mary and a spirit from Him", has been interpreted by some Christian apologetics as Mohammed's assertion of the divinity of Jesus. Charles-J. Ledit argues that Jesus, being the Word, proceeded from God's transcendent Being and emanated from his ineffable Self as thought is formed in a human mind before it is delievered.[14] His thesis, however, has been opposed by Islamic scholars. The Quran does not attach any importance to the reference to Jesus as Word or Spirit. Christians and Muslims mean two entirely different things when they refer to the Word and the Spirit. Jesus of the Quran is only Allah's messenger. Nothing more. Any other attribute given to Jesus to assert his divinity contradicts the very foundation of the Quranic message about One God. The Quran cannot be interpreted in the context of Christian doctrine. Islamic Godhead cannot be shared with any other person.

The word *Trinity* is not found anywhere in the Bible. The doctrine of the Trinity emerged as a concept at the end of the fourth century in order to end the Christological controversies perpetuated by heretics who denied either the divinity or humanity of Jesus. Arius, a Greek theologian of Alexandria, Egypt who became an influential teacher in the early fourth century, argued that God the Father was eternal and "unbegotten". In contrast to the nature of the Father, Jesus, the Word, was "begotten" and created like human beings. Hence Jesus was not divine and was subordinate to the Father. Jesus served only as a mediator between God and human beings, a kind of "halfway house" between the two.[15] Arius,

---

14. Charles-J. Ledit, *Mahomet, Israel et le Christ*, (Paris: La Colombe, 1956), p.152.

15. Williston Walker, et. al., *The History of the Christian Church*, fourth edition (New York: Charles Scribner's Sons, 1985), p.133.

therefore, negated the idea that a sovereign God could suffer and endure pain. It has been widely believed that Mohammed had met some of Arius' followers who were scattered all over Arabia and from there developed his understanding about the person of Jesus Christ.[16]

Arius carried his message to the people of his day who sang: "Once God was alone, and not yet a Father, but afterward he became a Father!"[17] The theologians of the early church tried to explain in clear terms by the doctrine of the Trinity that Jesus Christ and the Holy Spirit are essential for our salvation. The early Church leaders taught that the Word of God had the same Being as with God and he was pre-existent. If God could not experience human agony and share human misery, his redemptive act would stop short of genuine participation with human limitations. The Trinity, therefore, was defined as the nature of God (ousia) which existed as three hypostases. They instructed the early Church that the Sovereign God of the Hebrew Scriptures was fully present in Jesus of Nazareth and guided the believers who gathered together in koinonia fellowship as manifested in the Holy Spirit.

The Trinity

The doctrine of the Trinity is essential for the Christian understanding of sin and salvation as it expresses the unsurpassable love of God. The early expression for the Trinity is *tres personae et una substantia* (three persons but one substance). *Substantia* cannot be understood as a "thing" or a mere "substance". Rather, the qualities of God (such as justice, power, love, and goodness) as revealed in the Hebrew Scriptures are found in the person of Jesus also. In Christian theology, one cannot separate the expressions of Jesus from the fatherhood of God or the empowering of the Holy Spirit.

In order to explain the relation between God the Father and God the Son, the use of Greek philosophical terms such as *(homo-ousios)* "one substance" and "of the same being" were used by the early church. The usage of unambiguous language as expressed in Greek philosophical thought was necessary to settle the distinction btween the synoptic gospels and the fourth gospel.

---

16. Critics of Islam argue that Mohammed's theology was also influenced by Nestorian and Monophysite Christians. The Nestorians, for example, denied the divinity of Jesus and rejected the notion that Mary was the 'God-bearer'.

17. Jaroslav Pelikan, *The Emergence of the Catholic Tradition* (100-600), (Chicago: The University of Chicago Press, 1971), p.195.

The debate over the divinity of Jesus was defined and conclusively decided in 325 A.D., at the first ecumenical council held at Nicaea where the Nicene Creed was adopted. The Council condemned Arius and his ideas as heresy. He left Alexandria where he served as a priest and moved to Palestine where he gained a large following. The issue of Jesus the God-Man was finally and conclusively resolved at the Council by the clear definition of Christian belief which came to be known as the Nicene Creed. The Creed became a regular confession of the Church of Jesus Christ:

> We believe in one God, the Father, the Almighty, maker of heaven and earth, of all that is, seen and unseen. We believe in one Lord, Jesus Christ, the only Son of God, eternally begotten of the Father, God from God, Light from Light, true God from true God, begotten not made, of one Being with the Father; through him all things were made. For us and for our salvation he came down from heaven, was incarnate of the Holy Spirit and the Virgin Mary and became truly human. For our sake he was crucified under Pontius Pilate; he suffered death and was buried. On the third day he rose again in accordance with the Scriptures; he ascended into heaven and is seated at the right hand of the Father. He will come again in glory to judge the living and the dead, and his kingdom will have no end.

> We believe in the Holy Spirit, the Lord, the giver of life, who proceeds from the Father and the Son, who with the Father and the Son is worshipped and glorified, who has spoken through the prophets. We believe in the one holy universal and apostolic church. We acknowledge one baptism for the forgiveness of sins. We look for the resurrection of the dead, and the life of the world to come.

Jesus is of the same substance with God the Father and Johannine expression of "incarnationist" Christology became complete at the Chalcedonian Council in the fifth century. The Council approved:

> Therefore, following the holy fathers, we all with one accord teach men to acknowledge one and the same Son, our Lord Jesus Christ, at once complete in God head and complete in manhood, truly God and truly man, consisting also of a reasonable soul and body; of one substance with the Father as

regards his Godhead, and at the same time of one substance with as regards his manhood; like us in all respects, apart from sin; as regards his Godhead, begotten of the Father before the ages, but yet as regards his manhood begotten, for us men and salvation, of Mary the Virgin, the God-bearer; one and the same Christ, Son, Lord, Only-begotten, recognized in Two Natures, Without Confusion, Without Change, Without Division, Without Separation; the distinction of natures being in no way annulled by the union, but rather the characteristics of each nature being preserved and coming together to form one person and one substance *(hypostasis)*, not as parted or separated into two persons, but one and the same Son and the only-begotten God the Word, Lord Jesus Christ; even as the prophets from earliest times spoke of him, and our Lord Jesus Christ himself taught us, and the creed of the Fathers has handed down to us.

The Nicene Creed and Chalcedonian Creed accurately express the "two-nature" Christology of incarnationism - "the hypostatic union" of divine nature and human nature in one person whose actual being *(hypostasis)* is not that of a human but that of the divine Logos as presented in the fourth gospel. This Incarnationist Christology became the doctrine and the thought of the Church in later centuries.

The Christian doctrine of the Trinity is the attempt to comprehend the eternal mystery of God and his act of redemption as manifested in the person of Jesus, the Word of God and the Holy Spirit, the Indwelling Agent. The economy of redemption is the core and context in which statements about God were made. The relationship between the being of God and his act of redemption define the Christian belief of Trinitarian theology. The Sovereign and Creator God, who is beyond comprehension and understanding, by making himself visible in the person of Jesus Christ, has made tangible within human history the ineffable mystery of God. The God who revealed himself in Christ is the One Eternal Logos. When Jesus was questioned about the foremost of the commandments, he answered, "Hear, O Israel, the Lord our God is One". Commenting on Jesus's response Gregory G. Bolich writes:

> If Jesus, in his identity with God, is seen to be divine himself, this does not mean that there are now two Gods, one in rivalry with the other, or even two Gods cooperating with the other, but that there is **one** God, and that the authority of the one God is also the authority of Jesus. But this, if recognized in and of

itself, might nevertheless remain insufficient. Hence, we find James' warning in Chapter two that even the demons recognize that God is one, and yet their only response is to shudder at the awesome truth of this.[18]

John's Gospel opens with the message that the pre-incarnate Son himself is the Eternal God which Paul continues in his epistles, especially, in his epistle to the Colossians.

The Christian scriptures only echo the idea of the Hebrew Scriptures, especially the creation text, as documented in Genesis 1st and 2nd chapters and Proverbs 8th chapter. The Spirit, who was actively present from the very beginning, continues to guide the creation back to its origin, God, and the Church to its beginning, the Word. The followers of Jesus fully recognized Jesus's Godhead and his revelation only after his resurrection and the coming of the Holy Spirit at Pentecost.

The Holy Spirit, who was sent at the request of the Son, witnesses the preaching of the Word and strengthens the community of believers gathered together as Church. By the presence of the Spirit, the presence of Christ is continued. The Spirit continues to work among the believers to witness God's righteousness, convict the world of its sin, and warn humanity of the imminent judgment. Paul emphasizes that the Spirit is the agent of God whom, according to Bolich, "God has given as an earnest of redemption". Bolich continues:

> By the Spirit comes power, the same power by which God raised Jesus from the dead. Through the indwelling of the Spirit, [human being] receives the witness of God to his own relationship with God in Jesus Christ. This spirit is also a spirit of comfort who preaches Christ, but here the emphasis is on a preaching of the Christ known pre-eminently by the individual within the believing community. Yet this Spirit is also a spirit who makes his witness and his proclamation of Christ known throughout the community by the gifts that he engenders. These gifts, meant for the up building of the Body of Christ, all find their fulfillment in the proclamation or witness to Christ [as found in] Ephesians 4, I Corinthians 12 [and], I Corinthians 14.[19]

---

18. Gregory G. Bolich, *Authority and the Church*, (Washington D.C.: University Press of America, 1982), p.53.

19. Bolich, *Authority and the Church*, p.63.

The doctrine of the Trinity, the drama of redemption, and the working of the Holy Spirit are well described by Apostle Paul in his letter to the Ephesians 1:3-14, which is commonly known as the liturgical hymn of thanksgiving.

> Blessed be the God and Father of our Lord Jesus Christ, who has blessed us in Christ with every spiritual blessing in the heavenly places, even as he chose us in him before the foundation of the world, that we should be holy and blameless before him. He destines us in love to be his sons through Jesus Christ, according to the purpose of his will, to the praise of his glorious grace which he freely bestowed on us in the Beloved. In him we have redemption through his blood, the forgiveness of our trespasses, according to the riches of his grace which he lavished upon us. For he has made known to us in all wisdom and insight the mystery of his will, according to his purpose which he set forth in Christ as a plan for the fullness of time, to unite all things in him, things in heaven and things on earth. In him according to the purpose of him who accomplishes all things according to the counsel of his will, we who first hoped in Christ have been destined and appointed to live for the praise of his glory. In him you also, who have heard the word of truth, the gospel of your salvation, and have believed in him, were sealed with the promised Holy Spirit, which is the guarantee of our inheritance until we acquire possession of it, to the praise of his glory. (RSV)

The Christian Scriptures affirm that Jesus Christ has hidden God's glory even as he revealed it. A believer in Christ participates in the salvific activities of God revealed through Jesus Christ and manifested by the power of the Holy Spirit. By entering into a committed relationship with Christ, a Christian partakes in the mission of Christ, in the power and presence of the Holy Spirit, and in the service and life of all of God's creation.

Hence the doctrine of the Trinity is central in Christian theology of divine-human encounter with radical implications. The broken relationship between God and his creation was restored through the sacrificial death and resurrection of Christ. Jesus, the perfect image of the invisible God, took human form and humbled himself even to suffer and die on the cross. By doing so, the God of the Bible became a personal and relational God to exist in communion with Jesus and the Holy Spirit.

Christian theology is intrinsically connected to God's self-communication in Christ and in the Spirit. That the God of the Bible is personal or tri-personal is evident at the core of the doctrine of the Trinity. The Gospels and Epistles neither consider the doctrine of the Trinity a theological issue, nor debate whether God is one in three modalities or one nature in three persons. Rather, it deals with the drama of divine-human encounter and narrates the story of eternal redemption which the Bible calls a mystery. This salvific mystery, which was revealed in the person of Jesus Christ, which continues to manifest in the lives of the believers by the inner working of the Holy Spirit, gives the doctrine of the Trinity its unique place.

The doctrine of the Trinity was the one major doctrine which separated "orthodox" Christians in the early church from "heretical" Christians, which isolated Christianity from Judaism, which set apart the Church from idolaters and presented Christianity as a religion of salvation. Jaroslav Pelikan writes:

> In this dogma (of the Trinity) the church vindicated the monotheism that has been at issue in its conflicts with Judaism, and it came to terms with the concept of the Logos, over which it has disputed with paganism. The bond between creation and redemption, which the church had defended against Marcion and other Gnostics, was given creedal status in the confession concerning the relation of the Father to the son, and the doctrine of the Holy Spirit, whose vagueness had been accentuated by the conflict with Montanism, was incorporated into this confession. The docrtrine believed, taught, and confessed by the church catholic of the second and third centuries also led to the Trinity, for in this dogma Christianity drew the line that separated it from pagan supernaturalism and it reaffirmed its character as a religion of salvation.[20]

This mysterious unity between God and humanity continued even after Jesus rose from the dead by the coming and inner working of the Holy Spirit. The doctrine of the Trinity symbolizes this mystery and affirms that the biblical theology cannot be separated from soteriology. The deeper Trinitarian mystery validates that the Eternal God who

---

20. Jaroslav Pelikan, *The Emergence of the Catholic Tradition (100-600), The Christian Tradition: A History of the Development of Doctrine*, vol.I (Chicago and London: University of Chicago Press, 1971), p.172.

revealed himself in Jesus Christ and the Holy Spirit still remains unfathomable. Jesus Christ, who is the key to the understanding of God and the Holy Spirit, is the enabling power of salvation offered by God. Diogenes Allen writes, "At the core of the Christian life is the fact that Christians have a Lord, someone to whom they belong and to whom they are obedient."[21]

The Quran and the Bible

The Quran and the Bible are in agreement on a number of details. These include the story of creation, breathing of God's spirit into the first human being, Satan's temptation of Adam, the revelation of the Torah, the uniqueness of Psalms, the blessedness of the Virgin Mary, the divine birth of Jesus and the miracles he performed, his second coming and the Last Judgment.

The Quran refers to the Torah as an earlier revelation and calls it the Book (Sura 3:176, 5:44, 3:33). The Quran agrees with the Bible in saying that the Torah was written by God with his own hand (Deut. 9:10, Sura 7.145). After revealing his message to Moses and to the prophets, God took care of the Torah. God taught the Torah to Jesus, when he was in his mother's womb. Jesus learned it and "became its master, confirmed its teachings, and acted according to it."[22]

The Quran has a very high regard for the Hebrew and Christian Scriptures, and refers to them as The Book of God (Sura 5:48) or the Word of God (Sura 2:71), a light and direction to humanity (Sura 6:91), a guidance and mercy (Sura 6:155), and "a final judgment" in deciding human matters (Sura 2:101, 2:75, 5:46, 47, 6:91 and 3:184). The Quran acknowledges the divine revelation of the Book and says:

> O Muslims, say: 'We believe in Allah and the revelation given to us, and to Abraham, and Ishmael and Isaac, Jacob and the tribes; and that given to Moses and Jesus, and that given to (all) prophets from their Lord: We make no difference between one and another of them. (Sura 2:136).

This verse is generally considered the Creed of Islam. According to Yusuf Ali, the above verse was given to Muslims so that they may believe in Allah and the prophets who came before Mohammed.

---

21. Diogenes Allen, "The Paradox of Freedom and Authority", *Theology Today*, Vol.XXXVI, No.2 (July, 1979), p.167.

22. Al-Tabari, 5:110, 3:48

Believe in (1) the One Universal God, (2) the Message to us through Muhammad and the signs as interpreted on the basis of personal responsibility, (3) the Message delivered by other Teachers in the past. These are mentioned in three groups: (1) Abraham, Ismail, Isaac, Jacob, and the Tribes: of these Abraham had apparently a Book and the others followed his tradition; (2) Moses and Jesus, who each left a scripture; these scriptures are still extant, though not in their pristine form; and (3) other scriptures, Prophets, messengers of God, not specifically mentioned in the Quran. We make no difference between any of these. Their message (in essence) was one, and that is the basis of Islam.[23]

The Quran does not contain doctrines about God. It has no narrative to explain his nature. It only explains how humanity can experience his blessings and mercies by submitting to his will. The Quran corrects the corruptions the Jews and Christians have brought into their scriptures. The Quran emphasizes that God can only be known by his revealed message and we can speak about him only in signs and symbols. Since God is unknowable, the human mind cannot comprehend his ineffable nature.

The Quran speaks of the great resemblances it extends for the meditation of the believers. Unlike Christianity, a Muslim does not believe in a set of doctrines but in active submission to Allah's will. Those who submit to Allah's will in prayer and almsgiving are true believers. The Quran teaches:

Believers are those who, when God is mentioned, feel a tremor in their hearts, and when they hear His signs rehearsed, find their faith strengthened, and put (all) their trust in their Lord; who establish regular prayers and spend (freely) out of the gifts We have given them for sustenance: such in truth are the believers: they have grades of dignity with their Lord, and forgiveness, and generous sustenance. (8:2-4).

Islam strongly believes that the Christian understanding of God coming in the form of a human being and dying on the cross to save humanity from sin and condemnation is *zanna* (guesswork).

---

23. Ali, *The Holy Quran: Text, Translation and Commentary*, p.55.

The Quran also presents itself as the diary of the Prophet Mohammed. His loves and hates, doubts and questions have been expressed in various ways throughout the Quran. Consequently, the way in which Mohammed received the message has been challenged both by Jewish and Christian scholars. As the Quran has been literally taken as the message of God, Muslims would not subject it to critical inquiry. Mohammed himself has expressed the way in which he received the inspiration from Allah:

> At the moment of inspiration anxiety pressed upon the prophet, and his countenance became troubled. Sweat dropped from his forehead, and he would fall to the ground as in a trance. 'Inspiration', he said, 'cometh to me in one of two ways. At times, Gabriel speaketh the word unto me as one man speaketh to another, and this is easy. At other times it is like the ringing of a bell, it penetrateth my heart, and rendeth me, and this afflicteth me the most.'[24]

In his book *God and Man in the Koran: Semantics of the Koranic Weltanschauung*, Toshihiko Izutsu quotes the above passage and comments:

> What Muhammed is trying to convey thereby seems to be that while he is actually receiving revelation he does not have the consciousness of hearing any intelligible words spoken... (except) a mysterious indistinct noise... but the moment it ceases he realizes that the noise has already transformed itself into distinct meaningful words.[25]

The orthodox Muslim circle does not agree with the Hadith and insists that Mohammed was merely used as an instrument of Allah to recite the message that was dictated or shown to him. The entire revelation was given in a mechanical process. Kenneth Cragg summarizes the Islamic view of revelation succinctly:

> [The Quranic revelation] is understood as having been verbally received by Muhammed in entire, syllabic, stenographic

---

24. Sir William Muir, *Mahomet and Islam* (St. Paul's Churchyard: The Religious Tract Society, 1883), p.24. Quote taken from Phil Parshall's *The Fortress and the Fire: Jesus Christ and the Challenge of Islam*, (Bombay: Gospel Literature Service, 1976), p.5.

25. Toshihiko Izutse, *God and Man in the Koran: Semantics of the Koranic Weltanschauung*, (Tokyo, 1964), p.17

inerrancy, through the mediation of the very words of God. The Prophet's part was completely passive-indeed, not a part at all. Analogies used here are, for example, a robot, or, 'as a pipe conducting a jet of water through a stone lion in a Persian garden.'[26]

Unlike the Torah, which was revealed to Moses in one session during his forty day communion with YHWH at Mount Sinai, the Quran was revealed to Mohammed one part at a time throughout his life time. For twenty-three years, he received direct messages from Allah. As each new message was revealed to him, he recited it aloud to the listeners so that they might commit the message to memory. Some listeners wrote it down on parchments and papyrus.

Some Islamic scholars take a neutral position about the process of revelation and argue that both the divine and human elements were involved in the formation of the Quran. Fazlur Rahman, a Pakistani Muslim scholar, argues that the Quran is absolutely divine in spite of the involvement of human factors. The revelation was "brought down upon the heart of Mohammed" (26:192-194). On account of his genuine prophetic role, Allah revealed the pure divine Word to Mohammed, as known among the Christian theological circles, an organic doctrine of inspiration.

> When Mohammed's moral intuitive perception rose to the highest point and became identified with the moral law itself... the word was given with inspiration itself. The Quran is thus pure Divine Word, but, of course it is equally intimately related to the inmost personality of the Prophet Mohammed whose relation to it cannot be mechanically conceived like that of a record. The Divine word flowed through the Prophet's heart.[27]

It is not uncommon even in Christian circles to listen to enthusiasts who assert that the Bible was inspired by God and the prophets were used as mechanical means to transmit God's message.

The Inter-relations Between the Bible and the Quran

A number of stories narrated in the Quran have their origin in the Bible. Some stories have roots in Jewish Talmud, Midrash, Hebrew and Christian Scriptures, and Christian Apocrypha. For example, the names

---

26. Cragg, *International Bulletin of Missionary Research*, "The Riddle of Man and the Silence of God: A Christian Perception of Muslim Response", October 1993, p.161.

27. Fazlur Rahman, *Islam* (Chicago, 1979), p.33.

of the prophets such as Noah, Ibrahim (Abraham) Lot, Pharaoh, Moses, Aaron, Elijah, Elisha, Job, David, Solomon, Jonah, Michael, and Gabriel have biblical origin. The stories of these characters in the Hebrew Scriptures represent God's involvement in human history. The deeds of the prophets and the stories related in the Hebrew Scriptures have been interpreted by Christians from salvific and redemptive viewpoints. The Quran, on the other hand, includes those stories to support the claims of the prophets and divine judgment of events.

Critics condemn the Quran as a potpourri of religious thoughts from the Middle East. Thomas O'Shaughnessy writes:

> [The] Koran displays a cross-section of the religious ideas that prevailed in the Arabia of his day; Orthodox, Nestorian and Monophysite—all set against a backdrop of Biblical plagiarism and Jewish legend culled from the Talmud and Midrash.[28]

Stories retold in the Quran, at times, have been given a new meaning by putting several stories together. Some of the major Hebrew Prophets, such as Isaiah and Jeremiah, are not mentioned in the Quran. The fall of Satan as narrated in the Book of Isaiah has been connected to his refusal to worship Adam. The writer of the Epistle to the Hebrews mentions the superiority of Jesus over the angels and says, "And again, when he brings the firstborn into the world, he says, "let all God's angels worship him" (Hebrews 1:6). The Quran refers to this as God's summon to all the angels to worship Adam.[29]

The stories about Cain and Abel, Noah and the flood, the call of Abraham and his conversion to monotheism, Ishmael and Isaac, and Jacob and his decedents are given an elaborate space in the Quran. A detailed narration is given about Joseph's extraordinary intelligence, his handsomeness, the testimony of a child to prove the innocence of Joseph. Jacob's revelation about Joseph being alive and the rescue of Moses are also given a lengthy textual space.

The Quran gives a more detailed account of the life and ministry of Abraham and Moses than those any other prophets. The Quranic account

---

28. Thomas O'Shaughnessy, *The Koranic Concept of the Word of God*, (Rome: Pontificio Instituto Biblico, 1948), p.33.

29. Satan's refusal to "worship an inferior and younger being" is found in an apocryphal document. See Robert Henry Charles, *Apocrypha and Pseudepigrapha*, (Oxford: Clarendon Press, 1965), vol. II, p.137.

of Moses receiving the Law from God and providing water to the wandering Israelites in the wilderness differs vastly from the Biblical account of Moses' call to Egypt and his encounter with Pharaoh. The Quran says that Moses saw the burning bush on his way to Egypt and was sent to Pharaoh, Haman and Qarim (Corah). In contrast, that Bible says that God appeared to Moses in a burning bush and called him to leave Midian before he went to Egypt in order to stand before Pharaoh.

There appears to be plenty of confusion about the number of plagues God sent upon Egypt. The Quran, in one account, says that God sent nine plagues upon Egypt. "To Moses We did nine clear signs..." (Sura 17:101). In another account it says, "So We sent (plagues) on them: Wholesale Death, Locusts, Lice, Frogs, and Blood: signs openly self-explained: but they were steeped in arrogance, a people given to sin" (Sura 7:133). The Quran also talks about Moses' threat to kill Aaron and God's threat to let Mount Sinai fall upon the Israelites who rebelled against him. The story of Moses is often told in the Quran but his life in Midian is mentioned only once, in Sura 28.

The Quran also mixes up some of the stories narrated in Judges, Samuel, and Kings. It blends the character of the Bible with the accounts of Midrash and leaves out the context and important details.[30] David is presented in the Quran as a prophet and king. God revealed himself to David through the Psalms. David is also presented as a man gifted in making armour. His affair with Bathsheba is totally left out. The narration about Solomon comes very close to that of the Bible and the apocrypha. The number of wives and concubines Solomon had is vastly underestimated. The narratives about Solomon's wisdom comes close to the apocryphal accounts which portray him as the one who understands the language of birds and the one who has at his disposal the forces of the jinn.

The Gospel accounts may also have had an influence upon the making of the Quran. The parable of Jesus about the rich man and Lazarus is presented in a different form. "When their eyes shall be turned towards the companions of the fire, they will say; 'Our Lord! send us not to the company of the wrong-doers.'... The companions of the fire will call upon the companions of the Garden: 'Pour down to us water or anything that Allah doth provide for your sustenance'" (Sura 7:47,50). "And on the day that the unbelievers will be placed before the fire, (it

---

30. See for example, David and Nathan as narrated in Sura 38.20-23.

will be said to them): 'ye received your good things in the life of the world, and ye took your pleasure out of them: but to-day shall ye be recompensed with a penalty of humiliation: for that ye were arrogant on earth without just cause, and that ye (ever) transgressed'" (Sura 46:20).

Some Christian scholars argue that the Quran has a scrambled version of the parable of the foolish virgins (Sura 57:11ff), the wicked husbandmen (Sura 36:13ff), the Holy Communion (Sura 5:112ff), the miracles of Jesus (Sura 3:43), the story of the Nativity and the Annunciation (Sura 19:1-39 and 3:35-51). Stories about the conception of Virgin Mary (Sura 3:1ff) and the miracles Jesus performed as a child are found in the apocryphal literatures such as the Protevangelium of James, the Gospel of St. Thomas and the Arabic Gospel of the Infancy. Certain additions like Mary supporting herself on a palm tree during her pangs of childbirth could be traced to the Greek myth of Leto.

Islam's response to the repetition of stories from other religious literatures is that all divine revelation came from a single source - Allah. However, since the Quran is the ultimate revelation, it abrogates all the earlier revelations. There are no differences found in the Quran in relation to the narration of stories found in other scriptures; the later revelation supersedes the earlier; hence the Quran's version is final and authentic.[31]

The Christians give emphasis not only to the revealed, written Word of God but also to the incarnate person of Jesus Christ in whom God has fully revealed himself. The revealed Scripture is different from the revealed person of Jesus Christ although both of them are inter-connected. The Bible documents the event of revelation as made manifest

---

31. Frithjof Schuon finds an interesting correlation in Asian religious history: "The Quran enunciates a perspective which makes it possible to 'go beyond' certain formal aspects of the two more ancient monotheisms. Something analogous can be seen, not only in the position of Christianity in relation to Judaism—where the point is self-evident by reason of the messianic idea and the fact that the former is like a 'bhaktic' esotericism of the latter—but also in the attitude of Buddhism towards Brahmanism; here too the later appearance in time coincides with a perspective that is symbolically, though not intrinsically, superior. Of this fact the tradition that is apparently being superceded clearly has no need to take account since each perspective is a universe for itself—and thus a centre and a standard— and since in its own way it contains all valid points of view. By the very logic of things the later tradition is 'condemned' to the symbolical attitude of superiority, on pain of non-existence one might almost say; but there is also a positive symbolism of anteriority and in this respect the new tradition, which is from its own point of view the final one, must incarnate 'what came before', —or glory-is consequently its absolute anteriority. Frithjof Shuon, *Understanding Islam*, trans. by D.M. Matheson, (New York: Roy Publishers, Inc., 1964), pp.55-56.

in the person of Jesus Christ. "Revelation comes both *through* and *in* Scripture."[32] The Christians do not attach any magical or supernatural quality to the written word except that it witnesses the divine-human drama enacted on the hills of Calvary which brought redemption and forgiveness to humanity. Therefore, Christians bear witness to that event everywhere and proclaim the message of salvation. The message of redemption was attested to by Jesus' resurrection on the third day after his death on the cross of Calvary. Jesus was seen and testified as Lord and God.

The Church cannot exist without the Word; nor can the Word be proclaimed without the Church. Bolich aptly summarizes the function of Christian Scripture.

> The purpose of [Christian] Scripture is to witness to Christ, but it remains the peculiar character of the Bible that his witness is not fulfilled apart from the work of the Church. The Bible and the Church, the holy ones of God and the Holy Scripture are both of God and exist for one another. Their life is only in Christ. Without this kind of image the Church is fragmentation. When the Scriptures and the Church are placed together - where they belong - they speak with an authority that causes the proclamation of each to be acknowledged as the wisdom and Word of God.[33]

---

32. Bolich, *Authority and the Church*, p.71.

33. Ibid., p.71.

CHAPTER XIII
Sin and Salvation : Christianity and Islam

The existence of the sovereign Creator God of the Bible and the Quran is not established by evidence but by faith and by personal experience. The prophets of God bore witness not only to the tangibility of God but also to his involvement in human history. They passed on the message of the greatness of God and the need to worship him from generation to generation. They taught that God is not in contention with evil. His creation is not intrinsically evil. Unlike early Greek and Roman mythologies, the God of the Bible and the Quran does not have consorts. He does not need human aid to create. God creates and recreates to let His will be known to the whole universe.

Human beings occupy the pinnacle of God's creation. They are commanded to find comfort and joy in each other, and they are instructed to be fruitful and multiply. Human sexuality, therefore, is not considered profane and evil. Judaism, Christianity, and Islam teach that human beings are created for a purpose: to love and worship God. The presence of Satan, a force against God, is taken for granted. The sacred scriptures of these three religions agree that the Devil misguided the first parents to disobey God's command by tempting them to eat the forbidden fruit.

Human history is linear for these three religions and is directed toward an ultimate goal in which God triumphs, the righteous is rewarded, and evil punished. The revealed and written word given through the prophets serves as the cornerstone of their faith. The essence of their moral and ethical foundation goes way back to the Mosaic law, especially to the Ten Commandments. The prototype of worship is traced back to Abraham who worshipped the One God.

In spite of many similarities found in these three religions, each of them focuses on different aspects of their faith. Judaism is centered on the promises and blessings of God which were given to his chosen people. Christianity is founded on Jesus Christ, the Son of God and Messiah, who incarnated in this world to reconcile the rebellious humanity with God by his death on the cross and resurrection from the dead. Islam calls the whole of humanity to submit to Allah's will and worship Him, and Him alone.

However, Islam goes far beyond Judaism and Christianity by introducing a new paradigm. It negates the existence of other gods by saying, "there is no god but Allah". Islam demands religious action not theological analysis. It affirms that God has not revealed Him*self* in the Quran, but has only revealed His law. Therefore, humanity has to obey and observe the law. God is not the Father of humanity but the Sovereign Ruler of the universe. Hence, one cannot establish a personal relationship with him. This concept of a transcendent God who is distant and removed is a radical departure from the Christian concept of theophany and the immanence of God in Christ.

If we need to understand the difference between Christian and Muslim concepts of sin and salvation, we should pay close attention to the teachings of the founders of those two religious communities. Although the Quran clearly presents that Mohammed is not in anyway equal to Jesus in terms of birth and the performance of ministry, it is salutary for our study to compare and analyze the teachings of the originators of the two major world religions.

The Ministry of Jesus and Mohammed

Both Jesus and Mohammed were born humble and raised lowly in the backwaters of the Middle East. Their followers were poor, uneducated, and people of ordinary class. Jesus and Mohammed taught that the world was not a place to run away from but to live and celebrate God-given life. Both of them built their traditions on the heritage of the Hebrew Scriptures. They taught that their message was for all generations and they condemned violence and exploitation. Their followers emulated their leaders and built their lives around them.

The fundamental difference between Jesus and Mohammed is that the latter never claimed to be God. He never summoned his listeners to follow him. He said that he was only a Warner and an Apostle of Allah. There was nothing vicarious or redemptive about his life and death. The Prophet Mohammed presented Jesus with respect in the Quran and said ιe was God's special creation and he would come again at the end of ιys to judge the world and to establish Islam everywhere. The Jesus of the Quran has no redemptive feature. He was only Allah's special envoy who came to teach and guide the people into monotheistic worship.

The Christian Scriptures portray an entirely different picture of the person of Jesus. The central theme of the gospel is not merely the events surrounding the birth of Jesus but the person of Jesus himself: his incarnation, his proclamation, his relationship with God, the Father, and his redemptive suffering, death, and resurrection. The cross was the driving force of the ministry of Jesus. The name Jesus, given to him at his birth, summarized the very purpose of his mission. For, according to the Gospel of Matthew, "[Jesus] will save his people from their sins" (Mt.1:21).

Easter is more important than Christmas for the Christians. Jesus, by his death and resurrection, brought together God and humanity, and reconciled humanity's marred relationship with God which was brought into the world by the disobedient act of the first parents (Col.1:20). He reconciled the broken humanity by his shedding of blood on the cross (Col. 3:1-4, Jn. 12:32). The death and resurrection of Jesus serve as God's decisive act of salvation for the whole of humanity. The function of the Church, its sacraments, its mission, and its very foundation are based on the vicarious suffering of Jesus, his violent death on the cross, and his victorious resurrection from the dead (I Cor.15).

Jesus has not been presented in the gospels as a mere human being or the one who received revelation from God progressively like Mohammed did. Jesus has been presented in the gospels and (in the post-resurrection context) in the epistles as Messiah, Son of God, the only way to the Father, and the One who has brought the gift of God's love. He addressed God, "Abba, Father" and gave authority to his followers to do the same. Jesus himself declared that the one who had seen him had seen the Father. Matthew translates his name Immanuel as "God with us" (Mt. 1:23).

While he was an infant, Jesus was given this name because he was to save his people from their sins by being God incarnate in this world. The ministry of Jesus was challenged not by his opponents only but by the sins of humanity as well. He was constantly confronted and told to abandon his mission of delivering people from their slavery to sin. He was repeatedly questioned to prove his identity as the Son of God. He was unceasingly tempted to be a political Messiah and renounce his mission as the Lamb of God. However, Jesus proved himself to be victorious in his mission and glorious in his accomplishments.

The central part of his message was not a summon to submit to God's will nor to observe a catalogue of rules but a call to repentance and acceptance of the good news of God's Kingdom. His message to the listeners was: "The time is fulfilled, and the kingdom of God is at hand; repent, and believe in the gospel" (Mk. 1:15). His ministry was not merely to show the way to God, but to let his listeners know that he was The Way. Hence, Jesus demanded an absolute loyalty from his followers and instructed them not to worship idols nor follow any other gods. Jesus saw life on earth as corrupt and mortal. Yet, he assured his listeners that those who followed him would find eternal life.

Unlike Mohammed, Jesus never read nor recited words from a heavenly tablet. He was the Word and proclaimed his own. He never dreamt or retreated to caves to receive revelation. His teachings were original, authentic, and archetypical. He quoted from the Jewish scriptures only when he had to rightly interpret the legal matters of Judaism.

Jesus never undertook a battle nor encouraged his followers to establish a community. He never sought to bring the future by force. He never functioned as a statesman nor a general of an army to challenge any political power. He had no political agenda. He was unarmed and defenseless until he died a violent death on the cross. He showed the ardour of his mission in the Temple and in other places of interaction with Pharisees, Sadducees, and religio-political leaders. His only intention was to show God's love and to identify with suffering people. He talked of the kingdom of God in which all people will be included. He taught his followers to forgive enemies and love strangers. He even loved the Samaritans, the enemies of the Jews, and presented them as role models to the Jewish community.

Jesus was a public man not an ascetic who lived in seclusion. He was homeless, penniless, and an itinerant preacher. He was never married, and he never had children. He was not a successful man by worldly standards. His teachings were revolutionary. Contrary to the teachings of the world, Jesus said those who were last would be first in God's kingdom and lowliest would be the highest in God's sight. His sermon on the mount was contrary to the traditional thinking of the world. He did not impose celibacy, and taught that marriage or abstinence was a voluntary act.

Jesus used local verities to make his message known. He divided the people of the world as sheep and goats as those who entered the broad gate and narrow gate, children of darkness and children of light. He stood in religious traditions but challenged traditions which did not have mercy and compassion.

There was no sudden turning point in his ministry to receive revelation or to enter ministry. He was Divinity Incarnate and revealed himself and God. He lamented about the sinfulness of humanity and the need for inner redemption. He warned his listeners of the dangers of the end of days and summoned them to repent of their sins and turn to God. The gospels portray an incessant urgency in his message to repent of sins and not just to submit to God's will.

Jesus' ministry was both inward and outward. Jesus did not order any religious rituals nor prescribe any special costume. No special mode of prayer nor a creed of doctrine was given to his disciples. The Gospels attest that the ministry of Jesus was oriented to restore the lost humanity to God. The Epistle to the Hebrews narrates how Jesus' life was offered as a sacrifice in the manner stipulated in the Hebrew Scriptures. In accordance to the Hebrew tradition, Jesus acted as Prophet, Priest, King, Messiah and Son.

During the time of Israelites, Messiah was not the only one who was anointed. Priests were anointed when ordained (Ex.28:41) and some prophets were also anointed into office (I Kings 19:16). Leopold Sabourin observes in his book *Priesthood: A Comparative Study*:

> If Christ freely gave his life in sacrifices for the redemption of [humanity] it is as a priest that he did it. It should be legitimately concluded that even if Christ is not explicitly called priest outside [the epistle to the] Hebrews, it is implied that he is in texts that presents his death as a sacrifice.[1]

The Epistle to the Hebrews says that the priestly work of Jesus was evident in his sacrificial death on the cross. Jesus was the "sin offering" who served as the perfect high priest in the order of Melchizedek, who carried the sacrificial offering to the very presence of God and took responsibility for humanity's sin and evil. Having presented the sin offering for the whole of humanity and having fulfilled all the responsibilities of a high priest, Jesus sat at the right hand of God. The

---

1. Sabourin, *Priesthood: A Comparative Study*, p.101.

act of "sitting", metaphorically speaking, represents the rest one takes after completing an assigned task.

The Christian Scriptures also say that no one can draw near God except through the person of Jesus. What Jesus did with his life, death and resurrection, and what he does at the right hand of God as evidenced in the Epistle to the Hebrews represents the Christian concept of salvation.

The Gospels and the Epistles of the Christian Scriptures state that the sacrifice of Jesus on the cross was a once-for-all act, and his was the final and ultimate revelation given in reconciliation of the broken and estranged humanity with God. Paul writes, "In him we have redemption through his blood, the forgiveness of sins" (Eph.1:7). Christ's death was a victory over the forces of evil. "God made alive together with him, having forgiven us all our trespasses, having cancelled the bond which stood against us with its legal demands; this he set aside, nailing it to the cross. He disarmed the principalities and powers and made a public example of them, triumphing over them in him" (Col.2:14-15). His death liberates humanity not only from sin but also from death (Eph. 2:1-3, Heb.2:1-14).

The cross of Jesus Christ was a major offence and a serious scandal in the first century. There was nothing heroic about dying on the cross. Paul admitted the scandal when he wrote, "We preach Christ crucified, a stumbling block to Jews and folly to Gentiles" (I Cor. 1:23). One of the powerful images used by the followers of Christ after his death and resurrection was "reigning from the tree." Jesus reigns and lives forever because he rose from the dead on the third day. By his resurrection, he conquered death and evil. The accursed cross, "the tree", became a symbol of victory, not of defeat.

The idea of a crucified Messiah, nevertheless, was a horrifying blasphemy to the Jews of Jesus' time. Messiah, according to the Hebrew tradition, is a conqueror not a sufferer, a victor not a loser. For God's Chosen or Anointed One to suffer such a degrading death was inconceivable to Jewish minds. The intellectual listeners of the day could not comprehend the atoning effect attached to a common man who was brutally killed on the cross.

The Romans saw Jesus as a rebellious criminal who would not comply with the Jewish law of the day. His failure to come down from the cross proved to both the Romans and to the onlookers that he was indeed an ordinary man who was punished for his crime. The cross, to the Romans, was the "accursed tree". Cicero, before Jesus' time, said that a true Roman should not think or hear or see the cross. The cross was such an abomination and an ignominy to the Roman mind.

After the death and resurrection of Jesus, some of his followers attempted to give new meaning to the whole event. Some of them denied his divinity and a few denied his humanity. One of the formidable opponents of the death and resurrection of Jesus was an early writer and philosopher named Celsus. He challenged the idea of the incarnation and questioned the elevation of a common criminal's ignoble death. Celsus concluded that the vicarious death of Christ on the cross was "the most ridiculous make-shift of all."[2] Celsus challenged the followers of Jesus saying that if Jesus had been a Messiah, God would have transported him from the cross and proven his divinity.[3] Or, at least, God could have conceived a better way for Jesus to die. The Christian apologists countered Celsus' argument with the notion that the death of Christ on the cross was part of the Divine Plan. God chose to offer his grace to rebellious humanity and make restitution for their sins by the death of Christ on the cross.

Another fourth century British monk and theologian, Pelagius, argued that there was no corporate sin. Adam's sin had no effect on the succeeding generation. Pelagius maintained that human beings have freedom of will. He insisted that sin is personal and hence there is no need for grace. Humanity could attain perfection in this life. He also contended that Jesus was not the Messiah but an obedient servant of God who set an example for humanity. Pelagians had a stronghold in the Middle East during Mohammed's time. It has been widely believed that Mohammed was influenced by the Pelagian belief. The Prophet's teachings and the Quranic injunctions about Jesus' life and ministry reflect Pelagianism. The early church condemned Pelagianism as it attempted to diminish Christianity to a mere moral code and to a catalogue of ethical rules. It presented Jesus Christ only as a common inspiring role-model.

The Concept of Sin in Islam

Christianity places a great deal of importance on the historical events of Jesus' life: his birth, life, death, and resurrection. Christian faith is

---

2. *Origen* Contra Celsum, (Cambridge: University Press, 1953), 6:78.

3. See Martin Hengel, *Crucifixion*, (Philadelphia: Fortress Press, 1977).

founded on the principle that Jesus is the Christ, the God incarnate (Jn.
1:14). He made it possible for his followers to be born again and to
become children of God (Jn. 1:11-13). Islam, on the other hand,
condemns the Christian concept of Jesus, the Son of God. It denies the
need for a mediator and the necessity for one man to die vicariously for
somebody else's sins. Islam insists there was nothing soteriological about
the ministry of Jesus on earth. Furthermore, Islam has no doctrine of sin
in the Christian sense of the word.

Sin in Islam means enthroning one's ego as the centre of one's life
and refusing to submit to Allah's will. Associating an idol or a human
being with God and worshipping that object or person as God is the
ultimate and unpardonable sin (shirk) (Sura 31:13, 4:16). Shirk dethrones
the sovereignty of God and decentres the unity of the One Godhead. Shirk
also decimates the God-given sound constitutions (fitra, the primordial
norm) and displaces the truth he has implanted in human hearts. Loving
Allah and obeying his revelation manifested in the Quran is the paradigm
of Islamic concept of sin and salvation. Faith, not good works, will lead
a believer to eternal life. The Hadith says:

> Narrated Abu Dhar: Allah's Apostle said, "The Angel Gabriel
> came and said to me, 'Whoever amongst your followers dies,
> worshipping none along with Allah, will enter paradise.' I said,
> 'Even if he did such-and-such things (i.e. even if he stole or
> committed illegal sexual intercourse.' He said, 'Yes'" (S:337;
> 41.3.573).

However, shirk is not interpreted in a limited sense of associating
other gods with Allah. Hypocritical religiosity aimed at earning the
appreciation of believers is also appraised as Shirk for it deludes both
God and fellow believers. "Hypocrisy and true monotheism do not go
together. Pride too is a kind of Shirk. For these reasons, Islamic ethics
could delineate the 'lesser Shirk' (al-Shirk al-asghar) or 'hidden Shirk'
(hidden in the depth of the soul, (al-ashirk al-khafiy).[4] In other words,
Shirk is the opposite of Shahada and only idolaters and pagans associate
or add something to the Godhead. If they do, they become the enemies
of God.

Islam denies the fundamental Judeo-Christian concept of the
originial sin. Islam affirms that each child is born of God and, therefore,
is pure and sinless. Grown up adults are responsible for their own deeds.

---

4. Ignaz Goldziher, *Introduction to Islamic Theology and Law*, p.42.

As each human being is created by God with a *fitra*, he or she can commune with God both in this world and the next. Yet, both Islam and Christianity agree in principle that the central dynamic of sin is idolatry (Ex.22 and Rom. 1.18-32). And making finite objects into an ultimate concern for life and worship is a major transgression of God's law.

Islam has a two-tier notion of sin: *dhanb* and *ithm*. Dhanb is used for human error, mistakes, shortcoming or faults which human beings commit unconsciously, and its consequence is an endorsement rather than retribution. Ithm is more serious than dhanb. Ithm is applied for deliberate transgression and willful disobedience which incur punishment. Ithm includes both conscious and unconscious action against God and humanity. As Ithm engages the whole of human body to commit the willful rebellion against God and humanity, it encompasses the inadvertent faults and human frailties as well.

Since Adam's death, God has raised and sent messengers and prophets with special revelations to guide his people and deliver them from Satan. The greatest of these messengers was Abraham who wrote down God's message which has been lost. However, God continued to send prophets like Moses, David, Jesus, and Mohammed. Hence Islam has not felt the need for the development of a doctrine of salvation. Furthermore, in Islam, the remedy of sin does not entail a bloody sacrifice of an intercessor; rather a mere public confession of Shahda and the observance of the Five-Pillars of Islam will suffice.

Islam affirms the sinlessness *(Ismah)* of the prophets. They may have committed Dhanb, but not Ithm. The Shiites' doctrine of Imam says that the Imams are sinless as they are special creations of God. God has created them in a special way so that God's guidance and light may be transmitted through them to the people. Shiites insist that the Imams are absolutely necessary for the sustenance of God's creation and for the believer to obtain salvation. The function of the twelve Imams is to serve as mediators between God and humanity. However, the Sunnis strongly disagree with the mediatory role played by the Shiite Imams as it undermines Shahada and the demand for absolute submission to Allah. Ever since Hussein, Ali's son, was murdered at the Karbala, the Shiites have developed a doctrine that the Imams are half-divine and half-human, and they are sinless, super-humans.

Islam does not permit its followers to be called sinners. The term sinner is reserved only for an unbelieving rebel and an ungrateful dissenter. A Muslim is a believer not a sinner. He or she may err but cannot sin for he or she is always committed to Allah for His mercy and forgiveness. Islam does not have a liturgy for personal or corporate confession of sin. It does not accommodate any notion of the Judeo-Christian absolution of sin. God, who knows the hearts of men and women, forgives whenever his children turn to him in worship and service.

The vilest sins in Islam are disbelief in Allah and ingratitude for all of his mercies. The Quran says that God will abandon the unbelievers as they have forgotten him (Sura 7:51, 9:67, 45:34). Unbelievers will stray aimlessly and be lost without finding the road to paradise as God cannot guide the wicked (Sura 7:178, 42:46, 9:109). One of the Hadiths says even the father of Abraham (the first Muslim) was transformed into an animal and cast into the fires of hell. Even Abraham's prayers for his father, who was an infidel and an idolater, had no avail.

> Narrated Abu Huraira: The Prophet said, "On the Day of Resurrection Abraham will meet his father Azar whose face will be dark and covered with dust. [The Prophet] Abraham will say (to Him): 'Didn't I tell you not to disobey me?' His father will reply: 'Today I will not disobey you.' Abraham will say: 'O Lord! You promised not to disgrace me on the Day of Resurrection; and what will be more disgraceful to me than cursing and dishonoring my father?' then Allah will say [to him]: 'I had forbidden Paradise to the infidels,' Then he will be addressed, 'O Abraham! What is underneath your feet?' He will look and there he will see a *dhabh* (an animal) blood-stained, which will be caught by the legs and thrown in the fire." (4:365, 55.9.569).

Human beings are given the free will to choose good or evil, and they are judged according to their choice (Sura 17:84, 76:29). One resonant message which echoes throughout the Quran is that Allah is Sovereign. "Allah guides whomever he will and allows to go astray whomever he will" (Sura 6:110). Although the above sura comes close to the Christian concept of predestination, Islam has no room for such contemplation. The Quran states that Allah does not willfully guide anyone to darkness as it contradicts the bounteous divine mercy and abundant compassion promised in every chapter of the Quran. Nevertheless, the Hadith supports the concept of fore-ordination based on the Sura 18:28 in which Allah says he will mislead certain people and then punish them for their disobedience.

> Now have come to you, from your Lord, proofs (to open your
> eyes): if any will see, it will be for (the good of) his own soul;
> if any will be blind, it will be to his own (harm): I am not here
> to watch over your doings. (Sura 6:104).

> Verily We have revealed the Book to thee in truth, for
> (instructing) mankind. He, then, that receives guidance benefits
> his own soul: But he that strays injures his own soul, nor art
> thou set over them to dispose of their affairs" (Sura 39:41).

Human freedom and predestination as theological concepts have been
discussed at length by Herbert Grimme in his book *Muhammad*. Grimme
argues that the apparent contradictions of Mohammed should be
understood in the context of the deliverance of Mohammed's message.
In the first Meccan delivery, he talked about the absolute freedom of
the will, and in the later Medinan period, he reversed himself to advocate
surrender and service to God because humanity has no choice.[5]

The Quran enumerates the kind of blessings the believers will
receive when they inherit eternal life in paradise and the kind of pains
the infidels will experience when they are cast into hell. The end result
of a true Muslim is life in paradise. Although believers would enjoy life
in paradise after death by the mercies of God, a Muslim is instructed to
work for and strive to enter paradise while still living on earth.

The blessings of the paradise are obtained neither by the expiatory
mediation of others nor by the annihilation of the self, but by the
conscious striving and perfecting of one's own effort to live a righteous
life. Ali epitomizes the Islamic concept of salvation.

> This then is the Muslim concept of salvation. It consists, not in
> being saved from the consequences of our sins by the sufferings
> of the merits of others, nor in *Nirvana*, or annihilation or
> absorption, - but in the achievement of a perfected personality,
> a Bliss that grows up within us, and does not depend on external
> circumstances. It may require the utmost effort or striving
> (Jihad) of a lifetime or more. But it is the Supreme
> Achievement, the attainment of all desires, the felicity *in*
> *excelsis*.[6]

---

5. See Herbert Grimme, *Mohammed*, (Munster, 1892-1895), Vol.II, pp.105 ff.

6. Ali, *The Holy Quran, Text, Translation and Commentary*, p.1467.

The Quran also presents salvation as an escape from the approaching doomsday, a participation in the experience of resurrection with fellow believers, and an entry into the gardens of paradise. On the day of salvation, God will be merciful upon those who obeyed and those who paid heed to his prophets (22:38).

Obeying the law of God as revealed in the Quran is the precondition to obtaining salvation. The law of God may be anything from the practice of personal piety to physical purity. Both observing the five-pillars of Islam and complying with the Quranic instructions of food and hygienic habits have eternal consequences.

Muslims are instructed on food habits and social manners and the Muslims must refrain from them. Some food habits are an abomination or sin against God. "Do not eat of anything over which the name of Allah has not been uttered, for it is a *(fisq)* sin." Islamic law governs food habits, (Sura 2:173, %;1-3), marriage regulations (Sura 4:23), divorce, adultery, birth control (Sura 4:19-22), inheritance and communal living (Sura 4:4-12).

Mohammed offered the believers an irrevocable stipulation such as a blessing, including the name of Allah, which must be openly proclaimed before they may eat of the flesh of the animals which are allowed to be consumed. As it is difficult to know if the flesh had been blessed or not, the hadith encourages the believers to buy meat from Muslim business men only "for the flesh of an animal slaughtered by a Muslim is in all circumstances admissible as food, whether he (audibly) pronounced the name of God over it or not, (because) the Muslim is constantly mindful of God, whether or not he makes it obvious in so many words."[7] Eating pork, drinking wine, and touching anything abominable are violation of God's law.

The Concept of Salvation

In Islam, salvation as a concept is understood primarily as "deliverance" from danger and delusion. The story of Jonah as narrated in the Quran shows how he was delivered from the belly of a large fish. Salvation also means Allah's blessings upon material wealth and monetary success in one's endeavours. The Quran says:

---

7. Quoted in Ignaz Goldziher, *Introduction to Islamic Theology and Law*, tr. by *Andras and Ruth Hamori*, (Princeton, N.J.: Princeton University Press, 1981), p.58.

This is the Book; in its guidance sure, without doubt, to those who fear God; who believe in the unseen, are steadfast in prayer, and spend out of what We have provided for them; and who believe in the revelation sent to thee, and sent before thy time, and (in their hearts) have the assurance of the hereafter. They are on (true) guidance, from their Lord, and it is these who will prosper. (Sura 2:2-5).

Those who follow the law of the Quran and submit to the will of God will be amply rewarded on the final day of judgment. The blessings given to the righteous ones and the punishment bestowed upon the evil ones are explained with graphic detail in the Quran. Each individual, according to Islamic belief, is given two angels, and for each person a book of deeds is maintained which bears witness to his or her good or evil state (Sura 21:47). The fate of an individual greatly depends upon his or her own choices on earth. Although human beings are prone to stray and commit sin, those who choose to rely on God's mercy and follow his guidance as outlined in the Quran, will inherit paradise. Others will suffer damnation.

The Merciful God is a just God who rewards or punishes human beings according to their deeds on earth. While they are on earth, human beings can repent and turn to Allah for the forgiveness of their sins or go their own ways and face the consequences. The act of repentance involves openly acknowledging the Shahada and publicly observing the five pillars of Islam.

To Christians, all of those practices may appear to be a mere human practice with no intervention of the grace of God. For the Muslims, though, such practices may convey a profound sense of spiritual commitment to God and a deep experience of salvific determination. Christianity teaches that salvation is a gift of God, which can be obtained only by faith and by the grace of God. No one can earn salvation by merits. Islam absolutely rejects the Christian notion of justifiction by faith and the biblical unerstanding of the mystery of the sacraments. Observation of individual piety and compliance to the teachings of the Quran alone enable a believer to obtain salvation. In short, worship and submission are the foundations of the road to salvation.

Muslims claim that they stand in a long line of prophetic traditions. The rituals they observe are commemorative celebrations not mysterious sacraments as Christians practice in their churches. Andrew Rippin rightly observes:

The sacrifice of the hajj and the performance of the fast of Ramadan for the most part do not take on the character of sacraments, conceived to have specific effects for the believer, but rather remain acts which individuals do within their sense of obedience... Islam, in its construction of its rituals, is different from Judaism and Christianity and has rejected, or at least greatly modified, the central ritual activities of its predecessors. In this way, it has created its 'uniqueness' through difference, but that does remain a 'uniqueness' which cannot be systematized into a cohesive perspective, at least not within the framework of ritual.[8]

Islam teaches that the path to the next world begins in this world through spiritual discipline, political establishment and social order. The joys of life beyond the grave can be obtained not only through individual piety but also through collective human social, political and cultural order managed by Muslims themselves.

The Concept of the End of Days in Islam: Paradise and Hell

In Islam, the last days are characterized by the figures of Gog and Magog *(yajuj and majuj)*, the Mahdi (the rightly guided one), the anti-Christ and Jesus. The Muslim interpreters say God and Magog represent violence, annihilation, and rebellion and were thefore kept at bay by the building of an iron barrier (Sura 18:94). The barrier was built, according to the general consensus of Islamic teachings, by Alexander the Great who was commissioned by God.[9] In the last days, chaos and confusion will plunge the world into utter darkness. At that time, the Mahdi will appear and establish justice and righteousness.

However, Mahdi's reign will be followed by anti-Christ who will misguide and deceive people with false promises of peace and prosperity, which, eventually will lead to denial and disbelief in God. The Anti-Christ will perform miracles with his evil power and make sin virtuous. The Anti-Christ will gain a large following who will persecute Muslims all over the world and drive them into exile. When life becomes intolerant

---

8. Andrew Rippin, *Muslims: Their Religious Beliefs and Practices*, (Volume 1: The Formative Period), (London: Rouledge, 1990), p.99.

9. See Ali, *The Holy Quran: Text Translation and Commentary*, pp.716-765. The barrier was built mainly to ward off the wild tribes of Central Asia who were wreaking havoc to Greek and Roman kingdoms and the Persian Empire. Hence, China built the Great Wall to protect its inhabitation.

and persecution reaches its peak, Jesus will re-appear and enable the believers to discern the spirit. He will oepn the doors of paradise for believers and hell for unbelievers.

Only those who had followed the path of Allah will enter and enjoy the raptures of paradise (Sura 89:27-30, 88:8-15); others will be condemned to experience the pains of hell. It is reported that Mohammed had said, "Those who have merited paradise will enter it; the damned will go to hell. God will then say, 'Let those leave hell whose hearts contain even the weight of a mustard seed of faith!' Then they will be released, although they have already been burned to ashes, and plunged with the river of rain-water, or into the river of life; and immediately they will be revived." Mohammed reproved riches as being an agent of Iblis to entice believers from the path of Allah.

> Narrated Ibn Abi Laila; The Prophet forbade us to wear clothes of silk or Dibaj, and to drink out of gold or silver vessels, and said, "These things are for them [unbelievers] in this world and for you [believers] in the Hereafter... He who drinks from a silver vessel is but filling his abdomen with Hell Fire" (7:366-67, 69.28.538).

Islam has its own version of intermediary (limbo) state for not-so-serious rebels against Allah. Although the Quran does not mention anything like purgatory, the Hadith comes close to it when it says, "And God will say: the Angels, the Prophets, and the believers have all interceded for them [the sinners] save the Most Merciful of the Merciful. And he will grasp the fire in his hand and draw out a people who never did any good." Some Muslim theologians contend that if believers were indeed sent to hell for some of their "not-so-serious" sins, they will not be tortured "forever". Rather, they will be punished only for a short while so that their hearts and minds be utterly purified.[10] There are some who say that hell is not a place of eternal torture but only a place where one's egoistic personality will be totally annihilated and, eventually, the pure soul sent to heaven. As far as the children are concerned, they will go straight to paradise if they die before they reach the age of accountability. After they have attained the age of reason, they should be taught to practice Shahada and observe the five-pillars of Islam to avoid losing their souls and ending up outside of paradise.

---

10. See Cyril Glasse, *The Concise Encyclopaedia of Islam*, pp.107-109.

There are different levels of paradise. The believers will inherit them according to the deeds they performed and the level of spirituality they attained while they lived on this earth. Some of the names used for Paradise are: "gardens beneath which the rivers flow," "gardens of Paradise (Firdaws)," "gardens of Eden", "gardens of bliss". Only those who maintained their identity as God's agents on earth, who practiced Shahada, who obeyed or submitted to the teachings of the Quran will enter the Garden of Paradise and enjoy the nearness and blessings of God (Sura 3:14-15 and 89:27-30). In the presence of God, the Muslims will inherit the incorrupt total personality and the eternal bliss that flow from within. In paradise, one's own gifts and talents will be perfected and the desires of each one's personality will be satisfied to the fullest extent. A Hadith says the believers will be amply rewarded in Paradise.

> Narrated Abu Huraira: Allah's Apostle said, "The first batch of those who will enter Paradise will be [shining] like a full moon; and those who will enter next will be [shining] like the brightest star. Their hearts will be as if the heart of a single man, for they will have no enmity amongst themselves, and every one of them shall have two wives, each of whom will be so beautiful, pure, and transparent that the marrow of the bones of their legs will be seen through the flesh. They will be glorifying Allah in the morning and evening, and will never fall ill, and they will neither blow their noses, nor spit. Their utensils will be of gold and silver, and their combs will be of gold, and the matter used in their censers will be the aloes-wood, and their sweat will smell like musk" (4:307-8; 54.7.4.469).

The Day of Resurrection and the Day of Judgment are used interchangeably in Islamic literatures. The Islamic belief in the Day of Resurrection comes close to the Pauline narration of the end days in his epistles. The Quran says the Day of Judgment will be a day of stress and fear. Everything humanity took for granted as permanent and eternal will break asunder. The deeds of men and women will be weighed and judged accordingly. No one can escape from the Day of Judgment. The Quran portrays the Day of Resurrection graphically:

> One day the earth and the mountains will be violent in commotion. And the mountain will be as a heap of sand poured out and flowing down... Then how shall ye, if ye deny (God), guard yourselves against a day that will make children hoary-

headed? Whereon the sky will be cleft asunder? ...Verily, this is an admonition: Therefore, whoso will, let him take a (straight) path to his Lord! (Sura 73:14, 17-19).

He questions: 'where is the day of resurrection?' At length, when the sight is dazed and the moon is buried in darkness. And the sun and the moon are joined together,-That day will man say: 'where is the refuge?' By no means! No place of safety! Before they Lord (alone), that day will be, the place of rest. (Sura 75:6-12).

On the Day of Judgment, the trumpets will be blown, the earth will cease to exist, and the sky will be rolled up like a scroll. Before the Day of Judgment, the world would become increasingly evil and sinful. The world will be in dearth of honest people. Natural calamities and diseases will claim many human victims. The world will be enveloped in utter darkness, as sun and moon will not appear to give light and warmth. There will exist massive starvation and utter confusion. Rivers, lakes and seas will disappear from the face of the earth, which, consequently, will contribute to violent dust and sandstorm. Those who are left on earth will be tortured because of the vices they committed.

[When the first trumpet is blown, it will result] in the miserable death of the last people still alive, blinded by dust storms. At the sound of the second trumpet, the storm will blow the sand away from all the graves so that bodies, suddenly reunited with their souls, will rise and stand, lamenting their sinfulness and praying to God for forgiveness. After the third trumpet blast, Mohammed will rise, and mounted on his faithful Burak (used in the night journey), ride to the scales which have become visible in front of God's throne. Each person's sin will be weighed on the left scale, good deeds on the right scale. After individual judgment, Mohammed will lead the faithful into parade along the bridge over the fires of hell. The pressure of the crowd will be tremendous, causing all the sinners to fall into the fire, but the righteous will be saved.[11]

Islam does not say how the bodily resurrection will occur. However, the mystery of life entering dead body and dried-up bone is compared

---

11. John R. Hinnels, ed. *Textual Sources For the Study of Religion*, ed. and trans. by Andrew Rippin and Jan Knappert, (Chicago: University of Chicago Press, 1990), pp.10-11.

to rain water entering the dried-up land and revitalizing it. "It is God who sends forth the winds, so that they raise up the clouds, and We drive them to a land that is dead, and revive the earth therewith after its death: even so (will be) the resurrection!" (Sura 35:9). Everybody will be judged according to their conscious actions on earth, nobody else will be able to help them. For the evil doers, it will be a terrible day. "(It will be) the day when no soul shall have power (to do) aught for another: for the command, that day will be (wholly) with God" (Sura 82:19).

The Quran emphasizes in Sura 56:11ff, there will be two levels of Paradise for believers who enter there. The first level will be for those who were nearest to God while they lived on earth. They are called the honoured and exalted ones (56:11-26). The next level is for the "Companions of the Right Hand" (56:27-40) and they are called the Righteous Ones. Opposite to these groups are the sinners who lived a selfish and arrogant life without God and they will suffer in agony and loss, and they are called the Companions of the Left Hand (Sura 56:41-56).[12]

The Quran says paradise will be a place where the believers can enjoy peace and pleasure. As there are several degrees of spiritual experience, the believers would enjoy differing levels of bliss.[13] Cyril Glasse writes, "There is clearly a fundamental difference of degree here, which certain of the Sufis have not hesitated to define as that between those who merely achieve salvation and those who attain to Beatitude; salvation is the reward, they say, of the exoteric religion, and Beatitude the aim of the Sufis' esoteric Path."[14] Those who experience salvation will be many in number and those who experience Beatitude will be a few (Sura 56:13-14, 38-39). Hence Glasse continues, "as the end of time approaches, salvation remains open to many, but Beatitude to very few; this is not strange, since those 'brought nigh' include Jesus and other Prophets and, in fact, the line of Prophets was 'sealed' with the death of Mohammed."[15]

---

12. Yusuf Ali says, "There will be four-fold classification [in Paradise] according to the varying spiritual experience gained in this life: (1) the Prophets who taught and led mankind; (2) the sincere Devotees of Truth, who supported the Cause in their person and with all their resources; (3) the Martyrs and Witnesses, who suffered and served; and (4) the righteous people generally, those who led ordinary lives, but always with righteous aims. All these are united in one beautiful fellowship." *The Holy Quran: Text, Translation and Commentary*, p.1467.

13. See John 14:1.

14. Glasse, *The Encyclopaedia of Religion*, p.109.

15. Ibid.,

The Islamic Concept of Hell

Hell is mentioned by several names: "the fire", "Gehenna", "abyss", "crushing pressure", and "scorching fire". Those who come to this place of torture are the ones who are consumed with ego and have denied God's will. Several Muslim scholars say that God is eternal and eternity belongs to him alone. Hence, they argue, hell is not something that will last for ever. Glasse writes, "While paradise is not co-extensive with God, it is perpetual in that the blessed finally become one with their metaphysical possibility. The distinction applies all the more so to hell, albeit in another sense, in that hell ends for the individual once the consciousness of personality disappears, which happens sooner or later for all its inhabitants, even those whom Dante placed in the lowest circle".[16]

The Mutazilites believe, hell, in fact, both punishes and purifies the sinners. One's chaotic self-consciousness will be destroyed and the true nature God has placed in a human being would be restored. The al-Asharis believe that all those who have not committed idol-worship or Shirk in any other form will be temporarily punished in hell or left in the fires of hell until all the non-conformities are purged and removed so that they might become absolutely obedient to God's command. The prayers and petitions of God's Imams and messengers will also help them get out of the Burning Pit. This belief is founded on the sayings of the Hadith, "he shall make men come out of hell after they have been burned and reduced to cinders."[17] The Hadith corresponds the fires of hell to ordinary as found in this world.

> Narrated Abu Huraira: Allah's Apostle said, "Your [ordinary] fire is one of 70 parts of the [Hell] fire." Someone asked, "O Allah's Apostle! This [ordinary] fire would have been sufficient [to torture the unbelievers]." Allah's Apostle said "The [Hell] fire has 69 parts more than the ordinary [earthly] fire, each part is as hot as this [earthly] fire" (4:315; 54.9.487).

---

16. Glasse, *The Encyclopaedia of Islam*, p.152.
17. Ibid., pp.152-153.

CHAPTER XIV
Women and Jahiliyya

Before the advent of Islam, a large portion of the Arabs were tending camels and living as nomads of the desert in tents. By nature of their work, women in rural areas and desert region enjoyed considerable freedom in contrast to their counterparts in cities. Segregation of women and the imposition of the veil were unknown and unnecessary. Written evidences show women in jahiliyya[1] were protected and given special honour. Even after marriage, women were retained in their respective tribal communities or ethnic neighbourhoods. Women were offered protection and shelter by the entire tribe before and after marriage since there was a constant threat of kidnapping and capturing women by enemy tribes. Captured women were sometimes forced into marriage by rival tribes or ransomed for a high price. As female infanticide kept the female population to a bare minimum, threat of invasion to capture women constantly kept the tribal communities on edge. Since every tribe has to maintain its stability, often the tribes raided each other's territory to capture more women.

In jahiliyya, women chose their own husbands and monogamy was not strictly practiced. Children born to them became part of the mother's community, not the father's. Marriage would not subjugate a woman as she enjoyed the freedom to marry or dismiss a man at any time. She did not need a man's physical protection as it had been offered by her entire tribe. As the potential mother of valiant men, she was considered a prized possession. After all, the mothers of the tribe facilitated the community to sustain its energy and vitality, potency and durability, permanency and security.

The paternality of the children did not matter much. Husbands might be chosen from the same or outside of one's tribe, but children always remained in the tribe of their mothers. This was true even in the life of

---

1. The Quran calls pre-Islamic days as jahiliyya, a period of ignorance.

Mohammed. His mother, Aminah, continued to stay with her community ever after her marriage to Abdullah. He went to see his wife in her place regularly until he died before Mohammed's birth. Only after Aminah died, was Mohammed passed on to the custody of his father's relatives.[2] Abu'l-Faraj, the compiler of *Kitabul-Aghani* (the Book of the Arabs), says of women's marital freedom:

> The women in the jahiliyya, or some of them, used to divorce their husbands, and the form of their dismissal was this—if the women lived in a tent they turned it around, so that if the door had faced east it now faced west, and if it had faced Yeman it now faced Syria; and when the man saw this he knew that she had divorced him and did not go to her.[3]

Modern form of chastity or fidelity should not be applied to the warring, tent-dwelling nomads of the harsher days of Arab history. Marriage during those days did not involve any witness or contract. A prospective husband usually would take a *sadaq* (gift) and tender himself to a woman and say, *khitab*, the metaphorical translation of the word is "I am your lover". If the woman accepted the gift, she would tell him how long he might get to stay with her, which, of course, was likely to be extended if she liked him, and said *nikh*, "I thee wed". This union was called *sadiqa*.

During jahiliyya, women not only enjoyed freedom but occupied high places in society. They owned property and some of them were rich, wealthy herdswomen. This was true in cities as well. Khadijah, a wealthy widow and entrepreneur, lived a life of independence and respect in Mecca, which was a thriving metropolis. She must have owned movable and immovable property. She was a caravan trader who owned houses. She gave a house as a gift to her daughter, Zainab. Women of Mecca also shared in the sale and profits of merchandise. Abdur Rahim says, "Though a woman was debarred from inheriting, she was under no disability in the matter of owning property."[4]

---

2. Ahmed, *Women and Gender in Islam*, pp.43-44.

3. Abu'l-Faraj al-Isfahani, *Kitabul-Aghani*, Vol. XVI, (Bulak: Dar al-kutub, 1868), p.106.

4. Sir Abdur Rahim, *Muhammadan Jurisprudence*, p.12.

Robertson Smith says in his book *Kinship and Marriage in Early Arabia*, during jahiliyya there were queens, judges, poetesses, and rich business women.[5] When a husband became the "lord" of the woman (married or captured) in marriage, woman's freedom was diminished against her will and she became a man's possession for procreation. When the Arabs became Muslims, Mohammed condemned this reduced freedom and said, "It is not lawful for you to inherit women against their will" (Sura 4:23). In time, it led to all male members of a family claiming ownership over all women at home. Men became protectors of the chastity of women and negotiators or match-makers of their marriages. *Mahr*[6] became vogue and marriage became a male dominated institution. Mahr is a cash or in-kind compensation the groom gave to the family of the bride for losing a valuable member of the family and tribe who is a potential mother of a male soldier.

Mahr is not found anywhere in the Quran. Mahr gives the impression that a woman can be bought for a price. When the Quran directs a gift to be given to a woman, it refers to it as a reward and a reasonable restitution which the woman deserves in the event her husband divorces her. The woman can use the mahr in whatever way she likes (Sura 4:4). The practice of mahr is found in the traditions and Muslim literatures, and they present mahr as an important component of Islamic marriages. Some traditions say Mohammed himself paid mahr to his wives.[7]

The Quran uses three words which come close to mahr: *ajr* (reward), *sadiqa* (marriage gift), and *farada* (set aside a certain portion) (Sura 4:32, 5:7, 2:237). If the girl should marry her cousin on her father's side, mahr was not paid. After all, the family is not losing the girl to another tribe so there is no loss involved. If a woman was captured in a raid she was bartered and sold as a slave for money. However, widows were given to men who chose to marry them without mahr.

Slave trade was a prosperous and thriving business practiced both by Christians and Muslims in the Middle East. Muslim slaves were treated more humanely than the infidels. The Quran encourages Muslims to spend their fortunes as ransom to set the slaves free (Sura 2:177). Muslim masters were allowed to marry freed slaves and to have children.

---

5. William Robertson Smith, *Kinship and Marriage in Early Arabia*, (Cambridge: University Press, 1885), pp.125, 295.

6. *Mahr* is tantamount to dowry.

7. Some traditions say Mohammed gave five hundred dirhams (Arabian currency) to his wives except to war widows.

Such children will also be free. The masters also were given the right to keep the slaves as concubines. Their children, however, would not be free unless the master chooses to make them so. A free Muslim woman, unlike a free Muslim man, is not permitted to marry or have any intimate relationship with a slave man.

Women who were sold as slaves and children born to their masters could neither inherit any property nor carry the family name of their owners. When Mohammed tried to give a new social identity to those children born to Muslim fathers, he was faced with severe opposition. The Arabs refused to share any inheritance of property or name with children of slave mothers, claiming that their genealogy was not pure.

Female infanticide was a violent routine practiced in pre-Islamic Arabia. Fathers coaxed the mothers to abandon female children whom the fathers buried alive under the sands of the desert. Such practice was vehemently condemned by the Quran (Sura 16:60, 138, 81:8, 6:152, 17:33). Mohammed's strong imputation and vehement condemnation resulted in its gradual decline and final termination under Islam. Some scholars think female infanticide was a primitive form of sacrifice practiced by Arbas.[8] Others argue, hunger, poverty, drought, constant fear of females being taken alive as captives and made concubines or wives by tribals of lower status were some of the contributing factors for fathers to bury their daughters alive.[9]

Female infanticide was practiced by the Greeks and Romans prior to the arrival of Christianity. The Roman law said that the fathers were to raise all the boys and only one girl. The girls were, therefore, thrown alive at the dump sites but not buried. Christianity condemned this practice. Some forms of Christianity went so far as to say the exercise of abortion and the use of contraceptives were sinful. Some of the early church fathers (Tertullion, Origen, Augustine) devalued women in their writings. They believed, because of women, destruction was brought upon humanity and the Son of God had to die on the cross. As sex was considered shameful, women were considered inferior and representatives of evil and temptation.

Captured women prior to the arrival of Islam were expected to procreate children for the tribe in which they were kept captive. These

---

8. Reuben Levy, *The Sociology of Islam*, Vol.I, p.132.

9. L.E. Browne, *Eclipse of Christianity in Asia*, (Cambridge: University Press, 1933), p.83.

women were forced into marriage and stripped of their privileges as wives of another tribe. Captured women were controlled by their husbands. Unlike the free wives, the captured women could not divorce their husbands and their new born children belonged to the tribe of their fathers, not the mothers.[10] In some cases, women were sold as slaves and wives to men of another tribe for higher prices. Eventually, women became the property of men folks at home too. Fathers and male members of the family took control of women's lives. Suitors would come to the doors to negotiate with the fathers or kinsmen of women and pay mahr to get a woman in marriage. In these conditions, fathers rejoiced over the birth of a daughter as she would bring them an additional revenue.

During tougher economic times, the suitors would demand the girls to cease all ties with their families and tribes particularly with regard to the custom of returning children born to them. However, the fathers of the girls would not agree to that term as the suitors had paid mahr only for the brides not for their offsprings. If their offsprings had to stay with their fathers' tribes, more mahr or more negotiations were called for.[11] Consequently, women became a piece of property to be bartered, negotiated, and sold for profits by male members of families.

In course of time, a law which evolved out of the above negotiation said that all children born on a father's bed should belong to the father and to his tribe. The law al-walad li'l-firash was practiced even during Mohammed's days. The law accommodated the captors to marry even captured pregnant women and thus claim her offspring as his and the tribe's own. As all children belong to the tribe, fidelity among women was not given much thought. Wives were sent to other men in exchange for a favour or during husband's long journey or just to be impregnated by them. Since women's prices were set high by fathers and kinfolks, at times, several brothers from a family would pool all their resources and purchase a woman from another tribe to make her a common wife of all. As all children belong to the tribe and every one worked for the welfare of the kindred groups, no trouble was taken to authenticate the paternity of the children.

---

10. Robertson Smith, *Kinship and Marriage in Early Arabia*, p.91-94.

11. According to pre-Islamic jahiliyya custom, children born to mothers belonged to the families and the tribes of the mothers.

However, when women were captured or married from a respectable tribe or class, they would encourage their children to be in close relationship with their maternal uncles. Subsequently, children's loyalty was divided between two varying, at times, warring tribes. In order to avoid this split loyalty, men were often eager to find a suitable match within their paternal clan and safeguard the custody of their sons.

Robertson Smith claims that in order to retain all male children born to women within a tribe, a ritualistic ceremony called *aqiqa* was practiced by the Arabs.[12] *Aqiqa* means "cut" or "remove" like cutting the throat of a goat or a sheep or removing the foreskin in circumcision. In the ceremony, the throat of an animal was cut and the blood coated over the shaven head of a male child. The shaved hair or its comparable weight of silver was offered to the god of the father's tribe. The whole notion behind the sacrifice and the motive behind the offering was to avert any evil influence, the mother's tribe or her gods might bring upon the boy. The term *aqiqa* came out of this sacrificial act. The entire ritual was known as *aqqa I-rahima:*, "he severed the ties of relationship".[13]

As one can see in the later jahiliyya, husbands became the head of house and the sole owner of the wife. The family structure displaced the communal ownership of women and children. A progress was made toward the formation of marital fidelity.

Jahiliyya and Mohammed's Reform

Muslim apologists affirm that Mohammed was the one who reformed and transformed the Arab society. Before Mohammed, the early Arabs were plagued with superstition, idolatry, and infanticide. The seclusion of women, their subordination to men, and the wearing of the veil predate the advent of Islam and seventh century C.E. As the rise of Islam is treated as a new beginning by some Islamicists, some European scholars erroneously attributed the subjugation of women to Islamic teachings alone. Those scholars, who divide the Arab history into Islamic or Middle Eastern history since the arrival of Mohammed and Near Eastern history before his arrival, consequently associate the evil cultural practices such as infanticide and the veil which were in existent even before Mohammed's time with Islamic instructions.

---

12. Robertson Smith, *Kinship and Marriage in Early Arabia*, pp.179 ff.

13. Lane.

Islam came as a new revolutionary force amidst the existing cultural and social mores of the day and gave new social and moral instructions to its adherents in Arabia. Islam could not reform all of the social evils of the day since its main message was to abolish polytheism and assert the oneness of God.

Several Muslim scholars contend that the socio-economic condition which was passed on in the Middle East since neolithic times had committed women to secondary status. The origins of such practice have been traced back to Mesopotamia, the cradle of that time's civilization. Similar arguments, albeit from a different perspective, are presented with an elaborate accuracy by Leila Ahmed in the first two chapters of her book *Women and Gender in Islam: Historical Roots of a Modern Debate*.[14]

Ahmed argues that the advent of sedentary living and the slow transformation of nomadic living to agrarian, commercial, and urban lifestyles have served as major contributing factors for the division of labour between women and men, which eventually demoted women to a subordinate position. Women were possessed and used as property. Women were relegated to the task of staying home to procreate and raise children. Men travelled far and wide, worked in fields, managed all commercial, political, and social enterprises in order to provide for the needs at home.

The Mesopotamian civilization and laws made their imprint upon several cultures (Sumarian, Akkadian, Babylonian, Assyrian) for thousands of years. Mesopotamian laws influenced the formation of Hebrew and Islamic legislation. Enjoining concubines to bear children, the rights of the children to the fathers' property, and the exclusive right of a man to divorce his wife which Judeo-Christian and Islamic literatures talk about have their origins traced back to Mesopotamian civilization and jurisprudence.[15]

The Quran preserves the notion that during jahiliyya the birth of a daughter was not considered a blessing but a disaster. Fathers felt sad upon the birth of a female (Sura 16:60, 43:16). Muslim tradition says female children were buried alive. In the *Dictionary of Islam*, Hughes

---

14. Leila Ahmed, *Women and Gender in Islam: Historical Roots of a Modern Debate*, (Yale University Press: New Haven and London, 1992).

15. Ibid., p.16

mentions that the only incident which made Uthman shed a tear was when he was burying alive his little daughter, she reached out and "wiped the dust of the grave-earth from his beard."[16] When a girl was permitted to live, the parents had to live in constant fear that she might bring dishonour to the family by her misconduct. Therefore, she was given in marriage at the age of seven or eight.

Critics, however, contend that jahiliyya were not as bad as has been portrayed by the Muslim apologists. In fact, those days were better days for women as they were free, emancipated and unfettered. They were free to choose their own husbands and unconstrained to disown them.[17] R.A. Nicholson states that those were one of the glorious periods for women in Arab history. Poems were composed on women's chivalry. A hero's mother and sisters were honoured with high esteem.

> On the whole, their position was high and their influence great... They were regarded not as slaves and chattels, but as equals and companions. They inspired the poet to sing and the warrior to fight. The chivalry of the Middle Ages is, perhaps, ultimately traceable to heathen Arabia.[18]

In the same vein, S.Khuda Buksh, a Muslim literary critic, confirms in *Studies: Indian and Islamic*:

> During the highest bloom of Arab nationality, woman was not only man's equal, but was not infrequently the object of a chivalrous devotion.[19]

Angeliki Laiou suggests that women in Byzantium were active in the society serving as bath attendants, midwives, doctors, artisans, and food vendors. Women also worked as money lenders, traders, and investors.[20] Jahiliyya women enjoyed more freedom and autonomy than

---

16. Thomas Patrick Hughes, *A Dictionary of Islam*, (London: W.H. Allen, 1895), p.677.

17. Charles James Lyall, Translations of *Ancient Arabian Poetry*, (London: Williams & Norgate, 1930), p.xxi.

18. Reynold Alleyne Nicholson, *A Literary History of the Arabs*, (Cambridge: University Press, 1969), p.87.

19. S. Khuda Baksh, *Studies: Indian and Islamic*, (Delhi: Private Press, 1978), p.79.

20. Angeliki e. Laiou, "The Role of Women in Byzantine Society", *Jahrbuch der "osterreichischen Byzantinistik* 31, no.1, (1981), p.249. Quote taken from Leila Ahmed, *Women and Gender in Islam: Historical Roots of a Modern Debate*, p.27.

women under Islam, especially in marriage and leadership positions. Women, during pre-Islamic days, served as leaders and active participants in the community. For instance, Khadijah, Mohammed's first wife, was a wealthy widow who hired men to work for her. She hired Mohammed to oversee her caravan business and a little later, when she was pleased with him, she proposed and married him. She was the one who encouraged Mohammed to meditate and be open to the revelation he was receiving.

Khadijah's loyalty to Mohammed, her monogamous marriage, her economic independence, her own volition to marry a man much younger and lower in status than her prove that all was not bad during jahiliyya. Mohammed's monogamous marriage to Khadijah as long as she lived confirms that monogamy was indeed practiced in Mecca before Islam.

Critics also argue that Islam was the one that put so many restrictions on women and relegated them to a secondary place. The status of Aisha, Mohammed's favourite wife was cited to substantiate that claim. Aisha was born to Muslim parents and lived in a time of transition from jahiliyaa to Islam. In contrast to Khadijah's free and enterprising lifestyle, Aisha was expected to satisfy and serve her husband. Aisha wore a veil and stayed indoors most of the time. After Mohammed's death, she tried to become a community leader and led the warriors to fight against her political rival. She was defeated and sternly warned never to aspire for another leadership position in the community. She was not allowed to remarry as she and other wives of Mohammed were considered "the mothers of Islam". Although they were given respect and often consulted (especially Aisha) to interpret the customs and practices of Mohammed, which were documented and incorporated into Hadith and Sunna, their movements were very much restricted by men in power.

The Prophet's wives and daughters were often consulted by men on matters related to daily life and moral conduct. Women asked them questions on child-rearing, family, clothing, and cosmetics. Of all the wives of Mohammed, Aisha was consulted more often which resulted in attributing over two thousand traditions to her. About two hundred of these traditions have been included in the compilations of Bukhari and of Muslim, which are considered canonical.[21]

---

21. Walther, *Women in Islam*, p.106.

In his book *Muhammad at Medina*, Watt maintains that the pre-Islamic marriages in Arabia were significantly matrilineal.[22] It was a community in which paternity did not matter. Nonetheless, Watt states, a transition from matrilineal to patrilineal was in progress when Islam was spreading across the Arabian desert. The settled life of the dominant Qurayash tribal people, the rapid growth of commerce in and around Mecca during the fifth and sixth centuries, the break-down of communal property values to individuals owning business and wealth led the families to own and accumulate fortunes.

Increasing trade competition with little outside threat from desert pirates and moribund invaders resulted in the emergence of men as inheritors of everything, including women and children. Men desired to pass on their wealth as inheritance to male children.

Soon the society was transformed and paternity gained new importance. Consequently, matriliny was superseded by patriliny. Mohammed seized the moment of societal transition and consolidated it under Islam.

22. W. Montgomery Watt, *Muhammad at Medina*, (Oxford: Clarendon Press, 1956), pp.272-73.

CHAPTER XV
Marriage, Divorce and the Veil

The Myth of Female Inferiority

Islam does not have a hierarchy of religious priests and spiritual leaders as Christianity does. Nevertheless, Islam has Mullahs and Imams who are laymen who have a thorough knowledge of the Quran, Hadith, and Sharia. Men who are exceedingly informed of the scripture and laws of Islam call themselves to be leaders of the community. Since Muslims have been commanded to live together in unity and in harmony, and in oneness and solidarity, as we have already discussed in earlier chapters, the umma came into being. The umma today broadly means Muslim nations. The umma has enabled the Muslim community to practice the teachings of Mohammed freely and, especially, without outside political or social interference.

In Islamic countries, Allah alone is Sovereign. People are only his representatives. The guiding force and the governing principles of Islamic nations are the teachings given in the Quran. The interpreters of the Quran and the Islamic traditions are often consulted in matters pertaining to political and social principles of Islamic nations. Accordingly, the Imams and Mullahs of Islamic nations strive to combine both state and religion, and tend to give both political and spiritual leadership to the citizens.

Islamic society is primarily centered around men. The leaders at the mosques, teachers at instruction schools, and tutors at places of religious gathering are men. Male children, by and large, enjoy a lot more freedom than female children, particularly in dress code, social, and marital privileges. Men are placed at a higher level because of their economic superiority, physical vitality, and privileged sexuality. The often quoted Quranic passage to justify male superiority is:

> Men are the protectors and maintainers of women, because God has given the one more (strength) than the other, and because they support them from their means. Therefore, the righteous

women are devoutly obedient, and guard in (the husband's)
absence what God would have them guard. (Sura 4:34).

However, some Islamic scholars claim that the Quran is egalitarian
and it teaches that men and women are equal in the sight of God. Only
those who interpret the sacred scripture give slanted and biased opinions
about women as inferior creatures to men. Some modern Islamic women
scholars argue that the Quran, in fact, supports women and offers
preferential treatment to them. Riffat Hassan argues:

> Having spent seven years in study of the Quranic passages
> relating to women, I am convinced that the Quran is not biased
> against women and does not discriminate against them. On the
> contrary, because of its protective attitude toward all
> downtrodden and oppressed classes, it appears to be weighted
> in many ways in favour of women.[1]

In another context, Hassan presents that only men, who misinterpret
and misrepresent the Quranic and Islamic traditions, perpetuate the
discrimination against women in Islamic society. The Quran and the
hadith make up the sources of Sharia, which by a process of juristic
perception *(figh)* provides moral teaching, ethical instruction, and family
counselling. As men have controlled most of those offices of
interpretation and instruction, over the centuries women were given a
subordinate place and men were assigned a superior role. In her article
on *The Issue of Gender Equality in the Context of Creation in Islam*,
Hassan observes:

> Despite the fact the women such as Khadijah and Aishah (wives
> of the Prophet Muhammed) and Rabi'a al-Basri (the outstanding
> woman of Sufi) figure significantly in early Islam, the Islamic
> tradition has, by and large, remained rigidly patriarchal until the
> present time, prohibiting the growth of scholarship among
> women particularly in the realm of religious thought. This
> means that the sources on which the Islamic tradition is mainly
> based, namely, the Quran, the Sunnah, the hadith literature, and
> Fiqh, have been interpreted only by Muslim men who have
> arrogated to themselves the task of defining the ontological,

---

1. Riffat Hassan, "On Human Rights and the Quranic Perspective", in *Human Rights
in Religious Traditions*, ed., Arlene Swidler, (New York: The Pilgrim Press, 1982), p.63.

theological, sociological, and eschatological status of Muslim women.[2]

Hassan also maintains that Islam has relegated women to a subordinate position because of stories and fables borrowed from non-Quranic traditions, particularly from Jewish and Christian legends. Hassan observes that the Book of Genesis mentions that Adam was created first and Eve was created from his rib. Eve was given as a helper fit for Adam. According to the Genesis account, Eve was primarily responsible for the fall of Adam, which eventually had an impact on the entire humanity. Hence, all women folks down through the centuries were looked down as weak and vulnerable creatures. Contrary to the Biblical version, Hassan affirms, the Quran does not make mention of Eve as the reason for the fall of Adam. Adam and Eve both fall prey to the deception of Satan and commit the act of rebellion against God. Unlike the Hebrew term "Adam", which refers to an individual, the Quran considers Adam "as a collective noun [which] stands for humankind." The Quran itself does not discriminate against men and women.

> Analysis of the Quranic descriptions of human creation makes it clear that the Quran even handedly uses both feminine and masculine terms and imagery to describe the creation of humanity from a single source. That Allah's original creation was undifferentiated humanity and not either man or woman... is implicit in a number of Quranic passages, in particular (Surah 75:36-39).[3]

Only the Hadith, not the Quran, says Eve took the fruit of knowledge to Adam. Thus, Hassan concludes, the creation narratives mentioned in hadith "have had a formative influence upon the Muslim mind", and in the development of a theory that woman was irresolute and naive.

> According to the Quran, Allah created woman and man equal. They were created simultaneously, of like substance, and in like manner. The fact that almost all Muslims believe that the first woman (Hawwa') was created from Adam's rib shows that, in practice, the hadith literature has displaced the teaching of the Quran at least insofar as the issue of woman's creation is concerned.[4]

2. Riffat Hassan, "The Issue of Gender Equality in the Context of Creation in Islam", *Women's and Men's Liberation: Testimonies of Spirit*, Leonard Grab, Hayin Gordon, and Riffat Hassan eds., (New York: Greenwood Pr., 1991), p.56.

3. Ibid.

4. Ibid.

In the East, many Muslim families prefer male children to female. In more traditional and orthodox Muslim communities, female children are not expected to work outside of home and hence higher education to earn a living or to establish a career is not a necessity for them. Women are encouraged to stay home and be good wives and mothers. The role of a mother is so highly elevated in some communities that a mother is nurtured to believe and behave that her life should be centered around her husband and male children. Mothers are respected so much through oral and written traditions that the Hadith says, "paradise is at the feet of the mothers". Consequently, singleness and childlessness are discouraged; and all female children are raised to accept the idea that marriage and motherhood are ideal virtues.

Although the Quran does not talk about circumcision, it is widely being practiced in Islamic communities. Male children are usually circumcised when they are seven or eight years old, although no strict law governs it. Circumcision is not as much a religious celebration as it is a family festival. The same can be said of female circumcision also. It is a local tradition. Islam does not provide any written guidelines.

Islam gives much importance to the family unit. The Quran commands children to love and respect their parents.

> And that ye be kind to parents. Whether one or both of them attain old age in their life, say not to them a word of contempt, nor repel them, but address them in terms of honour. And, out of kindness, lower to them the wing of humility, and say: 'My Lord! bestow on them thy mercy even as they cherished me in childhood.' (Sura 17:23-24).

Children of believers are reminded that someday they will become parents themselves and they will receive similar respect from their children at old age. Children are raised to approach parents with kindness and gratitude, as they have shown love and care while children were helpless. Grown up children's responsibility is to return the love they received from parents when they were weak and vulnerable. Respecting parents in their old age has been given a spiritual dimension. Children are constanly reminded "of the great love with which God cherishes his creatures... it goes up into the highest spiritual region."[5]

---

5. A. Yusuf Ali, *The Holy Quran*, p.701.

Marriage in Islam

Marriage, not celibacy, is very much respected in Islam. Mohammed reformed some of the existing Arabic marriage laws and attempted to improve the plight of women. Some of the common Islamic sayings are, "Marriage is half religion", and "Only marriage makes a person whole". Mohammed once said, "Whoever gets married has completed half of his faith; therefore let him be conscious of Allah in the other half of his faith."[6] The Quran says marriage is a divine institution and everyone who is financially able must marry and bring forth children (24:32). Nobody, especially women, should be forced into marriage. The marrying members should have reached the age of discretion before they consummate their marriage. The Hadith says:

> Narrated Abu Huraira: The Prophet said, "A matron should not be given in marriage except after consulting her; and a virgin should not be given in marriage except after her permission." The people asked, "O Allah's Apostle! How can we know her permission?" He said, "Her silence [indicates her permission]" (7:51-52; 62.42.67).

A married couple who follows the principles of marriage as outlined in the Quran, Hadith, and Sunnah will certainly inherit Allah's blessings. Men are created by Allah to protect and take care of the family. Women are created mainly for procreation and to enjoy the pleasures that go with it.

> (The wives) are your garments and you are their garments. (Sura 2:187).

> He created wives from among yourselves that ye may dwell in tranquility with them, and he has put love and mercy between your (hearts). (Sura 20:21).

Commenting on the above verse Ali says, "A man's chivalry to the opposite sex is natural and God-given... And as woman is the weaker vessel, that tenderness may from a certain aspect be likened to mercy, the protecting kindness which the strong should give to the weak."[7] Marriage is not a sacrament and it does not necessarily have to be performed in a place of worship.

---

6. Quoted in W.O. Cole, ed., *Moral Issues in Six Religions*, (London: Heineman, 1991), p.126.

7. Ali, *The Holy Quran: Text, Translation and Commentary*, p.1056.

Marriage, in Islam, is primarily a social contract. Its legitimacy depends upon the proposal of one side and acceptance of the other. The whole concept of marriage is centred upon the consolidation of the family and procreation of children. The only pre-condition to marriage is that the involved parties must be mature in understanding, must have attained puberty, and should be free to say yes or no. Justice Aftab Hussain explains,

> The capacity to contract a valid marriage rests on the same basis and depends on the same conditions as the capacity to enter into any other contract... (1)...the parties must be able to understand the nature of their act. For, if either of them is *non compo mentis* or is incapable of understanding the nature of the contract, it is void. (2)...they must be adults. (3)...they must be acting of their free will and not under compulsion.[8]

The marriage ceremony must be performed in public in front of witnesses. The relationship between husbands and wives has a spiritual character as that which had existed between Allah and his prophets (Sura 4:21, 25). Mohammed is reported to have said, "God has instituted marriage from the days of Adam and it will continue in paradise as well."[9] As for marriage and sex the Quran says, "Your wives are as tilth unto you; so approach your tilth when or how ye will; but do some good act for your souls beforehand; and fear God, and know that ye are to meet him (in the hereafter) and give (these) good things to those who believe" (Sura 2:223). Commenting on this passage Ali says:

> Sex is not a thing to be ashamed of, or to be treated lightly, or to be indulged to excess. It is as solemn a fact as any in life. It is compared to a husband's tilth; it is a serious affair to him: he sows the seed in order to reap the harvest. But he chooses his own time and mode of cultivation. He does not sow out of season nor cultivate in a manner which will injure or exhaust the soil. He is wise and considerate and does not run riot. Coming from the simile to human beings, every kind of mutual consideration is required, but above all, we must remember that even in these matters there is a spiritual aspect. We must never forget our souls, and that we are responsible to God.[10]

---

8. Justice Aftab Hussain, *Status of Women in Islam*, (Lahore: Law Publishing Company, 1987), pp. 454-455.

9. W. Goldsack, *Selections from Mohammadan Traditions*, (Lahore: M.A. Academy, 1965), p.163.

10. Ali, *The Holy Quran: Text, Translation and Commentary*, p.88.

The Quran permits men to marry up to four wives. Modern day Islam is divided over such a practice. During Mohammed's days he gave permission to marry more than one wife because of the prevalent polygamous practices in Arabia and to take care of captives and widows whose husbands were killed in war after Uhud.[11] Some scholars disagree that polygamy was practiced in Arabia during pre-Islamic days, at least as far as Mecca and Medina are concerned.[12] Wiebke Walther holds that polygamy was indeed practiced in the Middle East. Nevertheless, she wonders if it was actually practiced in Mecca and Medina during Mohammed's days. Yet, she claims, the marriage contracts which women entered with men in Arabia one after another may have been considered by some early historians as a polygamous practice. During Mohammed's time, Walther asserts, free sexual practices were common in the Middle East. Serial monogamy was not an uncommon practice in pre-Islamic Arabia. Both men and women were married several times to one spouse after another. Nonetheless, Mohammed was the one who inaugurated the establishment of marriage among the tribal people of Arabia.[13]

The Quran lays down a number of conditions discouraging men from taking more than one wife.

> If ye fear that ye shall not be able to deal justly with the orphans, marry women of your choice, two, or three, or four; but if ye fear that ye shall not be able to deal justly (with them), then only one, or (a captive) that your right hand possess. That will be more suitable, to prevent you from doing injustice. (Sura 4:3).

This verse was revealed to Mohammed after Uhud, when the community was left with many orphans, widows, and a few captives of war. Mohammed was trying to be kind and just to those unfortunate ones by asking Muslim men to take in more than one wife and support them and their children.

Marrying orphans is permitted only if Muslims can protect the rights and properties of the orphans and the believers' dependents. If a believer cannot be fair and just to both of them, alternate arrangements should be made. The unchecked number of wives mentioned in the Quran

---

11. We will discuss it at length at a later part of this chapter.

12. G.Stern, *Marriage in Early Islam*, (London, 1939), pp.62, 81.

13. Wiebke Walther, *Women in Islam*, (Markus Wiener Publishing: Princeton & New York, 1993), p.57.

represents the prevailing cultural practices of the pre-Islamic days. Since it is nearly impossible for a man to treat all wives equally, Mohammed introduced a conditional clause for marriage: "if ye fear that ye shall not be able to do justly, then only one". Based on this stipulation, several modern Muslim scholars argue that a Muslim should have only one wife.

Islam offers guidelines to the believers whom to marry and whom not to marry.[14] Muslim men are absolutely forbidden to marry the following:

> And marry not women whom your father married...your mothers, daughters, sisters; father's sisters, mother's sisters, brother's daughters, sister's daughters; foster-mothers (who gave you suck), foster-sisters; your wives' mothers; your step-daughters under your guardianship, born of your wives to whom ye have gone in... those who have been wives of your sons proceeding from your loins, and two sisters in wedlock at one and the same time. (Sura 4:22-23).

Muslim men are encouraged to marry virgins and free women although marrying others is not forbidden (Sura 24:32). Marriage regulations strictly state that a Muslim should not marry a non-Muslim. If by necessity, one has to marry a non-Muslim, only men are permitted to do so. But even so, only on the condition that the bride is from the people of the Book.

A Christian or Jewish woman is permitted to practice her faith after marrying a Muslim man. However, she should not be higher in status (class, economy and society) than the man whom she marries. Children born to them must be raised as Muslims. If she becomes a widow, the children will be removed from her and given to the care of a Muslim relative unless she becomes a Muslim. She will not receive the widow's benefits and inheritance unless she renounces her faith to become a Muslim. As a result, many Jewish and Christian women, after marriage become Muslims themselves.

The Muslim marriage law becomes one-sided and ambiguous when it comes to women marrying outside of their faith. Although men are allowed to marry from the people of the Book, women are unequivocally forbidden. The Quranic assertion that "men are in charge of women"

---

14. See 4:26-28, 2:220, 24:3, 4:28.

(Sura 4:34) would make it hard for a Muslim woman to practice her faith while married to a non-Muslim. Anyone who wants to marry a Muslim woman must be a Muslim first. In some Islamic nations, young girls are prepared for marriage by keeping them at home and teaching them the art of cooking and maintaining the house. The preparation includes female circumcision, which is considered a highly controversial practice in some Islamic circles. Although the Quran does not talk about circumcision, male circumcision is widely practiced across the Muslim communities. Female circumcision is still practiced by the Shafiites and Malikites. The practice of circumcision predates Islamic era.

Female circumcision is opposed to by modern Muslims as it "mutilates" a woman's most intimate part. In female circumcision the clitoris or part of it is removed. In some cultures, parts of the inner labia of the vulva are removed which permanently scar a woman, and preclude her from deriving any sexual pleasure. In a boy's circumcision, only the outer skin of the male genital is removed which does not harm or mutilate him. In fact, the modern scientific community says circumcision is good for a male as it keeps his private part hygienically clean. Accordingly, the removal of foreskin is practiced by all religious communities as a principle of hygiene. Since having children is a religious duty, the Quran forbids "slaying of children" which is applied to the unborn too.

Abortion is also condemned by Islamic law. If the foetus becomes animated and a living being, abortion should not be performed. The Quran says: "Kill not your children for fear of want: We shall provide sustenance for them as well as for you. Verily the killing of them is a great sin" (Sura 17:31). Islamic law has provisions for the foetus to inherit property and hence abortion is vehemently condemned. Accidently induced abortion is considered "manslaughter" and the perpetrator should compensate the parents with "blood money". Mohammed is reported to have said, "The creation of each of you is brought together in your mother's belly for 40 days in the form of the seed, then you are a clot of blood for a like period, then a morsel of flesh for a like period, then there is sent to you an angel who blows the breath of life in you".[15] It is generally believed that life in a foetus is formed after 120 days and hence it is considered a murder to abort a foetus.

However, the Islamic jurists could not agree upon the controversy surrounding the debate. When exactly a foetus does become a living

---

15. Quoted in Cole, *Moral Issues in Six Religions*, p.120.

being is debated as intensely as it is done in some Christian circles. Some jurists argue that a woman can "abort her pregnancy by the use of medicines before the birth of foetus that is before 120 days of the pregnancy. She may also get the passage to the womb permanently sealed with the permission of her husband, so that sperm may not reach the uterus."[16] Abortion is permitted, if the mother's life is in danger, if the family's economic welfare is threatened, if the baby is not fully formed, and if the pregnancy is caused by rape. Compassion is the order of Islam not hardship (Sura 2:185).

Muslims do not oppose to artificial method of bringing children into the world (such as test-tube babies, artificial insemination etc.) as long as the sperm belongs to the husband. Implanting another man's sperm would constitute adultery. Islamic clerics are divided about the morality of surrogacy.

Family planning is permitted under Islamic law if it would save "a woman conceiving quickly and successively from the pangs of labour, stopping the transmission of infectious disease from one to the other and preventing the birth of children of weak muscles and weak nerves who may not be enabled to discharge their duties in the society."[17] The use of contraceptives, avoiding pregnancy through natural cycle, withdrawal (azl), and surgical procedures are also permitted by jurists. They argue that sex is for both pleasure and procreation. Mohammed was once asked, "What do you think of *coitus interruptus?*" He replied, "Ah well. There is no harm in it, because every single life which God has desired to bring into existence will come into existence."[18]

Divorce: Status of Men and Women

The Quran permits men and women to divorce. Men do not have to give reason to divorce their wives. Men, however, cannot divorce their wives while they are drunk or in a rage. Suras 2:226 and 227 outline the rules of divorce. When Mohammed appeared with his revolutionary message about One God and gave the call for believers to unite and form the umma, the Arab community at large had become a male dominated society. Men claimed ownership of women. Men could own or marry

---

16. Hussain, *Status of Women in Islam*, p.403.

17. Ibid., pp.403-404.

18. Quoted in Neal Robinson, *The Sayings of Muhammad*, (London: Duckworth, 1991), p.43.

any number of women and divorce them at any time. Such practice is mirrored in the Quran as well. The Quran places men above women and men are given more authority over women. In divorce proceedings, women have equal rights like men do; nonetheless, the Quran says that "men have a degree of advantage over (woman)" (Sura 2:228).

During Mohammed's time, two kinds of divorce were commonly practiced: *khula* and *talaq*. Khula was more formal than talaq. In khula, the wife was sent back to her father's or male guardian's house and mahr was repaid to the husband. By doing so, the husband freed himself of all the contract he had made with her father or male guardian. Khula could also become vile when the husband refuses to take mahr back and refuses to live with his · ife. In that case, the woman becomes helpless as the contract made between her husband and her father is still binding. The husband is still her owner and she is not free to do anything she wants.

In talaq,[19] which was widely practiced during Mohammed's days, the husband can pay up any remaining portion of mahr to the woman's father or male guardian, and take absolute control of the woman's life. And then, he can dismiss her with an oral proclamation of *anti taliq*, you are dismissed, three times. Until he pronounces three times, she is not free to go. He can say anti taliq in one day or in one year or more. The husband is not under obligation to give any reason for his dismissal. In between the, two pronouncements, or even after the second pronouncement of dismissal, he can repeal the divorce and take her back.

However, after the third pronouncement, the husband can remarry the divorced wife only after she marries another man who divorces her, or after her second husband dies and she becomes a widow. In all this, the woman has no right to divorce her husband. The Quran and Sharia give her power to claim separation from her husband by khula which allows the woman only to go back to be with her parents or male guardians. Yet, she is not allowed to remarry another man unless the husband divorces her.

The Quran, however, makes arrangements for the woman to survive. The divorcing husband is expected to be kind and to make provision for her living until she remarries. The Quran mandates that the divorced wife is not expected to suckle the child born in her marriage with the divorced

---

19. Talaq in Arabic means release from a knot.

husband. If she was asked by her former husband to suckle the child, she must be compensated as long as she suckles the child.

The divorce pronouncement becomes effective only after three menstrual cycles. The divorced woman should not remarry until the lapse of three months (three menstrual cycles) in order to make sure that she was not pregnant by her former husband. This practice is called *iddat* (Sura 2:28). The general meaning of idat is "a prescribed period". The same word is used for fasting also in the Quran (Sura 2:185). The three month waiting period gives an opportunity for the husband to change his mind in case he made the decision impulsively. During his three months, the husband has to provide for the woman's livelihood.

There are two other forms of divorce which are not very common. The first one is *Ila*, which is generally considered an instant separation or divorce. Again, it is to be initiated by the husband. Some scholars argue it is a suspensory divorce. The second one is *Zihar* which is recorded in the Quran also (Sura 33:4). A husband is not supposed to be intimate with the woman after the dismissal. Although zihar seems to be kinder than the other forms, the husband can continue to hold the ownership of his wife and give property rights to another man who enters into contract with him. Mohammed prohibited this practice (65:6).

Islam urges its followers to avoid divorce, if possible (Sura 2:226-242, 4:23-25, 33:4, 38-39, 58:2, 65:1-4). Nonetheless, the Quran places men above women as men enjoyed economic superiority in controlling the finances of the home. Men are offered privileged sexual freedom in practicing polygamy. Disobedient women are deprived of sexual pleasure and monetary privileges. "And women shall have rights similar to the rights againt them, according to what is equitable; but men have a degree (of advantage) over them" (Sura 2:228). Another sura says women are weaker than men and they should be protected by men as they protect their business or interests. As a wife, she should be submissive, obedient, and virtuous to him. She has to guard both his property and her personal virtue. Failure to do so will result in punishment. Penalty may vary from husband to husband or as the situation may warrant.

There are several kinds of discipline a husband may inflict upon his wife. The Quran documents the following four major disciplinary methods: a husband may use verbal warning, he may withdraw sexual intimacy, he may inflict physical punishment, or he may send her for family/community counsel. The Quran and the Hadith give the following guidance to the husband in correcting the unruly wife.

> As for those from whom ye fear rebellion, admonish them and banish them to beds apart and scourge them (Sura 4:34).

The Hadith says that a man should not go to bed with his wife at the end of the day after beating her.

> Narrated Abdullah bin Zama: The Prophet said: "None of you should flog his wife as he flogs a slave and then have sexual intercourse with her in the last part of the day (7:100-101; 62.94.132).

As the Muslims are commanded to live before Allah in devotion and veneration, the defectors should be corrected and punished. The role of administering justice is given to men. As Allah has created men and women with certain differences, and men have more strength than women, men have to take the leading role. It is men's duty to sustain and maintain women.

Mohammed introduced a number of injunctions to protect women from the hands of unscrupulous husbands. Since a husband may bring back his wife anytime during the three month waiting period and pronounce talaq again and again so that she may wait for three more months after every pronouncement until he or she dies, Mohammed intervened and introduced a new injunction to liberate women from the web of perpetual waiting and subjugation. Mohammed said that divorce can happen only twice and that man can take his wife before the end of three months only two times. Thereafter, the woman is free. The husband has to let go of the woman with kindness and she should be given whatever material benefits she rightfully deserves. She should not be deprived of her mahr (Sura 2:31 and 4:24).

The Quran makes possible for a woman to give up all her claim upon her husband and his property including mahr to secure freedom from him (Sura 2:229). The separated couple is free to marry again whom they like within their own faith. No further restrictions are imposed on them (Sura 2:232).

Islam also gives other innovations on divorce. It encourages the man to be more liberal to the divorced woman and pay her part of his property even if the marriage was not consummated.

> There is no blame on you if ye divorce women before consummation or the fixation of their dower; but bestow on them (a suitable gift), the wealthy according to his means, and

the poor according to his means;- a gift of a reasonable amount is due from those who wish to do the right thing. And if ye divorce them before consummation, but after the fixation of a dower for them, then half of the dower (is due to them), unless they remit it or (the man's half) is remitted by him in whose hands is the marriage tie; and the remission (of the man's half) is the nearest to righteousness. And do not forget liberality between yourselves. For God sees well all that ye do. (Sura 2:236-237).

The Quran attempts to make provision for a woman's growth and life after she is separated from her husband. The law is bare to the woman to pay whatever she owes to her former husband, for instance, in returning the mahr her family received from the husband at the time of marriage (Sura 4:39. 65:1-2).

Islamic tradition admits that problems do occur in all marriages. Even the prophet had to face misfortunes in his family life. When his wives demanded worldly comforts and pleasures which he could not afford, he had to face the issue of divorce. Aisha's father Abu Bakr and Hafsa's father 'Umar chided their daughters for demanding too much from the prophet.' Mohammed was saddened by the incident and stayed away from his wives for a month. During that time the following verses were revealed to him.

O Prophet! say to thy consorts: If it be that ye desire the life of this world, and its glitter, —then come! I will provide for your enjoyment and set you free in a handsome manner. But if ye seek God and His Apostle, and the home of the hereafter, verily God has prepared for the well-doers amongst you a great reward. (Sura 33:28).

It may be, if he divorced you (all), that God will give him in exchange consorts better than you, —who submit (their wills), who believe, who are devout, who turn to God in repentance, who worship (in humility), who travel (for Faith) and fast,— previously married or virgin. (Sura 66:5)

Biblical Injunctions on Divorce

In the Hebrew Scriptures, God commands his children to be faithful to their wives and declares that He hates divorce. "For I hate divorce, says the Lord God of Israel, and covering one's garment with violence, says the Lord of hosts. So take heed to yourselves and do not be faithless" (Malachi 2:16). The Hebrew Scriptures bestowed upon men absolute power to divorce his wife. It also says that the divorced couple cannot marry again.

> When a man takes a wife and marries her, if then she finds no favour in his eyes because he has found some indecency in her, and he writes her a bill of divorce and puts it in her hand and sends her out of his house, and she departs out of his house, and if she goes and becomes another man's wife, and the latter husband dislikes her and writes her a bill of divorce and puts it in her hand and sends her out of his house, or if the latter husband dies, who took her to be his wife, then her former husband who sent her away, may not take her again to be his wife, after she has been defiled; for that is an abomination before the Lord, and you shall not bring guilt upon the land which the Lord your God gives you for an inheritance. (Deut. 24:1-4).

The husband, however, cannot divorce his wife on false charges. If he accuses her of not being a virgin at the time of marriage and if the charge is proved false, he would be punished (Deut.22:17-19). A man who rapes a young girl has to pay bride money to her father and she becomes his wife and can never be divorced. (Deut.22:28-29).

Jesus also condemned divorce. When the Pharisees challenged him on the basis of the Mosaic law, Jesus said married couples were no longer two individuals but one entity. Divorce was not found at the time of creation. Moses granted divorce because of the hardness of human hearts. Jesus said to the Pharisees, "For your hardness of heart Moses allowed you to divorce your wives, but from the beginning it was not so. And I say to you: whoever divorces his wife, except for unchastity, and marries another, commits adultery". However, modern Christianity does not take the above teachings of Jesus literally and justifies divorce and remarriage. God's abundant mercy and abiding grace are called upon to vindicate the fallen nature of humanity and violation of biblical instructions.

The Veil

Wearing of the veil was common in Sassanian society and Christian communities in the Middle Est and Mediterranean regions. The high class women in Palestine and Syria wore veils, while the slaves were forbidden. The custom was common among Sassanians, Greeks, Romans

Jews, Assyrians. During the later part of Mohammed's life, his wives were instructed to wear veils. City women in pre-Islamic Arabia also wore the veil. In his book *Sociology of Islam*. R. Levy refers to a custom that was common in Mecca.[20] Fathers or the male members of the women's families would dress up their grown up daughters or female slaves, unveil their faces, and exhibit them to the crowd which gathered around kaaba. It was a way of looking for suitable husbands or buyers. After the suitable match was found, women would replace their veils.

Islam discouraged this practice of parading young women on the streets of Mecca. Some scholars interpret the Quranic verse, "Stay quietly in your houses, and make not a dazzling, like that of the former times of ignorance" (Sura 33:33), as Mohammed's way of encouraging his wives to be different from others. The Prophet's wives and the women of Islam were not like ordinary women. They had special privileges and responsibilities in guiding others to the path of Allah. They were not to deck themselves with ornaments or show themselves off.

The Quran does not say that women should wear the veil, although in several Muslim communities, girls are encouraged to wear the veil when they are eight or nine years old. Sura 33:33 gives suggestions to women living in Mecca and Medina to be modest, discreet, and careful in their dress and conduct. Urban centres were not congenial for women to be alone and to show themselves off.

The revelation about modesty and the dress code to Mohammed's wives were revealed in the Quran:

"O Prophet! Tell thy wives and daughters, and the believing women, that they should cast their outer garments over their persons (when abroad) : that is most convenient, that they should be known (as such) and not molested" (33:59).

Only Mohammed's wives were expected to be in seclusion and veil. His concubines and other Muslims women were not expected to be in veil.[21]

---

20. R. Levy, *Sociology of Islam*, Vol.I p.176.

21. During the classical period of Islamic power, however, male attitude toward women had changed and became misogynist and contemptuous. Men began to misuse Sura 4:4 and attempted to own as many captured non-Muslim women slaves as they could afford. They used such slaves as "objects for sexual use" which eventually obscured the distinction between the words "women", "concubine", and "objects for sexual use" in the male mind. Leila Ahmed argues that if the ethical teachings of the Quran are correctly understood, rather than its legal mandate, clarifications more beneficial to women can be heard. See Leila Ahmed, *Women and Gender in Islam*, (New Haven: Yale University Press, 1992), p.85.

The only instruction the Quran gives to Muslim women is to cover their private parts (Sura 24:31-32). Several stories and traditions are attributed to the Prophet in asking his wives to veil. One of the traditions says, during Mohammed's marriage to Zeinab bint Jahsh, some of the wedding guests stayed over in her room and conversed till late at night. Mohammed was displeased and disturbed by their callous insensitivity. When he was sitting outside the house and waiting for the guests to leave the revelation about seclusion was given. Another tradition adds, during the wedding reception, Omar's and a few other male guests' hands touched Aisha's. Mohammed felt insulted (aza) by the sight and the following revelation was given.

> O ye who believe! Enter not the Prophet's houses, - until leave is given you, - for a meal, (and then) not (so early as) to wait for its preparation: but when you are invited, enter; and when ye have taken your meal, disperse, without seeking familiar talk. Such (behavior) annoys the Prophet. And when ye ask (his ladies) for anything ye want, ask them from before a screen: that makes for greater purity for your hearts and for theirs. Nor is it right for you that ye should annoy God's Apostle, or that ye should marry his widows after him at any time. Truly such a thing is in God's sight an enormity. (Sura 35:53).

Ali says through the revelation the Prophet was only trying to teach etiquette and good manners to the "rude Arabs".[22] As Mohammed was becoming a powerful spiritual and political leader, both Arab converts and non-converts came to his court to strike deals with him. As they did not know the common etiquette, Mohammed had to keep his wives and daughters away from them and in seclusion. In the following verses, the Quran gives a list of people before whom those women could appear normally without veil.

After his death and the expansion of Islam all over the Middle East, the upper class Muslim women also began to wear veil just as the upper class women of other religious cultures did. As a sign of modesty and piety, all the Muslim women began to wear veils too. The demand for modesty is required for men and women as mentioned in Sura 24:30 and 31. Nonethless, Ali argues, "on account of the differences of the sexes in nature, temperaments, and social life, a greater amount of privacy is

---

22. Ali, *The Holy Quran: Text, Translation and Commentary*, p.1124.

required for women than for men, especially in the matter of dress and
the uncovering of the bosom."[23] While giving instructions to women, the
Quran does not say that they have to cover their faces and hands.

> And say to the believing women that they should lower their
> gaze and guard their modesty; that they should not display their
> beauty and ornaments except what (must ordinarily) appear
> thereof; that they should draw their veils over their bosoms and
> not display their beauty except to their husbands, their fathers,
> their husbands' fathers, their sons, their husbands' sons. (Sura
> 24:31).

Some Muslim scholars argue that the word "beauty" *(zinat)* in this
context refers to the jewellery women wear. Others argue it refers to the
natural beauty of the body. The two occurrences of the word "beauty"
are followed by an exception. Hence the Muslim community is divided
as some say that only ostentatious display of ornaments and jewellery is
forbidden, and others insist that the display of any beautiful part of a
woman (except hands and feet), particularly bosom, is forbidden and they
must cover themselves totally before the eyes of outsiders.

The habit of wearing the veil became common among the city-
dwelling upper-class women. It was not strictly practiced in rural centres
because of rare contact with strangers and for practical reasons as the
veil would interfere with their physical work. The Quran exempts elderly
women "who are past child-bearing" from wearing the veil (Sura 24:60).
Women, in general, are forbidden to make any eye contact with strangers;
and even if they have to speak to, give or receive anything from strangers,
it must be done from behind a curtain.

Since the wearing of veil prevents strangers from seeing the physical
beauty of women, marriages are usually arranged by elder members of
the families. The boys and girls express the kind of woman or man they
would like to marry to their parents and they "search" for them through
friends and relatives or through marriage brokers. This kind of "arranged
marriages" are common in other religious communities as well in the
East.

Young girls are taught and prepared right from their childhood to
be submissive to their fathers and husbands. After marriage, the bride is

---

23. Ali, *The Holy Quran: Text, Translation and Commentary*, p.904.

instructed to stay in her husband's home and take care of his affairs. As the girls are advised to believe that there is not much life left without their husbands, wives have come to accept their life within their husbands' home and community. Numerous songs, poems, and stories have been written about the plight of these young brides.[24]

Brides being married to strangers and going to a new and unfamiliar surrounding is not uncommon even today. The practice of parents picking partners for their children is common among Hindus, Christians, and Muslims in many parts of South Asia. The practice of giving dowry to the bridegroom is common among some Hindu and Christian communities. Although some governments and communities have made the practice illegal (Indian government has outlawed it), it is still being practiced by some communities in South-East Asia.

A married woman is expected to fulfill her assigned roles in a new surrounding. She is considered a part of a larger family, her husband's. One of the roles she is expected to fulfill is to bear children. Failure to do so will lead her husband to look for a second wife. The Quran affirms that wives and children are the comfort of man's eyes. He must pray for them for "he will be rewarded with the highest place in heaven" (Sura 25:74-75).

Adultery and Polygamy

Adultery and prostitution are strictly prohibited by the Quran and Sunna. Sleeping with one's own slaves is not considered adultery; sleeping with slaves of another man or with a woman who is not his wife is punishable by law. The Quran spells out the punishment: "The woman and the man guilty of adultery or fornication, - flog each of them with a hundred stripes: let not compassion move you in their case, in a matter prescribed by God and the Last Day: and let a party of the believers witness their punishment" (Sura 24:2). Fornication here, according to Ali, "implies that both parties are unmarried."[25].

The charge of adultery, which the Quran calls *zina*, should be supported by four eye-witnesses. Failure to do so will be considered slander and the slandered will be punished with eighty stripes and "be deprived of the citizen's right of giving evidence in all matters all his

---

24. See H. Granquist, *Marriage Conditions in a Palestinian Village*, Vols 1 &2, (Helsingfors: Finland 1931, 1935), pp. 143ff.

25. Ali, *The Quran: Text, Translation and Commentary*, p.896.

life, unless he repents and reforms, in which case he can be readmitted to be a competent witness."[26] In the case of a husband or wife bringing charge of adultery against each other while there is no outside witness available, the Quran says, "Their solitary evidence (can be received) if they bear witness four times (with an oath) by God that they are solely telling the truth; and the fifth (oath) (should be) that they solely invoke the curse of God on themselves if they tell a lie" (Sura 24:6-7). If the accused spouse denies the charge and bears witness by likewise vowing four times, both of them must call on God and his wrath upon the liar (Sura 24:8). The swearing is followed by the dissolution of marriage as they cannot live together harmoniously in marriage any longer.

False charges of adultery had been brought against Aisha also, the Prophet's favourite wife. Traditions say Aisha lost her necklace when the Muslim army and the Prophet's family were returning from the mission to the Banu Mustaliq. While she went out to search alone she was lost. On the next day she returned to the camp with a young man's help. Some of her rivals brought charges against her which divided the prophet's family and caused his temporary separation from his wife. Ali narrates:

> When the march was ordered (from Banu Mustaliq), Hadhrat Aisha was not in her tent, having gone to search for a valuable necklace she had dropped. As her litter was veiled, it was not noticed that she was not in it, until the army reached the next halt. Meanwhile, finding the camp had gone, she sat down to rest, hoping that someone would come back to fetch her when her absence was noticed. It was night and she fell asleep. Next morning she was found by Safwan, a Muhajir, who had been left behind at the camp, expressly to pick up anything inadvertently left behind. He put her on his camel and brought her, leading the camel on foot. This gave occasion to the enemies to raise a malicious scandal. The ring leader among them was the chief of the Medina Hypocrites, 'Abdullah ibn Ubai.[27]

After the incident Aisha fell sick and returned to be with her parents. Mohammed stayed away from her for a whole month. Soon, he was given a revelation about the truth and the matter was cleared.

---

26. Ibid., p.897, Sura: 24:4-5.

27. Ibid., p.898.

Mohammed was deeply disturbed about the incident and thanked God for saving him from evil consequences in this life and the next (See Sura 24;11-20). The Hadith gives a detailed account of Aisha's mortal agony and divine intervention.

> Narrated Aisha: By Allah I never thought that Allah would reveal Divine inspiration in my case, as I considered myself too inferior to be talked of in the Holy Quran. I had hoped that Allah's Apostle might have a dream in which Allah would prove my innocence. By Allah, Allah's Apostle had not got up and nobody had left the house before the Divine Inspiration came to Allah's Apostle. So there overtook him the same state which used to overtake him, (which he used to have on being inspired divinely). He was sweating so much so that the drops of the sweat were dropping like pearls though it was a (freezing) wintry day. When that state of Allah's Apostle was over, he was smiling and the first word he said was "Aisha! Thank Allah, for Allah has declared your innocence." My mother told me to go to Allah's Apostle. I replied, "By Allah, I will not go to him and will not thank but Allah" So Allah revealed: *"Verily! They who spread the slander are a gang among you..."* (Sura 24:11) (3:510-11; 48.15.829).

During jahiliyya, polygamous and polyandrous marriages were practiced in Mecca and Medina. What zina meant to those men and women is not apparent. In the early days of Islam, merchant class men and free women practiced zina openly.[28] Ahmed argues, zina probably referred to during Mohammed's time temporary (nikah) and some other forms of marriages practiced by men and women. As Islam could not transform the entire Arab society and its cultural practices, except in its strict teachings about God, it selectively approved some dominant conventions practiced by the Arabs while outlawing others. Male ownership of property, women, and practice of polygamy were assimilated while women were restricted and controlled in their sexuality and relegated to be under men.

Death of the Prophet and the Last Days of Aisha

Mohammed died in June 632 at Aisha's house when she was eighteen years old. Abu Bakr, who became Mohammed's successor, said he should be buried under the floor of the place where he died. After two

---

28. Ahmed, *Women and Gender In Islam*, pp.44-45.

years, Bakr died and he was buried right next to Mohammed. Caliph Umar became the next successor, and when he died he was buried next to Abù Bakr, much to the displeasure of Aisha. As Umar's daughter Zeinab, one of Mohammed's wives, was a constant pain to Aisha, Aisha was not too happy to have him buried in her room. Soon after that Aisha built a partition wall between her dwelling place and others, and lived the rest of her life in that small place of abode until she died at the age of 64.

CHAPTER XVI
Missiological Misunderstanding Between Christianity and Islam

Christians and Muslims see each other as unequal partners and one considers the other inferior in having divine revelation. Historically, Muslims judged Christians as "infidels" and Christians rated Muslims as "pagans" and "heretics". These two religious groups have deep, fundamental differences in revelation, belief, and redemption. Muslims believe in a Sovereign God who demands an unconditional obedience to his will and a complete turning away from idolatry. Christians emphasize on a God who mercifully has come in the form of a human being to redeem and reconcile the marred humanity with their Creator. For Muslims the revealed word is the Quran and for Christians the revealed Word is Jesus Christ. Christianity declares that it alone possesses the ultimate divine revelation in the person of Jesus Christ which Islam denies categorically. Islam affirms that it alone possesses the absolute divine truth as manifested in the form of the Quran which Christianity repudiates emphatically.

Theologically, Christians and Muslims often use the same words which, however, bear two distinctly separate meanings. When the leaders of these two religious groups come together with an earnest desire to understand each other's religious convictions, the basic differences of their faiths often keep them apart from arriving at an accord on a deeper level. In order to be faithful to their religious conviction, they either defy or disavow the other's faith.

Politically, Muslims accuse Christians of blocking the progress and development of Islamic civilization. The crusades of the Middle Ages are still considered the "Christian West's" systematic destruction of the Islamic Middle East's golden period. The Western colonialism during the nineteenth and early twentieth centuries is not only denounced of destabilizing the political sovereignty of the Ottoman Empire but also condemned of destroying the oneness and unity among the Arab nations. The anger and suspicion against the "Christian West" is not totally absent among some Muslims even today.

Modern European and North American countries are very much suspected of interfering with Arab religious and economic stability. The influence of Western civilization around the world, especially in the Middle East, is sometimes taken as Western Christians' covert plot against Muslims and their way of life. At times, the political, economic, and militaristic policies of the traditionally Christian countries of the West are confused with Christian faith itself.

Often Christians in the West consider Islam as a religion of violence and judge Muslims as an inassimilable religious community whose main goal in religious life is to disrupt the Western economic, political, and religious stability. Lack of knowledge of Arabic language and deep distrust of Islam as a faith and its religio-political culture contribute much to the Western Christians' ignorance of the Islamic way of life and its religious heritage. By the same token, the Muslims could not understand why Christians refuse to respect Mohammed as a prophet as much as Muslims respect Jesus as a prophet of God.

From the very beginning, Byzantine theologians viewed Islam as a Christian heresy. The Western Church charged Mohammed as an impostor who had falsely claimed divine inspiration for his recitations. In his book, *Religion in the Medieval West*, Bernard Hamilton narrates in detail, the ways in which Pope Innocent X (1243-54) curbed Muslims from preaching Islam in Christian nations as he was deeply convinced Islam was nothing but a Christian heresy. Muslim leaders held similar opinion about the Christian preachers in the Middle East. Hamilton writes:

> In both Islamic and Christian states apostasy was a capital offence, yet there were men in both cultures who were attracted to the other religion and who changed their faith. Like political defection in our own age, this involved a complete cultural break, for the only way of achieving one's aim was to go to live in the land of one's adopted faith. The Moorish traveller Ibn Jubayr met a merchant from the Meghrib, when he visited Acre in 1184, who had not only become a Christian, but also a monk, "thereby hastening for himself the pains of hell." But Christians also fled to Islamic territory and became Muslims, in sufficiently large numbers for thirteenth century popes to find

it necessary to arrange for those who decided that they had made a mistake to be received back into the Catholic Church. This presupposes that there were many more who had no wish to return.[1]

Christian leaders traditionally interpreted ancient philosophies, major world religions, and pre-Christian religious beliefs as a prelude to the Good News and *preparatio evangelica* (preparation for evangelism). When Islam came as a post-Christian religion and stood on the principles of Judeo-Christian traditions, Christian leaders often took Islam as a religious confrontation and rejected it as Christian heresy and "religious hodge-podge." Mohammed and the Quran were criticized for their misrepresentation of the Judeo-Christian faith, universal sin, human depravity, and the need for God's grace and divine redemption. The Muslim practice of the Five Pillars and other obligatory practices was accused of legalism and a burdensome demand which Islam inflicted upon God's children. Mohammed and Islam were associated with the deceptions of Antichrist as referred to in the book of Revelation. Since Islam denies the very foundation of Christianity, particularly the Christ event (the incarnation, crucifixion, resurrection, and the Trinity), Islamic claim as a post-Christian religion was absolutely disregarded. Christians often cite Mohammed's lifestyle, his mode of revelation, and the Quran's strong dependence upon Jewish and Christian scriptures as evidences to discredit Islam as a non-original religion.

Doctrinally, Islam asserts that a Muslim lives out his/her faith only by serving the One God and any association of a human being or an earthly creature with Godhead would break the first of the Ten Commandments. This central tenet of Islam denies the Christological teachings of the Christian Scriptures. Thus, the doctrine of Jesus, which is one of the common points of contact between the two faiths, has resulted in a conflicting claim and a dividing point. Affirming the Oneness of God and the refusal to accept Jesus' divinity, Maulana Abu Ala Maududi says:

> There is a Supreme Being, over and above all that our unwary eyes see in the universe, who possesses the Divine Attributes, who is the Will behind all phenomenon, the Creator of this grand universe, the Controller of its supreme law, the governor of its serene rhythm, the Administrator of all its workings. He

---

1. Bernard Hamilton, *Religion in the Medieval West*, (Great Britain: Edward Arnold Publishers Ltd., 1986), pp.149-150.

is *Allah*, the Lord of the universe and has none as associate in his Divinity.[2]

Yusuf Ali, standing on the tradition of Maududi, claims that each individual human being is responsible for his/her own sins. While commenting on Sura 6.164, Ali says, "We are fully responsible for our acts ourselves: We cannot transfer the consequences to someone else. Nor can anyone vicariously atone for our sins."[3]

Missiologically, the followers of these two religions often find each other in a collision course. The two religions call upon the believers to witness their faith in their God. Christians validate their belief in God with the teachings of the Bible, revelation in Jesus Christ, Creeds of the Church, traditions of the believers, and their personal spiritual experience with the inner working of the Holy Spirit. Muslims establish their faith on the teachings of the Quran, their unconditional submission to Allah's will, their obligatory practices to witness Allah's sovereignty over the entire world. Consequently, the two missionary religions compete for converts in the global arena.

Mission to the People of Other Faiths

The uniqueness of Jesus Christ and the universal meaning of his words, his deeds, his life, death, and resurrection constitute God's final revelation and serve as the foundation of the Christian faith. The person of Jesus Christ and his work constitute the heart and core of Christian tradition. Christian faith is the religion of a person, the Christ, not a "religion of the book" as Islam is.

The affirmation of Christian faith that Christ died for all that salvation is offered to every human being, and that it comes through the person of Jesus Christ is summarized by Hans Kung:

> The unconditionally reliable reality, to which men and women can hold fast for all time and eternity, is not the Bible texts and not the Fathers of the Church's magisterium, but God himself, as he spoke for believers through Jesus Christ. The texts of the Bible, the sayings of the Fathers and church authorities mean to be—with varying degrees of importance— no more and no less than an expression of this belief.[4]

---

2. Maududi, *Towards Understanding Islam*, p.97.

3. Ali, *The Holy Quran: Text, Translation and Commentary*, p.339.

4. Quoted in Nel Noddings, *Educating for Intelligent Belief or Unbelief*, (New York: Teachers College, 1993), p.86.

Therefore, the purpose of Church's mission is not an attempt to bring all religions together. Its task is not to "civilize" or "modernize" people who live in other parts of the world. The goal of Christian mission is not merely to foster an understanding between Christians and adherents of other faiths. The aim of Christian mission is not just to create a calm atmosphere or global peace and human reconciliation. The end of Christian mission is not in the mere alleviation of human suffering. The function and intent of Christian mission is to present Jesus Christ as Lord and Saviour of the world through words and deeds. Any other reason for engaging in Christian mission will de-throne Jesus Christ, de-centre the Gospel, and displace the gift of salvation offered through God's Son; it will eventually dislodge the very foundation of Christian faith.

To say Jesus of Nazareth is God is a biblical and eternally valid truth. The uncompromising teaching of the Christian Scriptures is that the God of the universe has identified himself with the person of Jesus Christ who identified himself with God. The One who invited people to believe in the eternal God became himself the content of faith. The one who proclaimed the message of the kingdom of God became himself the personification of the message. Any change in this biblical truth will entail misrepresentation of the Christian faith.

The Message of Salvation

In the Bible, salvation is a term used generally to describe the divine action of delivering humankind from evil and restoring it to a state of peace and prosperity. To the first Christians it meant what it had always meant in the Israelite traditions: security and prosperity in this life, bestowed by YHWH, the sole source of protection. It comprised the whole of human beings' nature and their contemporary existence. Primarily, it was a deliverance from any form of national calamities. Positively, salvation involved an exercise of strength that gained victory over hostile powers, and above all liberation from death and spiritual evil.

Salvation is the object of God's free and loving initiative, a hidden plan prepared for the benefit of human beings from all eternity and revealed in time. The revelation of this plan of salvation could only have been a progressive one. The progressive revelation of salvation takes place through history and in history. The series of events which make up human history, including all the happenings that are independent of human will, reflect and reveal to human beings the salvific plan of God

Thus salvation is revealed to human beings not only through the word of God, who speaks to human beings and tells them about some future event, but also through its own realization in history. Salvation is both revealed and realized in history, and for this reason human history is salvation history.

It is traditionally believed that there is no salvation outside the church because the church manifests and makes present the salvation of Christ through the proclamation of the gospel and the administration of the sacraments. Cyprian, a third-century bishop, taught *extra ecclesiam nulla salus* (outside the Church there is no salvation). Cyprian's teaching was affirmed at Lateran Council in 1215 A.D., and later at the Council of Florence in 1442 A.D. In 1854, Pope Pius IX had lamented over the error of teaching that there might be hope for eternal salvation for those not in any way part of the Catholic Church.[5]

Having reiterated the traditional Catholic exclusivism, however, Pius IX also followed with the classical exception, i.e., invincible ignorance of the true religion:

> That no one can be saved outside the apostolic Roman Church, that the Church is the only ark of salvation, and that whoever does not enter it will perish in the flood. Yet, on the other hand, it must likewise be held as certain that those who are in ignorance of the true religion, if this ignorance is invincible, are not subject to any guilt in this matter before the eyes of the Lord.[6]

This position was articulated again by the Papacy in 1949:

> The infallible dictum which teaches us that outside the Church there is no salvation, is among the truths that the Church has always taught and will always teach... The Saviour did not make it merely a necessity of precept for all nations to enter the Church. He also established the Church as a means of salvation without which no one can enter the Kingdom of glory. To gain eternal salvation it is not always required that a person be incorporated in reality... as a member of the Church, but it is required that he belongs to it at least in desire and longing...

---

5. J. Neuner, S.J. & J. Dupuis, S.J. *The Christian Faith in the Doctrinal Documents of the Catholic Church*, (Bombay: Catholic Book Publs., 1972). p.268.

6. Neuner & Dupuis, *The Christian Faith*, p.268.

> When a man is invincibly ignorant, God also accepts an implicit
> desire, so called because it is contained in the good disposition
> of soul by which a man wants his will to be conformed to God's
> will.[7]

But how does the church exercise its salvific role to those who live outside the fold of the Christian Church? What are the dimensions of the Church and how does Christ's salvific power operate in this world? Do other faiths have truth and revelation which Christians could recognize and employ for sharing the love of God? There is no easy answer to these questions.

Some Eastern Christian theologians challenge the Western systematic theologians for accepting and incorporating the Greco-Roman philosophies into the Christian thought and refusing to accept the validity of the Buddhist, Hindu or Islamic philosophies. Those Eastern theologians hold that when the Christian faith was a minority faith in the early days of Christianity, Christians took advantage of the surrounding dominant cultural and intellectual atmosphere of ancient Greece and Rome in communicating the Gospel. If early Christians could incorporate and utilize the existing revelations in communicating the Gospel, minority Asian Christians could also take advantage of the surrounding dominant religious faiths and present the good news of Jesus Christ.

Christianity thrived during the second and third centuries as it was able to communicate the message through the existing philosophical thoughts and ideas. The Hellenization of the ancient world, initiated by Alexander the Great three and a half centuries before Christianity came on the scene, had impacted Hebrew culture and paved way for the philosophical formation of Christianity.

After Alexander's conquest of the Middle East and Asia Minor during the fourth century BCE., a simplified form of Greek called *koine* became a common language for business and administration throughout the subdued land. Alexandria, the city which the Greeks built on the Egyptian coast, housed a great library and the city was known for its academic culture. Alexandria, which was often referred to as a "university town", later on became one of the five important centres of the Christian Church in the fourth and fifth centuries. The synagogue of Alexandria was significantly important for the development of Jewish and Christian

---

7. Neuner & Dupuis, *The Christian Faith*, p.236.

religious and philosophical thought. As the Jews in Alexandria could not understand the Hebrew Bible, it was translated into Greek. Jews in Jerusalem, the Galilean city of Sepphorus also exchanged Greek texts with Alexandrian Jews. Reading and speaking Greek became so common that multicultural trading cities often became the centres of transmitting philosophical, political, and religious thoughts between Hebrew scholarship and Greek scholarship. Soon Greek language and culture became such influencing forces that some Romans wanted to become Greek.

After Christ, the Christian Scriptures were written in the Greek language. Recent archaeological discoveries show that during Jesus' time the business correspondences and records were maintained in Greek.[8] In his book, *Bandits, Prophets, and Messiahs*, Richard A. Horsley reassembles the cultural, social, and intellectual history of the early Christian period:

> The Hellenistic Empires of Alexander's successors brought a systematic program of increased economic exploitation and a general policy of cultural imperialism that threatened the Jews' traditional ways of life. The ruling priestly elite, who maintained their privileged social position, attracted by the glories of Hellenistic civilization, began to compromise themselves culturally, religiously, and politically... Alexander and his successors founded numerous Hellenistic cities in Palestine, with the Greek-speaking citizens and their local gentry in control of the indigenous population, who had no citizenship rights in the cities proper.[9]

The application of philosophical thoughts of other religions, especially the Greeks, can be found in the works of Gnostics, Justin Martyr (100-165 CE), Clement of Alexandria (15-219 CE), Origen (185-255 CE), Augustine (354-430 CE). In the fourth century, Eusebius referred to the philosophical wisdom of other religions as *preparatio evangelica* as it served as a philosophical foundation for the Christian belief. The early church leaders called these pre-Christian philosophies and pre-Christian thoughts as the *logos spermatikos* (seminal divine word).

---

8. For detailed information see David E. Aune, *The New Testament in its Literary Environment*, (Philadelphia: Westminster Press, 1987).

9. Richard A. Horsley, *Bandits, Prophets, and Messiahs: Popular Movements at the Time of Jesus*, (San Francisco: Harper and Row, 1985), pp.10,11.

Hans Kung claims that the divine logos was active everywhere from the beginning, even in the second and third centuries when Christian theology was being developed. Kung inquires, "if the pagans Plato, Aristotle, and Ploginus, or later - for others even Marx and Freud could be 'pedagogues' leading men to Christ, why not also the philosophers and religious thinkers of other nations?"[10] Kung professes that the universalist view of the Christian Scriptures was soon undermined by the leaders of the Church Councils for political, economic, and military purposes which eventually held the Christian Church a captive of Western Christians.[11]

Respect for pre-Christian writers like Plato and Aristotle can also be found in the works of medieval and late medieval writers like Aquinas (1225-1274 CE), Bonaventure (1221-1274), Ramon Lull (1232-1316), Nicholas Cusa (1401-1464), Pico delta Mirandola (1464-1494) and Augustino Steuco (1497-1548). The end of Western colonialism opened people to look at each other's religion with a new pair of eyes and enabled them to acknowledge the positive values and lofty ethical and moral principles found in other religions too. Such a new outlook of the religions of the world made a tremendous impact on Protestant and Roman Catholic mission conferences in recent years.

The Christian Scriptures speak in many places of the universality of truth. Paul declared to the religious Athenians that, "God never left himself without witness" (Acts 14:17). The epistle to the Hebrews says that God had spoken to men and women at sundry times and in sundry ways; in the fullness of time, God spoke through his Son Jesus Christ. Does that mean no more divine revelation be given to humanity, especially through other faiths? Christian denominations and mission societies are divided and polarized on account of these missiological and theological concerns. An agreement has not been reached yet.

The Message of the International Missionary Conference
The first major World Missionary Conference held in Edinburgh in 1910 grew out of the nineteenth century European missionary movement, spiritual revival, and Student Volunteer Movement for Foreign Missions. The Conference was organized by the International Missionary Council

---

10. Hans Kung, *On Being a Christian*, trans. Edward Quinn (Doubleday: New York, 1968), p.113.

11. Ibid., p.113.

with an intention to take the Gospel in to "all the world." By "all the world", the organizers had actually in mind the image of the "non-European" and "non-Christian" world. The Conference recognized the names of the countries that were open and responsive to the Gospel.

The Conference encouraged its delegates to approach the adherents of other religions and their faith in other gods "with sympathetic attitude." With regard to the religious communities in India, the Conference said, "more harm has been done in India than in any other country by missionaries who have lacked the wisdom to appreciate the nobler side of a religion which they have labored so indefatigably to supplant."[12] However, the Conference went on to say that the people of other faiths, especially the Hindus, must be converted and brought into the church as the life and message of Christ will appeal to the Hindus in India.

The Conference did not debate on the theology of mission. It was just assumed. Christianity was considered the absolute and the fulfillment of all religions. Hence, the Conference affirmed that the Gospel must be preached to people everywhere and then be brought into Christ's Church. The Conference, therefore, encouraged the particicpants to convert the world to Christ.

The fundamental assumption of the gathering in Edinburgh in 1910 was that other religions were non-salvific and there was no salvation outside the Christian church. The participants were reminded that the Church of Christ was an evangelistic church and all the activities of the church, therefore, should be agents of the conversion of non-Christians. The nobler elements found in other faiths are evidences of the working of the Holy Spirit. However, only Jesus Christ can satisfy the longings of the human soul. The nobler elements found in other faiths should be used as points of contact in leading them to Christ.

But the Jerusalem mission conference held in 1928 had an entirely different agenda. While Edinburgh 1910 had been governed by the subject of evangelization of the world, Jerusalem was pre-occupied with theology. When the Christian message was presented at the Jerusalem conference there were two opposing viewpoints: one maintained the uniqueness and universality of the Gospel which demanded conversion of the people of other faiths, and the other upheld Christianity as

---

12. Vol.4; p.171.

fulfillment of all religions by stressing values in them and insisting conversion was not necessary. Arthur P. Johnson concluded the outcome of the Conference this way:

> ...the concept of salvation, evangelism, and conversion were changed at Jerusalem. The Jerusalem report stated its understanding of salvation: Christianity is concerned primarily with salvation. Religion is the attachment and expression of salvation. To be saved is to be delivered from all that mutilates, or fetters, or hinders the free growth of personality. It is to achieve wholeness, so that no part of man is wasted and all the human material in him gets a chance of expression and utilization. Salvation means fullness of life, well-being, strength, power, blessedness, happiness, righteousness, joy and peace. It is the complete penetration of the human by the divine.[13]

Jerusalem was the first Church mission conference to challenge the traditional Christian concepts of salvation, evangelism, and conversion. Each was restated with an attempt to understand non-Christian faiths. Conservative Christian scholars were distressed by the new course of direction the conference had taken and lamented that the concept of evangelism had become a process of religious educational improvement rather than confronting people with Jesus Christ. Theology of service had begun to displace the theology of conversion as a mission motivation.

One of the outspoken opponents of conservative theological doctrine was William Hocking, an American Professor in Philosophy from Harvard University. He asserted that the adherents of other religious faiths were not eternally lost and avowed "Christianity has many doctrines in common with other religions, and yet no other religion has the same group of doctrines."[14]

Hendrik Kraemer, a Dutch missionary to Indonesia, differed from William Hocking and declared that other religions "do not have the greatest gift of Christ—the forgiveness of sins", and hence Christian mission should be carried out with compassionate understanding.[15] Ten years after Tambaram Conference, held in 1938 Kraemer wrote:

---

13. Arthur P. Johnston, *World Evangelization and the Word of God,* (Minnesota: Bethany Fellowship, 1974), p.152.

14. William E. Hocking, *Rethinking Missions: A Layman's Inquiry After One Hundred Years* (New York: Harper & Bros., 1932), p.49.

15. Hendrich Kraemer, *The Christian Message in a Non-Christian World,* p.129.

The right attitude of the Church, properly understood, is essentially a missionary one, the church being set by God in the world as ambassador of His reconciliation, which is the truth that outshines all truth and the grace that works faithful love.[16]

Kraemer asserted that in other faiths all truth is relative and the final truth as revealed in the person Jesus Christ is unattainable in them.. "In practice", Kraemer maintained, "this fundamental relativism behaves itself as a militant absolutism."[17] The Christian revelation is absolutely *sui generis*. Kraemer drew a sharp difference between God's act of revelation and all religious experiences, be it Christian or other faiths. Kraemer maintained that the tolerance which Eastern religions display is only a pseudo-tolerance. Kraemer went on to extol the virtues of Christianity and wrote that only the Christian faith presents a religion of love and freedom.

The next major ecumenical mission conference held in Tambaram, South India, in 1938 came up with a higher regard for the Bible, mostly due to the influence of conservative scholars such as Hendrich Kraemer, Karl Barth, and Emil Brunner.[18] The Tambaram conference, like the Edinburgh 1910, emphasized the Christian Church as the focus of evangelism and upheld the conversion of the adherents of other religions. The theological contribution of Tambaram was conservative in nature and sustained the evangelistic goal of Edinburgh 1910. It offered Jesus as the "Word made flesh" in whom God acted for the salvation of humankind. Tambaram's approach to people of other religion was one of respect, but still a call for conversion was resonated throughout the Conference. The need for evangelism and the task of conversion were made a missional goal. Tambaram urged that turning to Christ means a radical break from the bonds of one's religious past but not an evolutionary fulfillment.

The New Delhi mission conference held in 1963 was preoccupied with the merger of the International Missionary Council (IMC) with the World Council of Churches (WCC). The conference did not vary much from its general understanding of the people of the faiths. The conference

---

16. Ibid., pp.129-30.

17. Ibid., p.206.

18. Tambaram is a suburb of the city of Madras in South India. The Conference was held on the campus of Madras Christian College, Tambaram, and hence it is addressed in several missionary journals as Madras Conference 1938.

was not too explicit about salvific effects of the non-Christian religions. It only expressed its concern for, as well as awareness of, the spiritual plight of human beings without Christ.

The Message of the WCC Conference

Uppsala 1968 was an important conference after the merger of the International Missionary Council with the World Council of Churches which was established in Amsterdam in 1948. Uppsala radically differed from the IMC's concept of mission and argued that God has been active in the world. In Section II, "Renewal in Mission" the Conference affirms:

> Much of the language of the frontier-crossing concern of the IMC theology of integration was quitely set aside for a fresh world-oriented statement of the missionary mandate, with "humanization" in Jesus Christ as its theological keyword.[19]

Salvation history at Uppsala was not understood as the proclamation of the Gospel but as God's intervention in world events which turned world history into salvation history. Therefore, to be a Christian was to desire the new and to actively participate in change. Salvation was interpreted as something which occurred in the world and not in the church. The church only shares in that salvation. In the commentary on revolution the Conference proclaimed:

> The Christian participation in mission...involves participation in the struggle for a just society...The churches, through the centuries, have been notorious for their hesitance in coming to terms with the oppressors in the name of law and order. In the process they have lost their authority to proclaim the Gospel to large segments of the nation.[20]

This existential notion of Christian mission was a radical departure from the IMC's concept of mission and salvation. As for the people of other faiths, Uppsala emphasized that dialogue was an indispensable part of the approach of Christians to others.[21]

---

19. James A. Scherer, *That The Gospel May Be Sincerely Preached Throughout the World.* (Geneva: LWF Report 11/12, 1982), p.89.

20. Norman Goodall. ed. *The Uppsala Report, 1968: Official Report of the Fourth Assembly of the World Council of Churches, Uppsala, July 4-20, 1968.* (Geneva: W.C.C., 1968).

21. *The Uppsala Report*, 1978. p.29.

The definition of Salvation Today as given at the Fourth Assembly of the World Council of Churches held at Bangkok in 1973 was very different from the traditional understanding of salvation. Bangkok defined salvation in broad neutral terms and affirmed that God is at work within and without the boundaries of the Church. The report said, "We see God at work today both within the church and beyond the church toward the achievement of his purpose that justice might shine on every nation."[22] Section II of Bangkok gives a comprehensive understanding of the concept of salvation. It says:

> Through Christ men and women are liberated and empowered with all their energies and possibilities to participate in this Messianic work... The salvation which Christ brought, and in which we participate, offers a comprehensive wholeness in this divided life... It is salvation of the soul and the body, of the individual and society, humanity and 'the groaning creation' ...As evil works both in personal life and in exploitative social structures which humiliate humanity, so God's justice manifests itself both in the justification of the sinner and in social and political justice. As guilt is both individual and corporate so God's liberating power changes both persons and structures. We have to overcome the dichotomies in our thinking between soul and body, person and society, humanity and creation. Therefore, we see the struggle for economic justice, political freedom and cultural renewal as elements in the total liberation of the world through the mission of God. This liberation is finally fulfilled when 'death is swallowed up in victory' ...This comprehensive notion of salvation demands of the whole of the people of God a matching comprehensive approach to their participation in salvation.[23]

Conservative mission scholars were sorely displeased with the position taken by the World Council of Churches. John R.W. Stott, an evangelical scholar from England, said that Bangkok placed all kinds of salvation experience from Eastern religions to the Pentecostal experience on the same level. The uniqueness of Christ was not clearly presented.

---

22. *International Review of Missions*, April 1973.

23. *Bangkok Assembly 1973: Minutes and Report of the Assembly of the Commission on World Mission and Evangelism of the World Council of Churches, December 31, 1972 and January 9-12, 1973,* (Geneva: World Council of Churches, n.d.), pp.88-89.

The fifth assembly of the WCC, held at Nairobi in 1975, sought to build bridges toward other groups in relation to the missionary and evangelistic work. M.M. Thomas said that the debate between social and personal salvation was meaningless as our hope in the coming Kingdom of God in Jesus Christ "provides us with an incentive to participate in efforts to build a more human social order in perspective of the Kingdom of God."[24]

Thomas also said that the church is the sign and bearer of salvation in the world. To avoid polarization and to promote reconciliation with the evangelicals who had their first large, global mission conference in Lausanne in 1974, Nairobi set aside all controversial matters of the Christian faith in relation to non-Christian faiths and reassured the participants by proclaiming, "We boldly confess Christ alone as Savior and Lord. We confidently trust in the power of the Gospel... we (confess)... his name is above every name."[25]

In the succeeding mission conferences at Melbourne 1980 and Vancouver 1983, the issues of salvation and relation to other faiths were discussed and the WCC continued to take its bold stand.

International Congress on World Evangelization : Lausanne 1974

Contrary to Bangkok 1973, Lausanne took a firm stand on Christocentric concept of salvation, including the lostness of human beings and their need for redemption. Lausanne strongly believed in conversion and proclaimed that evangelism was not an option but an imperative.

The Lausanne conference affirmed that salvation was offered in Christ Jesus alone and people were lost apart from him and hence evangelism and conversion were important in missionary work. As for other religious faiths, the Conference said:

> We recognize that all men have some knowledge of God... but we deny that this can save... we also reject as derogatory to Christ and the gospel every kind of syncretism and dialogue

---

24. David E. Johnson, gen.ed., *Uppsala to Nairobi: 1968-75. Report of the Central Committee to the Fifth Assembly of the World Council of Churches*, (New York: Friendship Press/London: S.P.C.K., 1975), p.231.

25. David E. Johnson, *Uppsala to Nairobi*, p.390.

which implies that Christ speaks equally through all religions and ideologies.[26]

Lausanne placed proclamation and conversion at the centre of evangelistic activity as "all men [without Christ] are perishing because of sin." Lausanne conclusively separated itself from the WCC concept of mission to the people of other faiths.

Roman Catholic Conference - Pre-Vatican II

Historically, the Roman Catholic Church held that there is no salvation outside the Roman Catholic Church. People were incorporated into the church through baptism which was regarded as the only means of salvation. Classical Catholicism has always maintained that salvation is only in the Catholic Church. It has also left the door open for those outside the Church to be the recipients of grace through the baptism by desire or by martyrdom.

In 1950, the First Plenary Council of India made a significant statement about the non-Christian religions. Neuner's and Dupuis' comment that this is the first official Catholic document "offering a clearly positive approach to the spiritual values of the world religions"[27] an attitude to be further reflected in the Second Vatican Council. The Council stated:

> We reject the view so widely spread in our regions which holds that all religions are equal among themselves, and that, provided they are adhered to with sincerity, all are various ways to one and the same end, namely God and eternal salvation. We equally reject the syncretism according to which the ideal religion or the religion of the future is conceived as a sort of synthesis to be worked out by men from various religions that exist.[28]

Despite its exclusive theological stand, the Council affirmed the positive values found in other religions.

> We acknowledge that there is truth and goodness outside the Christian religion, for God has not left the nations without a witness to Himself, and the human soul is naturally drawn towards the one true God.[29]

---

26. *Lausanne Covenant*, 3.

27. Neuner & Dupuis, *The Christian Faith*, p.272.

28. Ibid., p.272.

29. Ibid.

The Council also spoke of the serious errors and inadequacies of all non-Christian religions. "The inadequacies of all non-Christian religions are principally derived from this, that, Christ being constituted the one Mediator between God and men, there is no salvation by any other name."[30] This openness toward other religions gave an unclouded opinion and further concise expression in Vatican II.

Vatican II

The Second Vatican Council was one of the most important mission conferences of the twentieth century for the Roman Catholic Church. Pope John said that the Church must open the doors and windows and let a fresh wind blow through the Vatican. It was time, he declared, for *Aggiornamento*, the Church must update itself and reach beyond its visible boundaries. Vatican II acknowledged the Orthodox and Protestant churches as the Church of God comprised of members who were baptized Christians.[31] The Council also recognized that non-Christians, who seek the unknown God genuinely, were related "in various ways to the People of God."[32]

Nostra Aetate paid tribute to "perception" and "profound religious sense" found in other religions and affirmed that "The Catholic Church rejects nothing which is true and holy in these religions."[33] The Council demonstrated an extremely sympathetic attitude in interpreting the sincerity and beliefs of the followers of other faiths when it stated, "Those also can attain to everlasting salvation who through no fault of their own do not know the Gospel of Christ or His Church, yet sincerely seek God, and moved by grace, strive by their deeds to do His will as it is known to them through the dictates of conscience."[34]

Vatican II acknowledged the monotheistic belief of Islam and stressed Christianity and Islam share common religious beliefs such as prayer, almsgiving, fasting, honour for Mary as the mother of Jesus.[35] The Council also acknowledged the "many quarrels and hostilities" that

---

30. Ibid.

31. *Lumen Gentium*, 16.

32. Ibid.

33. Abbot, *The Document of Vatican II*, p.662.

34. *Lumen Gentium*, 16.

35. *Lumen Gentium*, 16, 22; *Nostra Aetate*, 3.

came between the two religious groups and desired to ignore the past and work for mutual understanding. A call to foster "social justice, moral values, peace and freedom" was given to both Muslims and Christians.[36]

In its Dogmatic Constitution of the Church, the Council referred to all religious people, Muslims in particular, as a religious community which is clearly situated in the history of salvation. "The plan of salvation also includes those who acknowledge the Creator. In the first place among these there are the Muslims, who, professing to hold the faith of Abraham, along with us adore the One and merciful God, who on the last day will judge [human beings]."[37] Pope John XXIII at the Council encouraged Christians every where to join with people of other faiths to engage in the ministry of peace and mercy. Pope John said:

> Christian charity truly extends to all, without distinction of race, social condition, or religion. It looks for neither gain nor gratitude. For as God has loved us with a spontaneous love, so also the faithful should in their charity care for the human person himself...[by] taking part in the striving of those peoples who are waging war on famine, ignorance, and disease, and thereby struggling to better their way of life and to secure peace in the world.[38]

In spite of the Council's openness to other religious faiths, Vatican II continued to hold Christianity, especially Catholicism, as "the all-embracing means" of human redemption and "the perfection of the means of salvation."[39]

CONTEMPORARY DEBATE

The Pluralists

J. Peter Schineller compared and sumarized the relationship of Christ and his Church with other religious faiths under four major categories: (a) Ecclesiocentric universe, exclusive Christology; (b) Christocentric universe, inclusive Christology; (c) Theocentric universe, normative Christology; (d) Theocentric universe, non-normative Christology.[40]

---

36. Ibid.

37. *Lumen Gentium*, 16.

38. *Ad Gentes*, 12.

39. *Unitatis Redintegratio*, 3.

40. See J. Peter Schineller, "Christ and Church: A Spectrum on Views", *Theological Studies* 37, (1976), pp.545-66. Walter J. Burghardt and William G. Thompson, eds., *Why the Church?*, (New York: Paulist Press, 1977), pp.1-22.

However, in recent years, some theologians moved away from the fourfold grouping of theological opinion to a threefold division: Christocentric, Theocentric, and Ecclesiocentric. In order to make it theologically functional and missiologically applicable, the threefold division has been further grouped and renamed into Exclusivism, Pluralism, and Inclusivism. As this grouping enables us to better understand the current missiological debate, we would like to explore this particular theological model in this chapter.

For the last three decades, a few Christian theologians have questioned the validity of the traditional missiological practices of the mission societies, have challenged the veracity of the salvific claims of the Church, and have called for a radical rethinking in its missional approach to the people of other faiths. Some of those theologians demand the Church to give up its exclusive claims that people are being saved only in and through the Church or even through their faith in Jesus Christ alone. Those theologians argue that all religions and non-religions are equally valid, and all of them have revelation and redemption which will eventually lead to the One Creator God whom all people worship. Those theologians who advocate theocentric pluralism, in spite of their differing opinion in various respects, have been broadly termed as Christian pluralists.

These theologians reject the salvific and mediatory representation of Jesus Christ which the Christian Scriptures, especially, Pauline writings represent. The theologians argue that it is no longer defensible to affirm that universal salvation is made possible only by the person and work of Jesus Christ. They contend that neither the Church nor the person of Jesus Christ can be used as the norm in evaluating the salvific claims avowed by other faiths.

The basic assumption these theologians bring into the contemporary theocentric debate and about the salvific claims of other faiths is that Jesus Christ came into this world to make "a contribution to the religious storehouse of humanity"[41] and, hence, the Christian Church should not strictly hold on to the traditionalist view of the uniqueness and universality of Jesus Christ. Therefore, the pluralists call for a shift in a paradigm from christocentrism to theocentrism, from inclusivism to pluralism, and from exclusivism to universalism. Some of the leading proponents of this pluralist view are John Hick, Paul Knitter, Alan Race, Alastair Hunter, Rosemary Ruether, and Wilfred Cantwell Smith.

---

41. W.A. Visser't Hooft, *No Other Name*, (London: S.C.M., 1963), p.95.

The pluralist theologians state that God has chosen to reveal himself in various ways through the cultures, geographical locations, and linguistic expressions of people everywhere. One particular religion should not claim that it has the whole truth and assert that it alone possesses the ultimate revelation. All religions are equally salvific. Christianity is just one of the many revelations given to humanity. This pluralistic view has been clearly exemplified through the well-known and popular story, *The Blind Men and the Elephant* of the King of Banares who invited six blind men into his court to feel and explain how an elephant looked like. One got hold of the trunk and said the elephant was like a rope; one of the leg and said the elephant was like a tree; one of the ear and said the elephant was like a winnowing fan; one of the abdomen and said the elephant was like a wall; one of the tail and said the elephant was like a broomstick; and the last one of the tusk and said the elephant was like a spear.

The pluralist theologians tend to prove their theocentric principles with complete modern theological and philosophical arguments and state that all religious views are equal paths to the one divine reality which no one religion totally contains. Just as the six blind men at the court, the adherents of each religion possess and experience only a partial revelation of the whole truth. No individual or religion can fully comprehend the Ultimate.

Ernst Troelstch's earlier claims that Christianity is the European religion just as Hinduism or Buddhism is an Asian one has been reaffirmed by these modern theologians. They affirm that each religion is relative and intrinsically intertwined with its own culture, time, and people. All the religions of the world have truth, revelation, and God's unquestionable presence. No religion of the world should be seen as manifestations of human pride or demonic deception. W.C. Smith asked the Christians to enter into dialogue with adherents of other religions with deep respect and profound admiration. Smith wrote, "From now on any serious intellectual statement of the Christian faith must include, if it is to serve its purpose among men, some sort of doctrine of other religions. He explains the fact that the Milky Way is there by the doctrine of creation, but how do we explain that the Bhagwad Gita is there?"[42]

---

42. Wilfred Cantwell Smith, "The Christian in a Religiously Plural World", in John Hick and B. Hebblethwaite, *Christianity and Other Religions*, (Collins, 1980), p.100.

Paul Knitter, a Roman Catholic theologian, argues that one can have strong faith in all the special revelations and redemptive work God has done in Jesus Christ without compromising the revelation given to others. Knitter writes, "In boldly proclaiming that God has indeed been defined in Jesus, Christians will also humbly admit that God has not been confined to Jesus."[43] As the salvation of humanity is concerned, Knitter calls for the Christians to move from orthodoxy to orthopraxis, and develop a theology which provides option for the poor as salvific values.[44]

John Hick, an English theologian and a leading champion of the pluralist theory, is a serious proponent of this theory. He calls for a "Copernican" type of revolution in Christian theology and calls for the Christians to move from the Christocentric view of the world to theocentric view of humanity and universe. In science, the Copernican system replaced the age old Ptolemaic system which taught for centuries that the sun revolved around the earth. Galileo and Copernicus challenged the belief and scientifically proved that the earth actually revolved around the sun. Hick argues that all religions, including Christianity, revolve around God, not the person of Jesus Christ. The preaching of the death of Christ on the cross as the door to eternal life is parochial and it presents God as a cruel blood thirsty tribal God of the West whom the West is thrusting upon the people all over the world. The Christocentric belief and teaching of salvation through the atonement of Christ on the cross must be challenged.

Other religions, Hick asserts, are centred around God not around Christianity. The Western Christians have falsely believed and fostered for centuries that all religions are centred around Christ and his teachings. A radical shift in paradigm, from Christocentric to theocentric model, not only necessitates the desertion of any superior claim Christianity imposes upon other faiths but also any lofty claims Christians make about Jesus Christ over other religions and their God. By calling for revolutionary change in paradigm, Hick rejects all inclusive Christology and contemporary missiological epistemology as useless human invention and willful, imperialistic imposition upon adherents of other faiths.

---

43. Paul Knitter, *No Other Name? A Critical Survey of Chritian Attitudes Toward the World Religions*, (New York: Orbis Books, 1985), pp.203-204.

44. See Paul Knitter, "Toward a Liberation Theology of Religions", *The Myth of Christian Uniqueness*, eds John Hick and Paul Knitter, (New York: Orbis Books, 1988), pp.178-200.

Hick continues to maintain that Jesus is just one of the many forms of divine revelation and he is certainly not the ultimate revelation of God given to humanity as Christians claim him to be. He warrants no one can conclusively reveal the ultimate reality of God. Hick, therefore, charges Christians of being parochial and having limited God's salvation only to a selected few. Hick emphatically denies that the loving God would seek to save only a small minority and make provision for them to receive God's salvation.[45] All revelations whether it was given to humanity in the form of YHWH, Krishna, Paramatman, Jesus, or Allah, according to Hick, "are all images of the divine, each expressing some aspect or range of aspects and yet none by itself fully and exhaustively corresponding to the infinite nature of ultimate reality."[46]

The fundamental weakness of pluralist theory, particularly Hick's in calling for a "Copernican" revolution in Christian theological thinking is the binary division the pluralist theory places upon the Christian concept of God. The pluralist theory divides the Christian understanding of God into two separate entities: God and Christ. The Christian Scriptures inform that God in Jesus Christ has totally revealed himself, and God and Jesus are one and the same. What Jesus brought into this world was not a mere gnostic understanding of the Divine Being but the absolute revelation of God himself by his own life, death and resurrection on the cross. By doing so, humanity was endowed with the gift of salvation which the Christian Scriptures call the Good News.

The biblical concept of God becoming a human being in Jesus Christ has been well-summarized by Edward Schillebeekx when he says: "Christ is God in a human way, and a human in a divine way."[47] Hick pejoratively calls this Christian message of salvation a mere "dogma". Gavin D'Costa, a Roman Catholic theologian from India, says Hick's either/or theory represents a rigid and self-contradictory position. His model of God is based on a monotheistic ultimate reality which not all world religions observe and nourish.

The second weakness of this pluralist theory is that it ignores the relevance of the cross of Christ through which God has communicated

---

45. John Hick, *God and the Universe of Faiths*, (London, 1977), p.122.

46. Ibid., p.140.

47. Edward Schillebeekx, *Jesus: An Experiment in Christology*, (New York: Crossroad, 1979), pp.626-69. See also *Christ: Sacrament of the Encounter with God*, (London: Sheed and Ward, 1963), pp.32-38.

to the people of this world. Jesus himself said, "The Son of Man must suffer." Anselm said, *nondum considerasti quanti ponderis sit peccatum*. If other religions have equal, if not superior, revelation, why would a God choose to send his own Son to die on the cross? Pluralist theory defeats the salvific and atoning purpose of the Christian faith won through the cross and resurrection. Any theoretical affirmation which says Christ's redemption is less than total, or any soteriological declaration which points out Christ's death on the cross is deficient, or any ethereal testimony which fosters the theological notion that humanity can be brought to God without the mediation of Christ stays clear contrast to the central teachings of the Christian Scriptures. By being open to the people of other faiths, these pluralist theologians undermine the very foundation of Christian faith and foil the unified witness of the Christian Scripture. Consequently, the pluralist theory strongly discourages Christian Church faith from engaging in mission evangelism and conversion of the adherents of other faiths.

The third weakness of this theory is that it ignores the serious problems each religion brings into the global theological town hall with conflicting claims on truth. For instance, the Christian doctrine is founded on the historic event of the death and resurrection of Christ and the coming of the Holy Spirit after his ascension into heaven. Islam denies this essential doctrine of Christianity and states that the coming of Mohammed was foretold by Jesus himself, which in turn, is denied by Christianity. Hinduism fosters the idea of reincarnation and the non-dualistic notion of God by stating that Atman is Brahman, which is repudiated by Christianity and Islam. Unfortunately, the pluralist theologians immensely overlook these major theological differences among religions.

Finally, in their burning zeal to bring harmony and unity among the religious people everywhere, the pluralist theologians are inclined to state that each religion brings in something unique and distinctive to meet the spiritual yearnings of humanity. Absolute submission to the sovereignty of God which Islam teaches its believers, undisputed belief in a moral universe which Confucianism talks about to its adherents, the earnest longing for spiritual detachment from the material world to find the truth which Buddhism outlines to its disciples as path to Nirvana, the eager expectation of a perfect ruler and a political messiah like King David whom the members of the Jewish community hope to receive, and the ultimate reign of a God-Human incarnated in the Person of Jesus Christ which Christianity teaches its followers are part of the whole truth about God and salvation. The pluralist theologians in their search for a common ground and desire for reconciled world religions isolate the values and merits other religions bring to their followers and fail to do justice to their essential nature. This theory not only removes the heart and the soul of missionary purpose of the Church but also fails to address the sufferings of Christians and the Church for their faith and witness in countries where Christians are a minority and under oppressive power of other religious political leaders.

In attempting to be open to the adherents of other religious traditions, the pluralist theologians have failed to recognize the lives and aspirations of millions of Christians who have left their former religious faiths to find shelter in Christ and experience the joy of the Holy Spirit under the shadow of the cross of Christ. If people are being saved in their faith, why would millions continue to join the Church of Jesus Christ every year in the non-Western world? The pluralist theory ignores to address the oppressive social, racial, cultural, caste, and economic burdens some religions impose upon their adherents in order to be faithful to their religious teachings. Eighty percent of Indian Christians are converts from Hinduism. The converts witness that they renounced Hinduism and embraced the Christian faith mainly because they found joy in Christ and experienced equality in the Christian community. Unlike Hinduism, Christianity did not impose any caste structure or hierarchical division among Christ's followers. Salvation in Christ for those Christian converts is not just an abstract intellectual assent but a psycho-somatic wholeness which enveloped the material and spiritual needs of a total human being.

The Inclusivists

The second group of theologians are the inclusivists who affirm the value of other religious faiths, other cultures and social orders, and recognize the involvement of God in the world and its people. The inclusivists insist that God's salvific activities as revealed through Jesus Christ is not limited to Christian faith alone. God has sent Jesus Christ to die for all people (II Cor. 5:14) and through his Spirit God is present in all cultures and he brings salvation to people everywhere, even to the ones who have not heard the Gospel. The inclusivists uphold Jesus Christ as God's absolute revelation, the means of salvation, and the universal Saviour. People of other faiths are saved by the grace of Christ which operates in and through other faith traditions, whether the followers of those traditions knew it nor not. Two of the leading proponents of this theory whom we could use for our study are Karl Rahner and Gavin D'Costa. Karl Rahner, a German Jesuit, said, "God desires the salvation of every one. And this salvation willed by God is the salvation won by Christ."[48]

Rahner upheld the view that God's grace is operative throughout human history and in all cultures, and so other religious faiths cannot fall outside of God's salvific purposes. Rahner, therefore, identified all those in other faiths who sincerely search for God's will for their lives as "anonymous Christians". Rahner maintained that the Trinitarian God's grace cannot be separated from Christ's absolute revelation. Therefore, he argued, whenever God's grace is mentioned, Christ's name is also included, not explicitly but implicitly, as he is part of the Trinity. Hence, all people experience the grace and salvation of Christ anonymously in the context of their own historical and religious reality. Rahner wrote:

> There is and has to be an anonymous and yet real relationship between the individual person and the concrete history of salvation, including Jesus Christ, in someone who has not yet had the whole, concrete, historical, explicit and reflexive experience in word and sacrament of this reality of salvation history. Such a person has this real and existential relationship merely implicitly in obedience to his orientation in grace towards the God of absolute, historical presence and self-communication. He exercises this obedience by accepting his own existence without reservation... Alongside this there is the fullness of Christianity which has become conscious of itself explicitly in faith and in hearing the word of the gospel, in the church's profession of faith, in sacrament, and in living an explicit Christian life which knows that is related to Jesus of Nazareth.[49]

Rahner's theory has been criticized as "staircase theory" of religion that still places Christianity over other faiths and that appropriates all the goodness and virtues found in other religions as Christian and relegates the world religions to a secondary position.

Gavin D'Costa, takes a middle position between the pluralists and the exclusivists, between Hick and Barth, and between the first and the

---

48. Karl Rahner, *Theological Investigations*, Vol.5; (London: Darton, Longman & Todd, 1976), p.122.

49. Karl Rahner, *Foundations of Christian Faith: An Introduction for the Idea of Christianity*, (New York: Herder, 1978), p.306.

second version of inclusivists theories. D'Costa says that two major doctrines of Christian faith which are axiomatic for the Church are the universal salvific will of God and the mediatory role of Jesus Christ operated through the Church. D'Costa writes:

> The form of inclusivism I have argued for tries to do full justice to [the] two most important Christian axioms: that salvation comes through God in Christ alone, and that God's salvific will is truly universal. By maintaining these two axioms in fruitful tension, the inclusivist paradigm can be characterized by an openness and commitment; an openness that seeks to explore the many and various ways in which God has spoken to all his children in the non-Christian religions and an openness that will lead to the positive fruits of this exploration, transforming, enriching and fulfilling Christianity, so much so that its future shape may be very different from the Church we know today.[50]

In refusing to believe that all non-Christian religions are invalid, he intends to go as far as risking his own Christian faith. He calls for a "committed openness" to all of human and religious history to be questioned, verified, and challenged for a deeper understanding of one's faith in God. In that process, he declares, one should be open to the "possibility of losing [his/her] faith altogether" and gain something new. He writes:

> "Real openness cannot but be vulnerable and precarious. But in that very opening it can also be receptive to riches and wealth from other religious and non-religious traditions. In fact, most of Christianity's history has been precisely this: an inculturation and incorporation of all that is worthwhile, true and good from cultures and religious traditions within which it has developed."[51]

D'Costa goes on to argue that his theory does not claim superiority over other religions, rather, it calls for committed openness "to the point where conversion cannot be precluded - hopefully on both sides."[52]

---

50. Gavin D'Costa, *Theology and Religious Pluralism: The Challenge of Other Religions*, (Oxford: Basil Blackwell, 1986), p.136.

51. Gavin D'Costa, *Dialogue and Alliance*, Vol.2, No.2, Summer 1988.

52. Ibid.

One other theological category which could be brought under the theory of inclusivism for the convenience of our study and the understanding of the ongoing theological debate about the concept of salvation is the theory of the presence of Christ. This theory affirms that the religions of the world possess salvific value by virtue of the presence of Christ and his salvific mystery operative in them. Jacques Dupuis aptly summarizes this theory's assumption in his book *Jesus Christ at the Encounter of World Religions*. According to Dupuis, the proponents of the theory of the presence of Christ believe that the adherents of other faiths are "saved by Christ not in spite of their religious allegiance and sincere practice of their tradition, but through that allegiance and practice. There is salvation without the gospel, then although none without Christ or apart from him. To be sure, the operative presence of the mystery of Jesus Christ in other religious traditions is concealed, and remains unknown by their members, but it is no less real for all that."[53]

An Indian born Roman Catholic theologian, Raymundo Panikkar has written extensively about the presence of Christ in Hinduism. In 1964, Swami Abhishiktananda, an Indian Roman Catholic theologian, called for an ecumenical relationship between Christianity and world religions. In his book *Hindu Christian Meeting Point*, Abhishiktananda remarked, "The time has...come for the Church to enter into official contact with...other religions."[54] Nevertheless, it is Panikkar who took the Christian doctrine of God into the depths of other faiths, especially into Hinduism. For Panikkar, according to Dupuis:

> Christ is the most powerful living symbol but not one limited to the historical Jesus - of the fully human, divine, and cosmic reality that he calls the Mystery. This symbol can have other names: for example, *Rama, Krishna, Ishvara, Purusha*. Christians call him "Christ", because it is in and through Jesus that they themselves have arrived at faith in the decisive reality. Each name, however, expresses the divine Mystery, each being an unknown dimension of Christ.[55]

Along with Karl Rahner, H.R. Schlette, and A. Roper, Panikkar affirms, "God provides to every [man/woman] coming into human

---

53. Jacques Dupuis, S.J., *Jesus Christ at the Encounter of World Religions*, (New York: Orbis Books, 1991), p.129.

54. Swami Abhishiktananda, *Hindu Christian Meeting Point*, (Delhi: ISPCK, 1976), p.1.

55. Dupuis, *Jesus Christ at the Encounter of World Religions*, pp. 185-86.

existence the means for his salvation."[56] If all men and women already possess the possibility of salvation, Panikkar believes, it amounts to "saying that Christ is present in one form or another in every human being in his religious way to God."[57] All religions then become paths to God in which Christ, somehow, incognito, is present. So the task of the church is not to convert people, it is rather to discover the unknown Christ who is already present in Hinduism. Panikkar's universalism consists in the way in which he believes God has made the means of salvation available to all men. "We may all say that sacraments are the ordinary means by which God leads the peoples of the earth towards himself" and these sacraments are present in the world religions too.[58] Hence, Panikkar concludes:

> The good and bonafide Hindu is saved by Christ and not by Hinduism, through the message of morality and good life, through the Mysterion that comes down to him through Hinduism, that Christ saves the Hindu normally. This amounts to saying that Hinduism has also a place in the universal saving presence of God.[59]

The problems we encounter with the inclusivist theory and the theory of presence of Christ are that they fail to respond to the question of the necessity of the cross. The inclusivist theory indirectly supports the traditional Roman Catholic dictum outside Church there is no salvation. As other faiths do not have salvific effect, an aggressive outreach conversion and evangelistic ministry is encouraged.

The theory of the presence of Christ talks about "good" people of other faiths who will be saved. Notwithstanding, it fails to address by what yardstick the goodness is measured. These measures do not relate to the Gospel message that the Son of Man came to redeem sinners not the righteous.[60]

The theory of the presence of Christ also assumes that religion is the sphere of salvation which goes contrary to the teachings of Jesus as

---

56. Ibid., p.51.

57. Ibid., p.34.

58. Ibid., p.54.

59. Ibid., p.54.

60. Hinduism teaches gods took the human form to kill the evil ones and uphold the righteous ones.

evidenced in the parable of the Good Samaritan in which two religious persons, a priest and a levite, are clearly on their way to perdition and the non-religious person on his way to salvation. While the theory of the presence of Christ recognizes in those religions normal means of salvation for their adherents, it reduces other faiths to mere religions of awareness or lack of the same regarding a reality equally possessed.

The inclusivist theory and the presence of Christ theory present Christianity as the consummation of all religions, although the genesis of faith journey is another religion. Lesslie Newbigin, former bishop of the Church of South India, is puzzled about the proposals of this theory and questions its validity. Newbigin writes:

> [Many of the Asian religions] turn... on many different axes, to fit them into this model is to lose any possibility of understanding them. Moreover what do the concepts of 'near' and 'far' mean in relation to the crucified and risen Jesus? Is the devout Pharisee nearer or farther than the semi-pagan prostitute? Is the passionate Marxist nearer or farther than the Hindu mystic? Is a man nearer to Christ because he is religious? Is the Gospel the culmination of religion or is it the end of religion?[61]

The theories do not offer any convincing answer to the questions raised by Newbigin.

The Exclusivists

The third group of theologians are called the exclusivist theologians. For the sake of simplicity and convenience of the study, we could include the theory of fulfillment also under this category. These theologians propose a radical discontinuity from all earlier revelations and insist that God has uniquely disclosed himself in the person of Jesus Christ. The religions of the world do not have salvific effect in themselves and they serve as a preparation for the gospel, just as Judaism prepared the way for the coming of the Messiah in the presence of Christ. The religions of the world will be judged in the light of Christ. J.N. Fraquhar in his book *The Crown of Hinduism* and P. Johanns in his book *To Christ Through Vedanta* strongly defended the theory of fulfillment.

---

61. Lesslie Newbigin, *The Finality of Christ*, (Richmond: John Knox Press, 1968), p.44.

These theologians argue that the mystery of Christ is actively present in other religious faiths in response to the human religious aspiration. However, the religious faiths themselves do not play any role in this mystery of salvation. The first chapter of Paul's letter to the Romans is often cited as an evidence to support this theory. In attempting to be faithful to God's total revelation in Jesus Christ, the exclusivists assert that all other religions are false and invalid. So they limit God's universal love and mercy to God's Church and to the Christian community, and persist that all those who fail to respond to the gospel will be lost for ever.

Their category of "lostness" includes people who have rejected the gospel and all those who have never heard the name of Jesus Christ. By doing so, the exclusivist theorists reduce the Merciful God of the Bible to a tyrant who makes a sweeping judgment upon billions in this world who have not even heard the gospel to make an intelligent decision. Henri de Lubac refused to attribute any positive salvific values to other faiths. He even challenged that anybody doing so would be establishing other faiths as analogous routes to salvation. Such an attempt would destroy the unity and oneness of the divine plan. Teilhard de Chardin, a naturalist theologian whom the fulfillment theoreticians often quote, said that the central point of convergence is neither the Church nor Christianity, but Jesus Christ. He wrote:

> [Christ] is the alpha and omega, the beginning and the end, the foundation stone and the keystone, Fulfillment and Fulfiller. It is he who consummates, he who gives all things their consistency. Toward him and by him, the inner Life and the Light of World, is wrought, in pangs and travail, the universal convergence of all created spirit. He is the one precious, solid Centre, gleaming on the future pinnacle of the world.[62.]

The exclusivist theologians maintain that God has made himself known fully and once and for all through a particular man at a particular time, and in a particular place. His coming has changed the human situation dramatically for ever. They derive support from Peter and Paul: Acts 4:12, I Cor. 8:6, Col.1:15-22, 2:9.

The strong proponent of the exclusivist view was Karl Barth, who rejected the value of other faiths and stated that all salvation is available only in Christ. Barth argued that other faiths are expressions of human

---

62. Pierre Teilhard de Chardin, *Science et Christ*, (Paris: Seuil, 1965), pp.60-61.

search for God and, hence, denied any salvific revelation found in other faiths. Barth declared that all religions, including Christianity, falls short of the revelation of God as they are all mere human expressions. Salvation and revelation are available to humanity only in and through the person of Jesus Christ, the Judeo-Christian Word, not through any other religion. Only those who respond positively to the Gospel of Jesus Christ will be saved. Hence, Barth invited the Christian Church to live out its salvation in faith and preach the Gospel so that people might hear and respond in faith.

Hendrik Kraemer presents Jesus Christ as the unique and final revelation of God who stands as judge over the religions of the world. Kraemer reduced other religions of the world as "erroneous" and "they are a fleeing from God."[63] He insisted Hinduism has no explicit means of salvation and called Islam a "riddle" for the religions of the world. In spite of its lack of originality and depth, Kraemer charged, Islam has excelled the religions of the world by "creating in its adherents a feeling of absolute religious superiority."[64] Kraemer agonized over Islam's exclusive claim and its "stubborn refusal towards another spiritual world" and hence he called Islam "an enigmatic missionary object."[65]

It will suffice for our study to cite two more historic incidents, one Roman Catholic and one Protestant, which took a strong exclusivist position. The Council of Florence affirmed in the fifteenth century, "No one outside the Catholic Church, not only pagans but also Jews and heretics and schismatics, can share in eternal life, but will perish in the eternal fire prepared for the devil and his angels." Almost a hundred years later, Martin Luther wrote, "Those who are outside of Christianity, be they heathens, Turks, Jews or even false Christians and hypocrites... cannot expect either love or any blessing from God, and accordingly remain in eternal wrath and perdition."[66]

The exlusivist theory presents Christianity and the Church as the visible depository of the mystery of Christ. This theory underestimates the values which the world religions treasure for their members. By

---

63. Hendrik Kraemer, *Why Christianity of All Religions*, (London: Lutterworth, 1962), p.95.

64. Kraemer, *The Christian Message in a Non-Christian World*, p.220.

65. Ibid., p.220.

66. Quoted in Maurice Wiles, *Christian Theology and Inter-Religious Dialogue*, (London: SCM Press, 1963), p.9.

limiting God's saving grace to only those who believe in Christ, the exclusivists violate the mode of revelation Christianity has received. Before Christ came, Judaism was considered a salvific revelation. Ruether, Mussner, and D'Costa censure that the exclusivist's theory stands in stark contrast to the biblical God of love, mercy, and justice.[67]

Several narratives in the Christian Scriptures attest that God accepts faithful people of other faiths as his own and Christian theology and Church have been built on the foundation of all the earlier revelations. In his letter to the Romans, Paul agonized over Israel's alienation from God's promises given through Christ, and yet made a provision that God in his abundant love made a way of salvation open for them (11:25-26) by including everyone who calls upon him (10:12-26). Therefore, it is preposterous to denounce other religious faiths as mere human invention and reduce them as beliefs which possess no positive values.

The Need for Dialogue

As mentioned in earlier chapters, Christianity and Isam have major theological and doctrinal differences. It would be naive to assume that the doctrinal differences between these two religions could be easily abolished. The authors of this book happened to participate in a Christian-Muslim dialogue which took place at Chicago a few months before completing this manuscript. After two days of intense dialogue and deep discussions between Christians and Muslims in the American Midwest, they drove home from Chicago. That evening TV news broadcast was saturated with the transforming events taking place all across South Africa, such as the lifting of the Apartheid and the preparation for the general election.

In a descriptive narration, a reporter from South Africa presented the joy and excitement of the people across the country and the eucharistic celebration conducted by Archbishop Desmond Tutu for thousands of people gathered in an open ground. At the conclusion of the report, the camera was focussed upon the Archbishop holding the chalice and broken bread in his hands, saying to the spiritually yearning and politically unfettered sea of people, "Christ has died, Christ is risen, and Christ will come again." The background images, sound bites, and

---

67. See Rosemary Ruether, *Faith and Fratricide*, (Seabury: Winston press, 1985), Franz Mussner, *Tractate on the Jews*, (Philadelphia: Fortress Press, 1984), Gavin D'Costa, *Theology and Religious Pluralism*, (Oxford and New York: Basil Blackwell, 1986).

symbols instilled a renewed meaning and revitalizing hope both to the Christian participants on the ground and TV audience around the world. The writers of this book were reminded again of the strong foundation and the deep underpinning of Christian faith.

The doctrinal difference between Christianity and Islam should not separate the two religious communities and divide the people of God from fulfilling their call to mission in this world. After all, we are all children of the One God who is the Creator of the universe, the Provider, Preserver, and Sustainer of the whole of humanity.

The God of the Bible is the God of history. The God who revealed himself to Abraham, Isaac, and Jacob has also given his "common grace" (as the Reformed theologians say) and general revelation to the people of other faiths also. Christians cannot make an exclusive claim that they alone possess the truth about God, world, human beings, and moral and spiritual values. As this is the only world which God has given for human beings to inhabit, religious people must first learn how to get along with each other as their hopes and aspirations are the same for every generation. God's people everywhere need to join hands to create genunine understanding based on authentic love and mutual respect. They should strive to work together to inspire human compassion and foster religious tolerance among the followers of different faiths. Despite major theological and doctrinal differences, human beings still can peacefully co-exist and non-violently build the Kingdom of God. Such a state can be realized only through dialogue and mutual respect.

Dialogue as a theological concept or even as missiological paradigm has been deeply criticized and profoundly misunderstood. An authentic dialogue would neither serve as a threat to one's religious faith nor function as a barrier for a believer's personal witness. So many volumes of books have been written on the importance and necessity of engaging in dialogue. So many conferences have been organized in promoting understanding and sesitivity in approaching the people of other faiths. One recent publication could be cited. Eeuwout Klootwijk wrote succinctly in the *Bangalore Theological Forum* that dialogue is part and parcel of Christ's mission as it brings Christians and followers of other faiths to serve the common concerns of people everywhere. He quotes extensively the works of Stanley Samartha, an Indian theologian, and attempted to clear the smoke surrounding the edifice called dialogue. Klootwijk affirmed:

> Dialogue is not incompatible with mission... Dialogue is a mood; a spirit; an attitude of love and respect towards neighbours of other faiths. The spirit of dialogue can be helpful in creating a climate of friendliness, trust and cooperation, in which there is room for mutual witness. The 'imperative of Christian witness in dialogue' does not stand in the way of other people's confessions and witnesses. Dialogue stands for new relationships with people of other religions. There need not be a contradiction between dialogue and witness/mission. Dialogue beyond mission and mission beyond dialogue implies openness to other people's faiths and commitment to one's own faith.[68]

Dialogue fosters mutual respect and creates an atmosphere for understanding each other's religious beliefs and doctrinal conviction. True dialogue draws the parties closer to each other to replace hostility and misunderstanding. Dialogue may not help parties find a common solution to all the problems of the world or for the parties to come to an agreement. Yet, dialogue clarifies the existing differences and opens up the debate. Dialogue continues to bring the parties to the table in order to find common ways to serve God's children everywhere. Michael Harper has rightly said:

> Dialogue does not have to mean either the collision of porcupines or the slither of courteous, civilized people who are divided by their interpretation of the meaning of life, yet united in their desire to understand, to discover points of contact and to face each other with the issues that hurt and anger.[69]

No matter how lofty the doctrine of dialogue or noble the intention be, authentic dialogue cannot take place in vacuum. It is only possible among real, living people. Dialogue is open-ended. It requires at least two people, with their distinct spiritual experiences, different religious perspectives, and diverse moral voices. Dialogue calls for the parties to review the past, plan for the future, and deeply establish themselves in the present. Dialogue does not produce an immediate or a long range end result.

---

68. Eeuwout Klootwijk, *Bangalore Theological Forum*, "Mission, Witness and Conversion in Relation to Dialogue", Bangalore, India, 1994, pp.44-45.

69. Michael Harper, *Male and Female in Church Family: Equal and Different*, (London: Hodder and Stoughton, 1994), p.216.

Dialogue is mainly a process. It is an ongoing event. It never ends. Dialogue brings back the parties involved back to the round table over and over again.

Those who plan only for the present will die with the problems of the present. History will view them harshly. Mikhail Mikhailovich Bakhtin, a twentieth-century Russian literary and cultural theorist who has strong roots in Russian Orthodox Christianity wrote, "Everything that belongs only to the present dies along with the present." Christians who are strongly committed to the ministry of reconciliation and ministry of service ought to take dialogue seriously.

Nevertheless, one needs to understand that dialogue is not going to serve as the panacea and an end result of all misunderstandings that exist between two varying religious communities. God may lead the groups to new ways and try new methods to bring harmony and unity among people of the world in future. Bakhtin suggests that "the present - whichever present - enjoys no exemption from superannuation...those incapable of such recognition in effect treat the present moment as essentially apocalyptic."[70]

As mentioned in the Introduction, when religions with diverse claims encounter each other in a spirit of dialogue and mutual respect, each is enriched, not only in the discovery of unsuspected riches in the other but also in the recognition of unnoticed postulates in itself. If we truly respect the deep spiritual yearnings, if we try to understand the genuine search for truth by the adherents of every religious tradition, and if we learn to appreciate the sincerity and commitment of every religious community, we can certainly help to liberate religions from "the captivity of time" and help the church to participate in God's mission. After all, Christian mission is, as Stanley Samartha aptly explains, "God's continuing activity through the Spirit to mend the brokenness of creation, to overcome the fragmentation of humanity, and to heal the rift between humanity, nature, and God."[71]

In order to accomplish it, Christians need to have a thorough knowledge of the values, traditions, and artifacts different from their own. It also requires a firm grasp of who Jesus Christ is all about, so that the encounter of Christianity and other faiths will be a profound and informed one, activating the potentials of each. Only then will that special sort of dialogue which Bakhtin calls "creative understanding" be possible.

---

70. Ibid., p.221.

71. Stanley Samartha, *One Christ - Many Religions: Toward Revised Christology*, (Maryknoll, NY. : Orbis Books, 1991), p.149.

GLOSSARY

Abbasid, the dynasty of caliphs who ruled from 750 A.D. till 1258. They succeeded the Umayyads in 749. The Abbasid dynasty was founded by Abul Abbas, called as *Saffah,* "the Spiller" of Umayyad blood.

Abu Bakr, the first caliph. He was a rich merchant in Mecca and was the second, after Khadijah, to believe in the mission of the Prophet. He was also known as *Siddiq,* the faithful. His daughter, Aisha, was the favorite wife of the Prophet.

Abus Hanifa, a theologian who founded the Hanafite school of law.

Abyssinia, modern-day Ethiopia. The Abyssinians are Monophysite Christians.

Ahl al-Dhimmah, literally, "People of the Covenant".

Ahl al-Kitab, literally, "People of the Book". They are: the Jews, the Christians, and the Zoroastrians.

Ahmadiyyah, a heterodox community founded by Mirza Ghulam Ahmad, 1251-1326, in Punjab, India.

Allah, Arabic word for God.

Allahu Akbar, God is great.

Ansar, helpers of Mohammed in Medina.

Aqabah, a hill in Mina just outside Mecca.

Arafat, an important pilgrim gathering place. It is a plain 12 miles South-West of Mecca.

Ashura, the first month of the Islamic year and the tenth month of the Muharram.

Ayatollah, a respectable title for high-ranking Shiite religious leaders in Iran and Iraq.

Banu Israil, Arabic and Hebrew words for "the Children of Israel".

Bashir, the one who brings good news.

Bismallah, the Quranic formula (bisillahi-ur-Rahmani-ur-Rahim): "In the Name of God, the Merciful, the Compassionate".

Battle of Badr, the first battle between the Meccans and the Muslims which took place at Badr which lies 90 miles to the south of Mecca.

Battle of the Camel, a decisive battle between Aisha's followers and Ali's followers. Ali won.

al-Buraq, the heavenly steed which Gabriel brought to the Prophet for the heavenly ascent.

Dajjal, a false prophet.

Dar al-Islam, house of Islam.

Dar al-adl-Islam, community of conscience.

Dar al-harb, the house of war.

Dhimmis, the "protected people" (the Jews, Christians and the Sabians) who were monotheists. They were granted freedom to practice their faith and given protection under Islam. In return, they were expected to pay poll-tax.

Fatihah, the name of the surah which is first placed in the Quran and which is the first chapter in the Quran.

Fatimah, one of the three daughters of Mohammed born to Khadijah.

Fatimids, the Ismaili dynasty which founded Cairo as Capital in 969. The Fatimids ruled a vast empire extending from Palestine to Tunisia.

Fidyah, give up one's life for a religious cause; redemption.

Fiqh, Islamic jurisprudence.

Five pillars: Shahada, Salat, Zakah, Sawm, and Hajj.

Hadith, traditions relating to the Prophet's deeds and speeches recounted by his companions.

Hajj, pilgrimage.

Hakim, governor or ruler of a province.

Hanif, one who practiced strict monotheism, the rightly inclined.

Hashimite, the Banu-Hashim, the Meccan clan to which Mohammed and Ali belonged.

Hawwa', the first woman, Eve.

Hijrah, the first migration of Muslims with the Prophet from Mecca to Yathrib (Medina).

Hussein, the second son of Ali and Fatimah.

Ibadah, act of ritual or worship.

Iblis, the devil or the slanderer.

Iddah, the time period a divorced woman (or a widow) must observe before she can remarry.

Ihram, the name of the costume the pilgrim wears to go to Mecca.

Ijma, consensus on a question of law.

Imam, the leader of prayer and the head of a community.

Injil, gospel.

Islam, comes from the word "shalom" (peace or salvation). It also means "surrender" and "reconciliation".

Isma, special grace of God.

Jihad, in Arbic means "effort" or "Holy War".

Kaaba, a large cube shaped stone structure, covered with a black cloth, stands in the centre of the Grand Mosque of Mecca. It is a spiritual centre and a holy house for Muslims. It is an important pilgrim place.

Karbala, the place where Hussein, grandson of the Prophet, was martyred. A pilgrim place for Shiite Muslims. It is in Iraq.

Khadijah, first wife of Mohammed.

Khalifa, trustees of God.

Kharijites, a sect which stood against both Ali and Muawiyah upon the arbitration that followed the battle of Siffin in 657.

Kismet, comes closer to Hindu concept of Karma or fate.

Laylat al-Qadr, the night of power, the night in which the Quran descended into the soul of the Prophet.

Light verses, See sura 24:35.

Mahdi, the guided one.

Masjid, mosque, a worship place.

Mawali, new Muslims.

Mihrab, a niche in the wall of a mosque to indicate the direction of Mecca (qibla), towards which all Muslims turn in prayer.

Minaret, a tower from which the Muezzin makes the call to prayers (a lighthouse).

Mosque, a place of worship. It is also called a place of prostration. In pre-Islamic times, the place in and around the kaaba was called mosque.

al-Muakkadah, that which is confirmed.

Muawiya, first caliph of the Umayyad dynasty who resisted Hasan, the son of Ali to abdicate. Muawiya, one of the sons of Abu Sufyan, led the first war of Islam for the right to rule the community.

Muhajirun, the faithful followers.

Mullah, religious or worship leader, scholar in the Quran.

Nadhir, the one who warns.

Qibla, the direction the Muslims face when they say their prayers or perform their salah.

Ramadan, the ninth month of the Islamic calendar. Fasting during Ramadan is one of the five-pillars of Islam.

Rasul Allah, the messenger of God.

Sabil Allah, the way of Allah.

Safa and Marawh, two small hills near the Kaaba. Pilgrims who go to Mecca walk or run between the hills as Haagar was walking or running in search for water between the hills with her infant son, Ishmael.

Salat, one of the five-pillars. The prescribed five prayers a Muslim must say in a day.

Sawm, fast.

Shahda, confession of the creed that is fundamental to Islam. The first and the most important of the five-pillars: "There is no God but Allah and Mohammed is the messenger of Allah."

Shahid, a martyr of Islam.

Shariah, the canonical law of Islam.

Shiites, the followers of Ali, the son in law of Mohammed. They attribute Ali and his heirs the status of imam and believe that they have the rightful leadership of the Muslim community.

Shirk, the crime of setting other gods along side of Allah.

Shubiha Lahum, literally means: "It was made only to appear so to them".

Sira, the biography of Mohammed.

Sufism, the mysticism of Islam.

Sunna, custom, the habits of Mohammed.

al-Sunnah al-Zaidah, that which is optional.

Sunni, those who follow the sunna.

Surah, a chapter in the Quran.

Tafsir, a commentary on the Quran.

Tawhid, the oneness of God.

Throne Verses, see Sura 2:255.

Umayyad, the first dynasty of caliphs (661-750).

Umma, Islamic community of believers.

Umrah, the lesser pilgrimage.

Yathrib, the original name of Medina.

Zakat, alms-giving, one of the Five Pillars.

SUMMARY OF ISLAMIC CHRONOLOGY

570 (?)	Birth of Mohammed.
610 (?)	Mohammed's first revelation in Mecca
615	Muslims emigration to Christian Abyssinia.
620-622	Mohammed's negotiation with tribal leaders from Yathrib.
622	Mohammed's migration to Yathrib *(Hijrah)*. Yathrib is named al-Medina, the city of the Prophet.
624	Battle at Badr.
625	Mohammed's defeat at the mountain of Uhud.
627	Battle of the Trench.
628	Treaty of Hudaybiyya with Meccans which opened passageway to kaaba.
630	Conquest of Mecca without bloodshed.
630-32	Conquest of the neighbouring tribes in and around Mecca.
632	Death of Mohammed. Abu Bakr became the first Caliph.
634	Death of Abu Bakr. Umar became the Caliph. Byzantine force overthrown in South Syria.
635	Damascus and a few other Syrian cities were taken.
635-38	Subjugation of Damascus and Jerusalem by Muslims.
639-40	Conquest of Egypt, Persia, and the end of Byzantine era in Syria.
642	Conquest of Alexandria.
644	Death of Umar. Uthman became the next Caliph.
645-46	Alexandria repossessed by Byzantine; retaken by Muslims.
652	Conquest of Armenia.
656	Death of Uthman. Ali, Mohammed's son in law and the husband of Fatimah became the next Caliph. Battle of the Camel.
657	Battle between Ali and Muawiya called battle of Siffin.

658	Arbitration between Ali and Muawiya. Rebellion of Kharijites.
661	Death of Ali. Inauguration of the rule of the Umayyad dynasty. Muawiya became the Caliph.
680	Death of Muawiya. Hussein, son of Ali, led rebellion in Kufa and was killed at Karbala. Muawiya's son Yazid became the Caliph.
684	Marwan I became Caliph.
685	Abdul Malik became the Caliph.
691	Building of the Dome of the Rock in Jerusalem.
711	Muslims expansion towards West. Muslim army attacked southern Spain under Tariq's leadership.
712	Muslim conquest of Central Asian Countries.
713	Muslims penetrate Indian subcontinent.
728	Death of theologian and preacher al-Hasan al-Basri.
746	Rebellion of the Kalb in Syria and of the Kharijites in Iraq.
749	Conquest of Kufa. All of Persia under Abbasid dynasty. Abbasid revolution against the Umayyads.
750	Beginning of the Abbasid Caliphate (750-1258).
756-929	Spain independent under Umayyad Caliphs.
762-763	Establishment of Baghdad as cultural and commercial centre and capital of all Muslim territories.
763	Baghdad was founded as the capital of the Abbasid empire by Al-Munsur.
765	Death of Jafar al-Sadiq imam of Shiites who held to a Fatimid line; their divisions date from al-Sadiq's death.
767	Death of Ibn Ishaq, historian, biographer of *(Sira)* of Mohammed. Death of Abu-Hanifa, the master of Islamic law and theologian. The School of Law of the Hanifites in Iraq was named after him.
793	Death of Sibawayhi, Arabic grammarian from Basra.
795	Death of jurist Malik ibn Anas in Medina.
813	Death of Maruf al-Karkhi who carried Sufism to Baghdad.
823	Death of al-Waqidi, the historian.
855	Death of Ahmad ibn Hanbal, jurist-theologian, teacher of hadith and the authority of the law school of the Hanbalites.

870	Death of al-Bukhari who put together the canonical collection of hadith.
873	The twelfth imam of the Shiites disappeared. He will return as the mahdi at the end of time.
909	Rise of the Ismaili Fatimids dynasty who drove the Aghlabids out of Ifriqiyya (Tunisia, North Africa) and established Fatimid dynasty (909-934).
923	Death of al-Tabari, master exegete and hadith-based historian.
935	Death of theologian al-Ashari who established the traditionist doctrine of the *ahl al-hadith* with the manner of *kalam.*
944	Berber revolt against Fatimids.
951	Conversion of Seljuk turks began.
956	Death of al-Masudi, traveller, historian and philosopher.
965	Death of al-Mutanabbi, an Arab poet.
968	Byzantium recaptured Sicily and Northern Syria.
969	Fatimids conquered Egypt and founded Cairo. Became a strong power in the Mediterranean.
973	Cairo became the capital. Al-Azhar (mosque and university, a spiritual centre for Ismaili Shiites) was founded.
1002	Death of Ibn Jinni, the philologist who codifed Arabic grammar.
1021	Death of mystic al-Sulami who put together a Sufi commentary on the Quran.
1031	End of Umayyad rule in Spain.
1055	The Seljuks came to power. Toghril became a ruler in Baghdad.
1076	Fatimid rule in Syria ended. Turkish general conquered Damascus. Suljuks power was sought.
1091	Seljuks took control of Syria. Baghdad became their capital.
1096	First Crusade by Pope Urban II.
1098	Crusaders captured Antioch.
1099	Crusaders captured Jerusalem.
1111	Death of al-Ghazzali, sufi theologian.
1147-49	Second Crusade
1166	Death of Sufi Abd al-Qadir in Baghdad.

1171	Saladin became the Abbassid Caliph in Egypt.
1179	Saladin defeated the Crusader army led by Baldwin IV at Marj Uyun.
1187	Saladin defeated Crusaders at Hitti. Recaptured Jerusalem.
1188	Third Crusade began.
1193	Death of Saladin in Jerusalem. His empire divided.
1200-18	al-Malik, Saladin's brother became Sultan of Egypt and Syria.
1202	Fourth Crusade.
1204	Crusader's conquest of Constantinople.
1227	Death of Genghis Khan.
1228	Crusade of Frederick II, who was excommunicated by Pope Gregory IX.
1229	Jerusalem came under Frederick II when Al-Malik relinquished it in a treaty.
1237	Mongols invaded Russia.
1244	Turks captured Jerusalem.
1249	Crusade of St. Louis IX.
1258	Beginning of Mongol period. Baghdad was destroyed by Mongols.
1270-72	Crusade of Edward to Tunisia and Palestine.
1289	Tripoli was delivered from the Crusaders by the Mamluks.
1326	Death of Osman. Successor Orkhan began Ottoman expansion towards Europe.
1328	Death of theologian, lawyer and reformer, Ibn Taymiyya.
1347-58	Ala al-din Hasan Bahman Shaf founded the kingdom of Madura after subduing Hindu kings in Northern India.
1351-1413	Tughluqids dynasty in power in Delhi.
1453	Ottoman Turks conquered Constantinople and made it capital of Ottoman kingdom and Islamic centre. Byzantine Empire ceased to exist.
1492	Muslims were expelled from Spain.
1498-1509	Portuguese supremacy in the Indian Ocean and establishment of trade posts in India.
1517	End of the Mamluk era. Beginning of the Ottoman Empire.

1526	Hungary was conquered by the Turks. Battle of Panipat: Lodi, Sultan of Delhi, was defeated and the Mogul emperors were established in India.
1550	Suleiman mosque was built in Constantinople. Islam's expansion to Far East.
1556- 1605	Akbar in Delhi, founded Din-illahi, a syncretistic universal religion in India. Mogul empire expanded in North and Central India.
1605-27	Jahangir, Mogul Emperor, in Delhi.
1628-58	Shah Jahan, Mogul Emperor in India.
1657	Turkey's control over Danube power again.
1736-39	Ottomans war against Austria and Russia.
1738-39	Nadir Shah invaded India and despoiled Delhi temples and treasuries.
1747	Death of Nadir Shah.
1768-74	Russian-Ottoman war
1784	Treaty of Aynali Kavak, a settlement between Russia and Ottoman empire; the Crimea was given to Russia.
1794-94	The Qajar dynasty took control of Persia. Shah was crowned in 1796.
1797-1834	Fath Ali Shah became the ruler of Iran.
1798	Napoleon invaded Egypt. Ottoman made political alliance with England and Russia.
1802	Egypt was returned to the Ottoman Empire.
1834-48	Mohammed Shah became the Shah of Persia.
1853-56	The Crimean war.
1859	Construction of the Suez canal began.
1860-61	Civil war in Lebanon. Christians were massacred.
1866	American University of Beirut was established by Protestant missionaries.
1869	Suez canal opened.
1881-83	French colonization of Tunisia.
1883	Ahmadiyya Movement in India.
1906	Iranian Constitution was published.
1908	Bulgaria declared independence from Ottoman Empire. Bosnia and Herzegovina were appropriated by Austria.

1908	Civil war in Iran. Shah escaped to Russia.
1914-18	World War I
1917	Balfour declared, British foreign minister, declared the establishment of "homeland" for the Jews in Palestine.
1921	Iraq became a constitutional monarchy under Faysal ibn Husayn.
1923	Constitution of Egypt proclaimed.
1924	Caliphate in Turkey was abolished and Turkey was made a secularized nation. No more *Sharia* courts. Civil courts were established. Ottoman era was put to rest.
1925	Qajar dynasty was ended in Iran. Rida Khan became the Shah.
1928	Islam as state religion was abolished in Turkey.
1932	Iraq declared independence. Joined League of Nations.
1937	Egypt joined League of Nations.
1945	Syria and Lebanon joined League of Nations.
1946	Jordan, Lebanon joined League of Nations.
1947	Pakistan was created for Muslims. Israel was created for Jews.
1953	Egypt became the Republic.
1979	Revolution in Iran. Shah Mohammed Rida Pahlavi was exiled. Islamic Republic of Iran was established. Ayatollah Khomeini, a Shiite Cleric, became an influential leader. Pakistani reformer and politician, Mawlana Mawdudi died.

THE NINETY NINE NAMES
OF ALLAH MENTIONED IN THE QURAN

The First, *Al-Awal* (Sura 57:3).

The Last, *Al-Akhir* (Sura 57:3).

The One, *Al-Ahad* (Sura 112:1).

The Originator, *Al-Badi* (Sura 2:117).

The Producer, *Al-Bari* (Sura 59:24)

The Beneficent, *Al-Barr* (Sura 52:28)

The Seeing, *Al-Basirn* (Sura 57:3)

The Expander, *Al-Basit* (Sura 13:26)

The Inner, *Al-Batin* (Sura 57:3)

The Raiser, *Al-Baith* (Sura 16:89)

The Enduring, *Al-Baqi* (Sura 20:73)

The Relenting, *Al-Tawwab* (Sura 2:37)

The Irresistible, *Al-Jabbar* (Sura 59:23)

The Majestic, *Al-Jalil* (a derived one)

The Gatherer, *Al-Jami* (Sura 3:9)

The Accounter, *Al-Hasib* (Sura 4:6)

The Guardian, *Al-Hafiz* (Sura 11:57)

The Truth, *Al-Haqq* (Sura 20:114)

The Wise, *Al-Hakkim* (Sura 6:18)

The Judge, *Al-Hakam* (Sura 40:48)

The Kindly, *Al-Halim* (Sura 2:235)

The Praiseworthy, *Al-Hamid* (Sura 2:269)

The Living, *Al-Hayy* (Sura 20:111)

The Well-Informed, *Al-Khabir* (Sura 6:18)

The Abaser, *Al-Khafid* (A derived name)

The Creator, *Al-Khaliq* (Sura 13:16)

The Benevolent, *Dhu-Jalal* (Sura 55:27)

The Gentle, *Ar-Rauf* (Sura 2:143)

The Merciful, *Ar-Rahman* (Sura 55:1)

The Compassionate, *Ar-Rahim* (Sura 2:143)

The Provider, *Ar-Razzaq* (Sura 51:57)

The Guide, *Ar-Rashid* (A Traditional name)

The Exalter, *Ar-Rafi* (Sura 6:83)

The Vigilant, *Ar-Raqib* (Sura 5:117)

The Peace, *As-Salam* (Sura 59:23)

The Hearer, *As-Sami* (Sura 17:1)

The Grateful, *Ash-Shakur* (Sura 64:17)

The Witness, *Ash-Shahid* (Sura 5:117)

The Forbearing, *As-Sabur* (A Traditional Name)

The Eternal, *As-Samad* (Sura 112:2)

The Afflicter, *Ad-Darr* (Sura 48:11)

The Outer, *Az-Zahir* (Sura 57:3)

The Just, *Al-Adl* (Sura 6:115)

The Mighty, *Al-Aziz* (Sura 59:23)

The Great, *Al-Azim* (Sura 2:255)

The Pardoner, *Al-Afuw* (Sura 4:99)

The Knowing, *Al-Alim* (Sura 2:29)

The High One, *Al-Ali* (Sura 2:255)

The Forgiver, *Al-Ghafur* (Sura 2:235)

The Forgiving, *Al-Ghaffar* (Sura 2:235)

The Rich, *Al-Ghani* (Sura 2:267)

The Opener, *Al-Fattah* (Sura 34:26)

The Seizer, *Al-Qabid* (Sura 2:245)

The Power, *Al-Qadir* (Sura 17:99)

The Holy, *Al-Quddud* (Sura 62:1)

The Victorious, *Al-Qahhar* (Sura 13:16)

The Strong, *Al-Qawi* (Sura 22:40)

The Self-Subsistent, *Al-Qayyum* (Sura 3:2)

The Great, *Al-Kabir* (Sura 22:62)

The Generous, *Al-Karim* (Sura 27:40)

The Gracious, *Al-Latif* (Sura 42:19)

The Deferrer, *Al-Muta'akhkhir* (Sura 14:42)

The Believer, *Al-Mumin* (Sura 59:23)

The Self Exalted, *Al-Mutali* (Sura 13:9)

The Superb, *Al-Mutakkabir* (Sura 59:23)

The Firm, *Al-Matin* (Sura 51:58)

The Founder, *Al-Mubdi* (Sura 85:13)

The Responsive, *Al-Mujib* (Sura 11:61)

The Glorious, *Al-Majid* (Sura 11:73)

The Counter, *Al-Muhsi* (Sura 19:94)

The Giver of Life, *Al-Muhyi* (Sura 30:50)

The Abaser, *Al-Mudhill* (Sura 3:26)

The Separator, *Al-Muzil* (Sura 10:28)

The Shaper, *Al-Musawwir* (Sura 59:24)

The Restorer, *Al-Muid* (Sura 85:13)

The Honourer, *Al-Muizz* (Sura 3:26)

The Giver, *Al-Muti* (Sura 20:50)

The Encricher, *Al-Mughni* (Sura 9:74)

The Maintainer, *Al-Muqit* (Sura 4:85)

The Prevailer, *Al-Muqtadir* (Sura 54:42)

The Bringer Forward, *Al-Muqddim* (Sura 50:28)

The Equitable, *Al-Muqsit* (Sura 21:47)

The King, *Al-Malik* (Sura 59:23)

The Sovereign God, *Malik al-Mulk* (Sura 3:26)

The Slayer, *Al-Mumit* (Sura 15:23)

The Avenger, *Al-Mutaqim* (Sura 30:47)

The Vigilant, *Al-Muhaimin* (Sura 59:23)

The Propitious, *An-Nafi* (Sura 48:11)

The Helper, *An-Nasir* (Sura 4:45)

The Light, *An-Nur* (Sura 24:35)

The Guide, *Al-Hadi* (Sura 22:54)

The Unique, *Al-Wahid* (Sura 74:11)

The Loving, *Al-Wadud* (Sura 11:90)

The Inheritor, *Al-Warith* (Sura 19:40)

The Vast, *Al-Wasi* (Sura 2:268)

The Steward, *Al-Wakil* (Sura 6:102)

The Patron, *Al-Waliy* (Sura 4:45)

The Protector, *Al-Wali* (Sura 13:11)

The Bestower, *Al-Wahhab* (Sura 3:8)

SELECTED BIBLIOGRAPHY

Abbat, Nabia. *Aisha, the Beloved of Mohammed*, (Chicago: University of Chicago Press, 1942).

Ahmed, Leila. *Women and Gender in Islam*, (New Haven: Yale University Press, 1992).

Al-Kalbi, *Kitab Al-asham*, ed. Klinke-Rosenberger (Leipzig: Otto Harrassowitz, 1941).

Ali, Amir. *The Spirit of Islam*, (London: Methuen, 1967).

Ali, Michael Nazir. *Frontiers in Muslim-Christian Encounter*, (Oxford: Regnum Books, 1987).

Al-Isfahani, Abu'l-Faraj, *Kitabul-Agahani*, vol.16, (Bulak: Dar al-Kutub, 1868).

Ali, Yusuf, A. *The Holy Quran: Text, Translation and Commentary*, (Brentwood, Maryland: Amana Corp., 1983).

Ansari, F.R. *Islam and Western Civilization*, (Karachi: World Federation of Islamic Missions, 1975).

Armstrong, Karen. *Muhammad: A Biography of the Prophet*, (New York: Harper, 1992).

Ati, Hammudah Abd-al. *Islam in Focus*, (Indianapolis: American Trust Publications, 1977).

Aune, David. E. *The New Testament in Its Literary Environment*, (Philadelphia: Westminster Press, 1987).

Ayoub, Mahmoud M. *The Qu'ran and Its Interpreters*, vol.1, (Albany: State University of New York Press, 1984).

.... *Redemptive Suffering in Islam: A Study of the Devotional Aspects of 'Ashura' in Twelver Shiism*, (New York: Mouton Publishers, 1986).

Azzam, Abd al-Rahman, *Batal al-Abtal Muhammad*, 2nd edition. (Cairo: The House of Arabic Books, 1954).

.... *The Eternal Message of Muhammad*, trans. Caesar E. Farah, (Cambridge: The Islamic Tracts Society, 1993).

Barton, James. *The Christian Approach to Islam* (Boston: Pilgrim Press, 1918).

Bethmann, Erich W. *Bridge to Islam*, (Nashville: Southern Publishing Association, 1950).

Bolich, Gregory G. *Authority and the Church*, (Washington, D.C.: University Press of America, 1982).

Borrmans, Maurice. *Interreligious Documents: Guidelines for Dialogue Between Christians and Muslims*, trans. R. Morston Speight, (New York: Paulist Press, 1990).

Brandon, S.G.F. *A Dictionary of Comparative Religion*, (New York: Macmillan, 1970).

Brady, James R. *Jesus Christ; Divine or Son of God*, (Lanham, Maryland: University Press of America, 1992).

Brink, Gijsbert van den. Ed., *Christian Faith and Philosophical Theology* (Essays in Honor of Vincent Brummer), (The Netherlands: Pharos, 1992).

Brown, Stuart. *The Nearest in Affection: Towards a Christian Understanding of Islam*, (Geneva: WCC Publications, 1994).

Browne, L.E. *Eclipse of Christianity in Asia,* (Cambridge: University Press, 1933).

Burghardt, Walter J. Thompson and William G. Eds., *Why the Church?* (New York: Paulist Press, 1977).

Chardin, Pierre Teilhard de. *Science et Christ*, (Paris: Seuil, 1965).

Cohen, R. Cohen. *Under Crescent and Cross: The Jews in the Middle Ages*, (Princeton: Princeton University Press, 1994).

Cole, W.O. Ed., *Moral Issues in Six Religions*, (London: Heineman, 1991).

Cox, Harvey. *Many Mansions: A Christians's Encounter with Other Faiths*, (Boston: Beacon Press, 1985).

Cragg, Kenneth. *The Call of the Minaret*, (New York: Oxford Press, 1956).

.... *The Dome and the Rock: Jerusalem Studies in Islam*, (London: S.P.C.K., 1964).

.... *The House of Islam*, 2nd Edition, (Encino, Ca.:Dickenson, 1975).

Daniel, Norman, *The Making of an Image*, (Oxford: One World, 1993).

.... *The House of Islam*, 2nd Edition, (Encino, Ca. Dickenson, 1975).

D'Costa, Gavin. *Theology and Religious Pluralism*: The Challenge of Other Religions, (Oxford: Basil Blackwell, 1986).

Denny, Frederick M. *Islam and the Muslim Community*, (San Francisco: Harper, 1987).

Dunn, James D.G. *Unity and Diversity in the New Testament*, (London: SCM Press Ltd., 1977).

Dupvis, Jacques, *Jesus Christ As The Encounter of World Religions,* (New York: Orbis Books, 1991).

Endress, Gerhard. *An Introduction to Islam*, trans. Carole Hillenbrand, (New York: Columbia University Press, 1988).

Gairdner, W.H. Temple. *The Reproach of Islam*, (London: Student Volunteer Missionary Union, 1909).

Glasse, Cyril. *The Concise Encyclopaedia of Islam*, (San Francisco: Harper, 1991).

Glubb, John Bagot. *The Life and Times of Muhammad*, (New York: Stein and Day, 1970).

Goldziher, Ignaz. *Muslim Studies*, vol. 2, ed. S.M. Stern, (London: George Allen & Urwin, 1971).

.... *Introduction to Islamic Theology and Law*, trans. Andras and Ruth Hamari, (Princeton, N.J.: Princeton University Press, 1981).

Goodall, Norman. ed., *The Uppsasla Report, 1968: Official Report of the Fourth Assembly of the World Council of Churches, Uppsala July 4-20, 1968*, (Geneva: W.C.C., 1968).

Granquist, H. *Marriage Conditions in a Palestinian Village*, Vols. 1 & 2, (Helsingfors, 1931, 1935).

Grimme, Herbert. *Mohammed*, vol.2, (Munster, 1985).

Halen, Henry H. *Halley's Bible Hand Book*, 24th Edition (Grand Rapids: Zondervan Publishing House, 1965).

Haley, Alex. *The Autobiography of Malcolm X*, (New Yok: Ballantine Books, 1965).

Hamilton, Bernard. *Religion in the Medieval West*, (Great Britain: Edward Arnold Publishers, 1986).

Harper, Michael. *Male and Female in Church Family: Equal and Different*, (London: Hodder and Stoughton, 1994).

Hassan, Riffat, Hayin Gordon, Leonard Grab, Eds., *Women's and Men's Liberation: Testimonies of Spirit*, (New York: Greenwood Press, 1991).

Hayek, Michael. *Messiah*, (Beirut: Catholic Press, 1961).

Henneck, Edgar. *The Infancy Gospel of Thomas and the Protevangelism of James, New Testament Apocrypha*, ed. and trans. R. McL Wilson, (Philadelphia: Westminster Press, 1963).

Hengel, Martin. *Crucifixion*, (Philadelphia: Fortress Press, 1977).

Hick, John. *God and the Universe of Faiths*, (London, 1977).

Hick, John and Hebblethwaites, B. *Christianity and Other Religions*, (New York: Collins, 1980).

Hick, John and Knitter, Paul. *The Myth of Christian Uniqueness*, (New York: Orbis Books, 1988).

Hinnels, John R. ed., *Textual Sources for the Study of Religion*, trans. Andrew Rippin and Jan Knappert, (Chicago: University of Chicago Press, 1990).

Hitti, Philip K. *The Arabs: A Short History*, (Chicago: Henry Regenry, 1943).

.... *History of the Arabs*, 9th Edition, (New York: St. Martin's Press, 1966).

.... *Islam: A Way of Life*, (New York: Henry Regenry, 1971).

.... *History of the Arabs*, 10th Edition, (New York: St. Martins Press, 1974).

Hocking, William E. *Rethinking Missions: A Layman's Inquiry After One Hundred Years*, (New York: Harper and Bros., 1932).

Hooft, Visser't W.A. *No Other Name*, (London: SPCK, 1963).

Horsely, Richard A. *Bandits, Prophets, and Messiahs: Popular Movements at the Time of Jesus*, (San Francisco: Harper and Row 1985).

Hughes, Thomas Patrick, *A Dictionary of Islam*, (London: W.H. Allen, 1953).

Hussain, Justice Aftab. *Status of Women in Islam*, (Lahore: Law Publishing Company, 1987).

Hussein, Kamal. *City of Wrong*, Trans. E.T. Amsterdam, (London, 1959).

Izutse, Toshihiko. *God and Man in the Koran: Semantics of the Koranic Weltanschauung*, (Tokyo: Keio Institute of Cultural and Linguistic Studies, 1964).

Johnson, David E. ed., *Uppsala to Nairobi: 1968-75. Report of the Central Committee to the Fifth Assembly of the World Council of Churches, December 31, 1972 and January 9-12, 1973*, (New York; Friendship Press, 1975).

Johnson, James Turner and Kelsay, John. eds., *Cross, Crescent and Sword: the Justification and Limitation of War in Western and Islamic Traditions*, (New York: Greenwood Press, 1990).

Johnston, Arthur P. *World Evangelization and the Word of God*, (Minnesota: Bethany Fellowship, 1974).

Jones, Bevan L. *The People of the Mosque*, (London: S.C.M. Press, 1932).

Kateregga, Badru D. and Shenk, David W. *Islam and Christianity: A Muslim and A Christian Dialogue*, (Grand Rapids: Eerdmans, 1980).

Kedar, Benjamin Z. *Crusade and Mission: European Approaches to the Muslims*, (Princeton: Princeton University Press, 1984).

Kelly, J.N.D. *The Early Christian Doctrines*, (London: A & C. Black, 1968).

Kelly, Marjorie. Ed., *Islam: The Religious and Political Life of a World Community*, (New York: Praeger, 1984).

Khan, Inamullah. *God and Man in Contemporary Islamic Thought*, ed. Charles Malik (Beirut: American University, 1972).

Khan, Muhammad Muhsin. *The Translation of the Meanings of Sahih al-Bukhari*, 6th edition. (Lahore, 1983).

Knitter, Paul. *No Other Name? A Critical Survey of Christian Attitudes Toward the World Religions*, (New York: Orbis Press, 1985).

Kraemer, Hendrich. *Why Christianity of All Religions?* (London Lutterworth, 1962).

.... *The Christian Message in a Non-Christian World*, (Grand Rapids, Michigan: Kregell Publishers, 1963).

Krey, August C. *The First Crusade: The Accounts of Eye-Witnesses and Participants*, (Princeton and London: Harper, 1921).

Krejci, Jaroslav. *The Human Predicament, Its Changing Image: A Study in Comparative Religion and History*, (New York: St. Martin's Press, 1991).

Kung, Hans. *On Being a Christian*, trans. Edward Quinn, (Doubleday: New York, 1968).

Laffin, John. *Holy War, Islam fights*, (London: Grafton Books, 1988).

Lane-Poole, Stanley. *The Speeches and Table, Talk of the Prophet Mohammed*, (London: Macmillan & Co., 1882).

Lapidus, Marvin. *A History of Islamic Societies*, (Cambridge: Cambridge Press, 1988).

Latif, Syed Abdul. *Islamic Cultural Studies*, (Lahore: Shaikh Muhammad Ashraf, 1947).

Ledit, R.P. Charles-J. *Mahomet, Israel et le Christ*, (Paris: La Colombe, 1956).

Lewis, Bernard. *Race and Color in Islam*, (New York: Harper and Row, 1971).

.... *The Jews of Islam*, (Princeton, N.J.: Princeton University Press, 1984).

.... *Islam: From the Prophet Mohammed to the Capture of Constantinople*, (New York: Harper & Row, 1974).

Lings, Martin. *Muhammad: His life Based on the Earliest Sources*, (London: Inner Traditions International, 1983).

Macdonald, Duncan. *Development of Muslim Theology*, (Lahore: Premier Book House, 1964).

Mahmudunnasir, Syed. *Islam, Its Concept and History*, (New Delhi: Kitab Bhavan, 1981).

Maududi, Syed Abul A'la. *Unity of the Muslim World* (Lahore: Islamic Publications, 1967).

.... *Fundamentals of Islam*, (Lahore: Islamic Publications, 1975).

.... *Islamic Way of Life*, (Kuwait: ILFSO, 1977).

Mawdudi, Abu al-Ala. *Khutubat* (An English Version), 2nd ed. (Chicago: Kazi, 1977).

.... *Towards Understanding Islam*, 6th Edition, (Salimiah, Kuwait: International Islamic Federation of Student Organization, 1982).

Muir, William. *Mahomet and Islam*, (St. Paul's Churchyard: Religious Tract Society, 1883).

Mussner, Franz. *Tractate On The Jews*, (Philadelphia; Fortress Press, 1984).

Neuner, John and Dupuis, Jacques. *The Christian Faith in the Doctrinal Documents of the Catholic Church*, (Bombay: Catholic Book Publs., 1972).

Newbigin, Lesslie. *The Finality of Christ*, (Richmond: John Knox Press, 1968).

Norton, Charles Eliot. Trans. *The Comedy of Dante Alighieri,* (Chicago: University of Chicago: University of Chicago Press, 1977).

O'Shaughnessy, Thomas. *The Koranic Concept of the Word of God,* (Rome: Pontificio Instituto Biblico, 1948).

Padwick, Constance. *Muslim Devotions,* (London: S.P.C.K., 1961).

Parrinder, Geoffrey. *Jesus in the Quran,* (New York: Barnes and Noble Inc., 1965).

Parshall, Phil. *The Fortress and the Fire: Jesus Christ and the Challenge of Islam,* (Bombay: Gospel Literature Service, 1976).

Pelikan, Jaroslav. *The Emergence of the Catholic Tradition (100-600), The Christian Tradition: A History of the Development of Doctrine,* vol.1 (Chicago and London: University of Chicago Press, 1971).

.... *Towards Understanding Islam,* 6th Edition, (Salimiah, Kuwait: International Islamic Federation of Student Organization, 1982).

Pipes, Daniel. *In the Path of God: Islam and Political power,* (New York: Basic Books, 1983).

Prideaux, Humphry. *The True Nature of Imposture, Fully Displayed in the Life of Mahomet,* (London, 1708).

Qutb, Sayyd. *The Mission of Muhammad,* (Karachi: Islamic Foundation, n.d.).

.... *Milestones,* (Cedar Rapids, Iowa: Unity Publishing, n.d.).

Rabbath, E. *L'Orient chretien a la veille de l'Islam,* (Beirut: Librairie Orientale, 1980).

Ragg, Lonsdale, ed. *Gospel of Barnabas,* (Oxford: Clavendon Press, 1907).

Rahman, Fazlur. *Islam,* (New York: Double Day and Co., 1968).

Rahner, Karl. *Foundations of Christian Faith: An Introduction for the Idea of Christianity,* (New York: Herder, 1978).

.... *Theological Investigations,* Vol.5 (London: Dorton, Longman & Todd, 1926).

Riley-Smith, Jonathan Simon Christopher. *The knights of St. John in Jerusalem and Cyprus,* 1050-1310, (London: 1967).

Rippin, Andrew. *Muslims : Their Religious Beliefs and Practices,* Vol.1. (London and New York: Routledge, 1990).

Robinson, Neal. *Christ in Islam and Chrsitanity: The Representation of Jesus in the Quran and the Classical Muslim Commentaries,* (London: Macmillan Press Ltd., 1991).

.... *The Sayings of Muhammad* (London: Duckworth Press, 1991).

Rodinson, Maxine. *Mohammed,* Trans. Ann Carter, (New York: Penguin Books, 1971).

Ruether, Rosemary. *Faith and Fratricide,* (Seabury: Winston Press, 1985).

Sabourin, Leopold. *Priesthood: A Comparative Study*, (Leiden: E.J. Brill, 1973).

Sachedina, Abdulaziz. *The Development of Jihad in Islamic Revelation and History*, (New York: Greenwood Press, 1976).

.... Ed, *Human Rights and the Conflicts of Cultures: Western and Islamic Perspectives on Religious Liberty*, (Columbia, S.C.: University of South Carolina Press, 1988).

Said, Edward. *Orientalism*, (New York: Vintage Books, 1979).

Samartha, Stanley. *One Christ - Many Religions: Toward Revised Christology*, (Maryknoll, NY.: Orbis Books, 1991).

Savory, Roger. *Introduction to Islamic Civilization*, (Cambridge: Cambridge University Press, 1976).

Schaff, Philip. *The Creeds of Christendom*, Vol.3, (Grand Rapids: Baker Books House, 1977).

Scherer, James A. *That the Gospel May Be Sincerely Preached Throughout the World*, (Geneva: LWF Report, 1982).

Schillebeex, Edward. *Christ: Sacrament of the Encounter with God*, (London: Sheed and Ward, 1963).

.... *Jesus: An Experiment in Christology*, (New York: Crossroad, 1979).

Seale, M.S. *Quran and the Bible*, (London: Groom Helen Ltd., 1978).

Shuon, Frithjof. *Understanding Islam,* trans. D.M. Matheson (New York: Roy Publishers, 1964).

Slomp, J. *Pseudo-Barnabas in the Context of Muslim-Christian Apologetics*, (Rawalpindi: Christian Study Centre, 1974).

Smith, Jane Idleman. Ed., *The Precious Pearl: A Transition from the Arabic*, (Missoula, Mt.: Scholars Press, 1979).

Smith, Roberton, *Kinship and Marriage in Early Arabia,* (Cambridge: University Press, 1985).

Southern, R.W. *Western Views of Islam in the Middle Ages*, (London, 1962).

Sweetman, Windrow J. *Islam and Christian Theology: A Study in the Interpretation of Theological Ideas in the Two Religions*, (London and Redhill: Lutterworth Press, 1945).

Swidler, Arlene. ed. *Human Rights in Religious Traditions,* (New York: Pilgim Press, 1982).

Taymiyya, Ibn. *A Muslim Theologian's Response to Christianity*, trans. Thomas F. Michael (New York: Caravan, 1884).

Thomas F. Michel, S.J. (Delmar, New York: Caravan Books, 1984).

Ur-Rahim, Muhammad 'Ata. *Jesus Prophet of Islam.* (Diwan Press: Norfolk, England, 1977).

Walker, Williston. Richard A. Norris, David W. Lotz, Robert Handy. *The History of the Christian Church*, 4th Edition, (New York: Charles Scribner's Sons, 1985).

Walther, Wiebke. *Women in Islam*, (Princeton and New York: Markus Wiener Publishing, 1993).

Watt, Montgomery W. *Muhammad At Mecca* (Oxford: Clarendon Press, 1953).

.... *Muhammad At Medina*, (Oxford: Clarendon Press, 1956).

.... *Muhammd, Prophet and Statesman*, (London: Oxford University Press, 1961).

Wiles, Maurice. *Christian Theology and Interreligious Dialogue*, (London: SCM Press, 1963).

Wright, Robin, *Sacred Rage; The Wrath of Militant Islam*, (Sussex, U.K.: Linden Press, 1985).

Zaehner, R.C. *At Sundry Times: An Essay in Comparative Religions*, (London: Faber and Faber, 1958).

Magazines/Journals

Allen, Diogenes. "The Paradox of Freedom and Authority", *Theology Today*, vol.xxxvi, no.2, (July, 1979).

Ayoub, Mohammed M. "Towards an Islamic Christology", *The Muslim World*, vol.I xvi, no.3, (July 1976).

Bates, Searle. "Islam and Religious Society" *The Muslim World*, vol.xxxvi, (Jan., 1946).

Cragg, Kenneth. "The Riddle of Man and the Silence of God: A Christian Perception of Muslim Response", *International Bulletin of Missionary Research*, (October 1993).

Klootwijk, Eeuwout. "Mission, Witness, and Conversion in Relation to Dialogue", *Bangalore Theological Forum*, (UTC., Bangalore, India, 1994).

Kerr, David. "The Challenge of Islamic Fundamentalism for Christianity", *International Bulletin of Missionary Research*, (October 1993).

Sanneh, Lamin. "Can a House Divided Stand? Reflections on Christian-Muslim Encounter in the West", *International Bulletin of Missionary Research*, October 1993.

Schneller, Peter J. vol.xxxvii, "Christ and Church: A Spectrum on Views", *Theological Studies*.

Syrdal, Rolf A. "Christ In The Chinese Koran," *The Muslim World,* Vol. xxvii, (Jan. 1935).

INDEX

MINNALIS

"I do hope you will keep me entertained. Hee-hee! Hee-hee-hee!!"

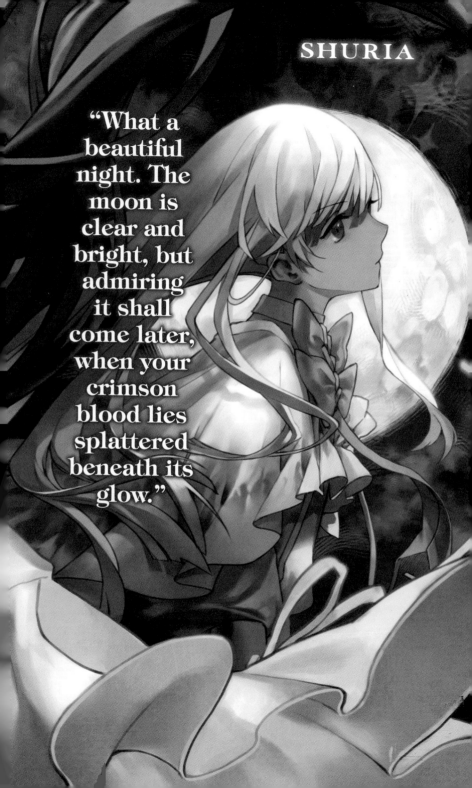

SHURIA

"What a beautiful night. The moon is clear and bright, but admiring it shall come later, when your crimson blood lies splattered beneath its glow."

"My name is Leticia.

A super-ultra-mega-pretty name, is it not?"

DEMON LORD
Leticia Lu Harleston

The Hero Laughs While Walking the Path of VENGEANCE a Second Time

3 The Spellcaster of Deceased Dreams

NERO KIZUKA

Illustration by SINSORA

YEN ON

NEW YORK

The Hero Laughs While Walking the Path of VENGEANCE a Second Time

3

NERO KIZUKA

TRANSLATION BY JAKE HUMPHREY • COVER ART BY SINSORA

NIDOME NO YUSHA WA FUKUSYU NO MICHI O WARAI AYUMU Vol. 3
BOMU NO MAJYUTSUSHI
©Kizuka Nero 2017
First published in Japan in 2017 by KADOKAWA CORPORATION, Tokyo.
English translation rights arranged with KADOKAWA CORPORATION, Tokyo,
through TUTTLE-MORI AGENCY, INC., Tokyo.

English translation © 2022 by Yen Press, LLC

Yen On
150 W 30th Street, 19th Floor
New York, NY 10001

Visit us at yenpress.com • facebook.com/yenpress • twitter.com/yenpress
yenpress.tumblr.com • instagram.com/yenpress

First Yen On Edition: August 2022
Edited by Yen On Editorial: Maya Deutsch
Designed by Yen Press Design: Wendy Chan

Yen On is an imprint of Yen Press, LLC.
The Yen On name and logo are trademarks of Yen Press, LLC.

Library of Congress Cataloging-in-Publication Data
Names: Kizuka, Nero, author. | Sinsora, illustrator. | Humphrey, Jake, translator.
Title: The hero laughs while walking the path of vengeance a second time /
Nero Kizuka ; illustration by Sinsora ; translation by Jake Humphrey.
Other titles: Nidome no yusha wa fukushuu no michi wo warai ayumu. English
Description: First Yen On edition. | New York, NY : Yen On, 2021.
Identifiers: LCCN 2021038196 | ISBN 9781975323707 (v. 1 ; trade paperback) |
ISBN 9781975323721 (v. 2 ; trade paperback) | ISBN 9781975323745 (v. 3 ; trade paperback)
Subjects: LCGFT: Fantasy fiction. | Light novels.
Classification: LCC PL872.5.I97 N5313 2021 | DDC 895.63/6—dc23
LC record available at https://lccn.loc.gov/2021038196

ISBNs: 978-1-9753-2374-5 (paperback)
978-1-9753-2375-2 (ebook)

1 3 5 7 9 10 8 6 4 2

LSC-C

Printed in the United States of America

3 The Spellcaster of Deceased Dreams

The Hero Laughs While Walking the Path of VENGEANCE a Second Time

NERO KIZUKA

CONTENTS

"Just you wait. It will be **painful,** but we will be there to **nurse you** back to **health.**"

"If you can help me exact **revenge** against Eumis, then take my **body,** my **heart,** my **mind,** my **soul.**"

PROLOGUE

O Lady of Light, please spare my little sister..."

I was praying at the town chapel, as I had been doing every day since Shelmie fell ill. The medicine to treat her was so expensive that I wouldn't be able to afford it, even if I worked for the rest of my life.

It was then that Eumis appeared.

"Oh my, you're even more adorable than I imagined," she said to me.

"Huh?"

"Are you Shuria? My name is Eumis. I'm your elder sister. Pleased to make your acquaintance."

As I stared in confusion, she cupped my cheek, smiled lovingly into my eyes, and whispered:

"You've worked so hard, haven't you? Good girl."

Hearing that made me happy.

So very happy...

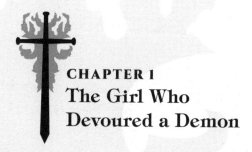

CHAPTER 1
The Girl Who
Devoured a Demon

Hmm? I don't know who you are, but I like the smell of your soul, boy. Though, you do seem familiar somehow... But no matter. You look scrumptious. I shall feast on you next."

"Ha, thanks. I guess that means a lot coming from a demon. Doesn't mean I have to like it, though."

I sneered at the demon's words and readied the Mystic Blade of Soulfire in my hand.

"By the way, you're no ordinary swordsman, are you, boy? You sliced my arms off real good."

"Is that a problem?" I retorted. "You all don't have bodies anyway."

"Hmm?" He gave me a curious look. "I doubt you could tell that just by looking. Does that mean you've dealt with my associates before?"

Demons were a kind of spirit, a bundle of mana possessing a will of their own. Just like spells, they came in six varieties: Fire, Water, Wind, Earth, Light, and Dark. Unlike Affinities, however, there were no Null or Miscellaneous spirits. Instead, there were two other types: angels and demons.

These two groups did everything in extremes, so I wasn't particularly fond of either of them. For now, though, I only had to think about the spirit in front of me.

"Something like that," I responded. "Anyway, I wouldn't say you guys really 'associate,' do you?"

"You have a point, my boy. I never did get along with my own kind. None of us do. And so? If you knew all that, why bother trying to wound me?"

The demon smirked as he regrew his lost arms. The ones on the floor dispersed into nothing, becoming mana once more before they joined back with his body.

It was Shuria who spoke next. "Why...?" she asked quietly. I glanced over to find her kneeling, the hem of her dress stained by the dirt floor of the basement.

"You just sit tight," I told her. "Don't die before I can recruit you."

And with that, I turned back to my opponent.

"Let me give it to you straight. You're kinda in my way. You wouldn't mind getting lost, would you?" I pointed at him with the Mystic Blade of Soulfire. "I'd like to keep my mana usage to a minimum, so I'll let you go if you make yourself scarce."

"Run away? Me? You must be joking, boy. Why would I do that when there's such a tasty-looking morsel in front of me?"

"I see. In that case...die."

As I channeled mana into my soul blade, it erupted into pale-blue flames. The demon recoiled at the light, which gave me a chance to lop off his forearm. The limb fell to the ground, azure fire dancing across the wound.

"Oh? You're a spellsword, boy? Well, too bad. You can't harm me, and those flames won't change anything!"

Ignoring the demon, I continued to hack at the arm on the ground, mincing it into tiny pieces.

"Are you deaf? There's no point! Any time you cut a bit off me, I can just..."

Suddenly, the demon's face fell.

"Wh-what? What did you do to me?"

"Oh, I wonder?" I smiled. "What do you think?"

A demon's body contained neither flesh nor bone. Rather, it was a shell composed of partially materialized mana. If I mixed my mana in with his, he wouldn't be able to reabsorb it without first separating it again—a task akin to sorting grains of sand. And while the demon stood there floundering, the blue flames had quickly disintegrated his severed arm so significantly that it was now completely irretrievable.

This was the Mystic Blade of Soulfire's true power. It didn't just grant me incorporeality. That was merely one application of its ability to give my mana ghostly form. I could also use that same power to hinder a spectral opponent, as I had here. Additionally, the blue flames spouting from its blade could deal damage to life-forms that lacked a physical body.

"I-impossible! H-how could you...?"

"Wrong answer."

"Grargh!"

Normally, demons were immune to all but Holy Magic, the highest tier of Light incantations. Consequently, they tended to ignore their opponents' attacks completely to focus on casting slow, powerful spells, and their actual fighting ability was relatively poor. Deprive them of that one advantage, however, and they would have a lethal opening.

Stepping in close, I performed a rising slash to tear off the demon's other arm, along with one of the wings sprouting from his lower back.

"Damn you!"

"Wrong again."

The demon attempted to completely dematerialize and flee, but the passive ability of the Mystic Blade of Soulfire allowed me to see spirits even when they were incorporeal. With a single diagonal slice, I severed his right leg at the hip, and his left at the knee, then proceeded to dice them up so finely that the limbs couldn't be reabsorbed.

"H-how?! How can you see me?! I'm not even corporeal!"

"Do I really look dumb enough to give my advantage away? Besides, you can see our souls, so it's only fair."

"Damn you! Who the hell are you?!"

The demon's top half toppled to the floor. With only one wing remaining, he was now completely immobile, and I was close enough to cut him down immediately if he so much as tried to cast a spell.

"Your kind puts too much trust in your immunities, and your evasive skills are all the worse for it. There, how's that for an explanation? Aren't I nice?"

I grinned at the trembling spirit, but he gave no response. He *had* asked me to explain, right? How rude.

"W-wait! Please! I was just…following orders! My contract! Eek!"

I channeled more mana into the Mystic Blade of Soulfire, causing the blue flames to burn even brighter. He recoiled in terror.

"Yeah, I know," I said. "Demons can't help or harm anybody without contractual approval. I know that."

"S-so…let me off, please? Look, I'll leave the girl alone! Her soul was just my payment; I'm not contractually obliged to take it. And I'll never make another deal again! Just…"

"Just? Just what?"

I raised my soul blade above my head.

"Just…do me a favor and let me live… Please?"

"Oh, no can do. There's nothing I hate more than strangers asking favors of me."

Because I'd learned the hard way that no good ever came of giving help to people who asked for it.

"S-stop! Let me gooo!"

"No."

Just as I was about to swing my sword down and end it, there came a voice.

"Please wait!"

"Hmm? What do *you* want?"

It was Shuria, clinging to my waist. The girl whom the demon had been tormenting moments before. I briefly considered the possibility that he had charmed her with his magic, but I had been paying close attention the whole time, and I had seen nothing of the sort.

"You can't, Kaito. Please don't kill him."

When I saw the fire lurking behind her scarlet eyes, however, I was ashamed I hadn't realized it sooner.

"I must be the one to end him," she said. "Please don't take that away from me."

"Ah, of course. How could I forget? I could never stand idly by while someone snatched away one of my mortal enemies."

If another person swooped in and took out my opponent without knowing the depths of my hatred, then looked at me like they'd done me a favor, I think I'd murder them on the spot. It wasn't like I objected to other people taking part in my revenge if we had different motives, but I couldn't allow them to exclude me from it entirely. Watching from the sidelines would be like sitting upon a chair of searing iron.

Hmm. Well, it'll take a while for the demon to regenerate.

I flashed a quick glance at the fiend, who was scrambling to retake his lost mana and activate his regenerative powers. Had he still not realized what I'd done, or was this simply the only option left to him? Either way, I had plenty of time to complete my recruitment first.

"Hey, Shuria. I actually came today to offer you an invitation," I told her.

I quelled the flow of mana into the Mystic Blade of Soulfire and recalled the sword into myself. Then I turned to face Shuria and lightly pushed her back, whereupon she fell to the ground, hands between her legs, and stared up into my eyes.

"I know what you've been through," I said. "You want to take revenge on Eumis, don't you? You hate her so much, it's all you can think about."

As I spoke, Shuria pulled the most disgusted face I'd ever seen. If looks could kill, this one would tear you apart. I knew it well.

She was thinking I could never understand how she felt.

She was appalled that I was rattling off about her thirst for vengeance, as though I could empathize.

I continued, "You hate this demon, don't you? And you'd never allow his existence to be snuffed out without having a hand in his death yourself."

She was right. Even if we were cut from the same cloth, we weren't *partners* yet. For that, we had to truly understand each other. It wasn't enough to have a few points in common. I really *didn't* comprehend her pain, nor she mine. No number of words could get it across.

"But right now, you're not strong enough to do the deed. Weak as this demon is, you still can't land so much as a single scratch on him."

"Th-that doesn't matter!" she cried.

I hit her back with a fierce, intimidating glare that was laced with mana. Rooted to the spot in sheer terror, Shuria lost whatever urge she had to resist.

"It's pathetic. But that's not the end of it. You won't have a hand in Eumis's death, either. I'll kill her myself. I don't care what she did to you. Suffer in powerlessness forever for all I care."

"Graaargh!" Shuria screamed. Overcoming her fear, she launched herself at me. No plan, just a mindless assault at the enemy standing before her. I effortlessly stepped aside, grabbed her by the scruff, and tossed her face-first into the dirt floor. She squealed as I stepped on her back.

"Grr! Get off…!"

"Right now, you have nothing. You've lost it all. Because you were clueless. Because you didn't try to understand."

"…"

"It was not power you lacked—it was determination. Your heart was full of love, when it should have been filled with enough poison to paint the whole world black."

"…Know that."

"You only saw what you wanted to see. You never tried to understand her motives. You just said, 'I trust her,' like that *meant* anything. *That's* why you're suffering now. It wasn't because of anything you did. It was because of what you *didn't* do."

"I get it! I get it! Stop lecturing me!"

The flames in her eyes flickered. Black flames of pure, directionless rage. They would devour her before long.

"You're in pain," I told her. "If you promise to give up on revenge, I'll let you go."

"Grr! Gah! Do not…mock me…! Eumis is mine and mine alone!"

"Do as I say, and you can leave this place alive. I'll hand you all the money you want, and you can go live in a nice house in the countryside somewhere. I really do feel sorry for you, you know."

"Keep your coin!" she cried. "A life like that is no better than death!" Shuria howled like a trapped beast. She really would expire if she couldn't exact her revenge. "I'll kill her I'll kill her I'll kill her! I'd sooner die than cast my anger aside!"

Any trace of rationality had left her. She was in hysterics, acting solely on emotion.

But what she'd just said, they were the first words of a newborn rebel desperately clinging to life.

"I see," I remarked, removing my foot. As I did, she sunk her teeth into me. Not lightly, to warn me off, but as if to tear my flesh apart.

9

"Yowch. You don't show mercy, do you?"

"Wh-why aren't you fighting back?" she asked, relaxing her jaws in suspicion.

"I was testing you. Believe me, I know how awful the things I just said were."

"…"

She locked eyes with me, trying to probe my true motive.

"But remember what I told you? This is an invitation."

"An…invitation…?"

"Yep," I said, squatting down before her.

"You told me you'd rather drop dead than cast your anger aside." I paused and looked her in the eye. "That's what I'm here to offer you. Die and be reborn."

Then I held out my hand and asked, "Shall we take revenge together, Shuria?"

☆

Today had been like a nightmare. Everything I had was taken from me.

No, that wasn't right—I realized for the first time that it had all been an illusion to begin with.

Still, it had been a dreadful day. I'd lost so much.

And yet…

"It's pathetic. But that's not the end of it. You won't have a hand in Eumis's death, either. I'll kill her myself. I don't care what she did to you. Suffer in powerlessness forever for all I care."

I threw myself at him before I could stop myself. But I wasn't strong enough to hurt him, of course, so he tossed me to the ground. He was like a wicked sorcerer from a fairy tale.

It was as if he knew everything about me. He presented me with every one of my flaws and laughed in my face.

And he threatened to take my sworn enemy away from me.

"You're in pain," he said. "If you promise to give up on revenge, I'll let you go."

How could he say that? It was enough to make my ears ring.

"Do as I say, and you can leave this place alive. I'll hand you all the money you want, and you can go live in a nice house in the countryside somewhere. I really do feel sorry for you, you know."

What's the point in that? I can't go back. I'm broken. There's nowhere for me to return to. There's no way I can just live a quiet life by myself anymore.

"I see."

He stepped off me, and I looked up at his face. Kaito was smiling at me. The threatening aura I felt before was nowhere to be found.

Isn't he a spirit? I thought briefly, but I could no longer find it in myself to care about such things.

If I did nothing, if I didn't fight back, he would take away my mortal foe, the only thing I had left. Then I would truly have nothing. I couldn't let that happen, even if it killed me. So I went for his leg. Surely, he would just dodge it and finish me off. Of course he would. He came to save my life, and look at how I repaid him. I didn't even take him up on his offer when I'd had the chance. He had every right to kill me.

I'd refused my chance to give up on revenge.

Because when I'd been lying there broken, ready to give up and accept death, I made a choice. I decided to do something about it, swore that I would see it through to the end.

Yet strangely, my foolish attack struck true. I had meant to tear him apart, but I could not continue against an unresisting opponent.

"Wh-why aren't you fighting back?"

"I was testing you. Believe me, I know how awful the things I just said were."

11

"…"

Then, for the first time, I looked into Kaito's eyes. They were deep, dark, and empty, like a bottomless swamp. I contemplated this man who would take my vengeance away from me.

"But remember what I told you? This is an invitation."

"An…invitation…?"

"Yep."

The emotion in his voice was now totally different. It pried apart the pieces of my shattered mind and wormed its way inside.

"You told me you'd rather drop dead than cast your anger aside. That's what I'm here to offer you. Die and be reborn."

He grinned. The smile of a devil.

"Shall we take revenge together, Shuria?"

His hand looked like a normal human's. But it belonged to an infernal creature. To take it would be to plunge myself into an infinite darkness from which there was no escape.

"…Together?" I asked.

"That's right. Choose. Between becoming my partner in crime or becoming a bystander. If you take my hand, you will be granted great power, but there will be no turning back. Your vengeance will fuse with mine, so even after we're done with Eumis, you'll have to continue working toward my goals. Our contract is bound by something thicker than blood, and I'm not being metaphoric. If I die, you die, and vice versa."

His voice came to me as if through deep water. This man was surely the real demon here. Like the ones from my books. An evil being who lured mankind into straying from the true path. But that was okay.

"That is all fine by me," I said. "I only want to know one thing. If I take your hand, will she suffer? Will I be able to see her brought low by pain and ruined with grief?"

That was the only thing that mattered to me. Together or alone, I didn't care so long as I could exact my revenge.

"Why are you still talking like a bystander? We'll be partners in crime. She won't just suffer; *you'll* make her suffer. This is what I've been saying. *You* have to decide. *You* have to choose. *You* have to think about it. I'm not going to do it for you. You have to make it happen."

"...Oh, you really are just like a devil. Here to lure me astray without any comforting words or hard promises."

"You already know what a lifetime of being dependent on others gets you, don't you?" He grinned. It was so dark, the word *smile* didn't seem to fit. But I knew the look on my own face was probably the same.

That hand was everything I had ever wished for. It offered me salvation, but it would make a demon of me.

"Please, Kaito," I said. "If you can help me exact revenge against Eumis, then take my body, my heart, my mind, my soul. Take everything and turn me into a devil like you!"

I reached out and took it.

"Please, Kaito. If you can help me exact revenge against Eumis, then take my body, my heart, my mind, my soul. Take everything and turn me into a devil like you!"

She wrapped her tiny, pale hand tightly around mine.

"First, I'm a ghost, then a spirit, and now a demon?" I remarked incredulously. "You're all over the place. I hate to break it to you, but I'm just an ordinary human."

I pulled Shuria up to her feet and conjured the Holy Sword of Retribution—in its shortened form for making contracts—into my hand.

She stared at me in disbelief. "What ordinary human can turn their body into mana and conjure swords out of thin air?"

"…Well, this blade right here will answer one of those questions for you. The other, I'll explain later. Here, take it. It'll tell you what to do."

As Shuria took hold of the weapon, a deep, dark, yet dazzlingly bright black light burst from the blade, as if in acceptance of her.

"What a strange glow," she murmured. "It's cold, dark, and hot." Her scarlet eyes twinkled as she gazed at the sword in wonder. Specks of black light drifted about the blade, like confetti inaugurating the rise of a new avenger.

Then as though she was embracing a prized possession, she turned the tip of the sword in on herself and plunged it into her chest. The blade shone before disappearing into a shower of brilliant particles like the blooming of a flower. There was no sign of a wound where the girl had stabbed herself.

Shuria murmured as dreaming. "Kh… Ah… Mm…" She was reliving my memories, just as Minnalis had. I, too, watched the scene through her eyes and witnessed again an experience even more powerful than if I were really there. The second time didn't get any easier, and try as I might, I found myself unable to bear it without scowling in disgust.

By the time the last of the dark specks of light had winked out, there was no longer any distinction between her vengeance and mine.

"It's nothing like having it explained, is it?" I remarked.

"No. I was surprised. I never expected to meet someone who has gone through something so similar to what I have."

Shuria let loose a mixed sigh, tinged with resolution.

"It felt very strange. But…what a wondrous power you have given me."

She opened and closed her hand several times before glancing around the room. As her eyes fell on what she was searching for, her face brightened, and she let out a quiet chuckle.

"What a wonderful thing to be left lying around. Let us make him our first subject."

It was a stuffed cat, sitting in the corner of the room. Shuria walked over to it and crouched, holding her hand out over its belly.

"Pussycat, pussycat, where did you go?

"Death has come to the land of snow.

"In the magic kingdom, time stands still.

"Come on, little pussycat, eat your fill.

"…Dance for me: *Puppet Possession*."

Combined with Shuria's swelling mana, her strange, singsong chant sent a number of red, yellow, and black particles dancing into the air. The mana flowed into the doll until, at last, the particles, too, were sucked inside.

"Mm… Ah… I feel giddy… The MP drunkenness… Ah-ha… Ah-ha-ha-ha-ha-ha! Now, rise!"

Slowly, but surely, the doll reacted to Shuria's voice. It sat up, shook, and rose to its feet.

"Huh," I said. "Now that's interesting."

"The interesting part comes next!" Shuria grinned. "Hee-hee! Hee-hee-hee!" she giggled, swept away on a wave of emotion. The doll turned neatly to face its master and bowed. Shuria flashed it a satisfied smile and bestowed on the puppet its first orders.

"Devour that pitiful clown. And make sure you savor it, okay?"

"Hee-hee-hee! Hee-hee-hee-hee!" the doll cackled and nodded. It turned and waddled toward the demon, trailing a knife and fork in its hands along the floor. I had planned on finishing the spirit off myself, but it would have been rather rude of me to intervene, so I instead opted to take a step back and watch what played out.

"C-curse you! Who are you? What are you?!"

15

The demon's regeneration was only half complete, but in a last-ditch effort, he had quickly recreated the rest of his body with a minimal amount of mana. As he tried to flee, however, the stuffed doll kicked him to the dirt floor.

"You dare mock me? Get off!" yelled the demon, shaking his hand to free himself from its grip.

"Hee-hee-hee!" laughed the puppet.

"Wh-what?!"

Ignoring him, the stuffed animal raised its knife, which grew to an enormous size, before swinging it down and severing the demon's arm.

"Ha...ha-ha..." the demon chuckled in relief. *"That knife's not like the other guy's sword. I can just absorb that mana back into me like so..."*

However, his relief proved short-lived.

"Didn't Shuria tell it to 'devour him'?" I pointed out. But before the demon could work out what that meant, the faithful puppet gave a helpful demonstration.

"Hee-hee-hee!"

It stabbed a fork into the demon's severed arm, then sliced up the limb with its (now normal-sized) knife before tossing a chunk into its mouth.

The demon watched in shock. *"...What?"* The pussycat doll gobbled up the rest of his arm before his very eyes while he struggled to process what was happening.

"Whoa, whoa, what the hell? It ate it? That thing ate my arm?"

"Ah-ha-ha-ha!" The mocking tones of Shuria's laughter rang out before the puppet joined in with a mischievous chuckle. "What's that look on your face? Is something the matter?"

As the demon's question went unanswered, the pussycat doll turned to face him once more, then clanged its knife and fork together twice.

"Dammit! Dammit, dammit, dammit, dammit! What the hell is

wrong with you?! First, a sword that burns mana, now a doll that eats it? That's not fair! It's against the rules!"

"*Pfft!* Pretty rich, coming from a demon," I remarked. I hadn't wanted to intervene, but he walked right into that one.

"*Don't you get it?! You lower life-forms are beneath me! So how come—? Goddammit!*"

The pussycat doll continued to do battle with the demon, if such a phrase applied to this one-sided slaughter. Though the demon couldn't feel pain, terror gripped him all the same. That was plain to see on his face as the doll consumed his body from the extremities inward.

Eventually, the only thing left was the demon's head. "*How could I be done in by a filthy human and a damn elf...?!*" By now, the mana that composed his body had completely dispersed. Before long, the rest of him would decompose to join it.

"Aww, that was boring. I wish my doll could've had a little more to do; it was his first fight and everything... You're no fun."

"Don't worry, Shuria," I consoled her. "We've still got Eumis to go, remember? We don't need to stretch out this part too much."

"I know...," she said dejectedly as she crouched. "Okay... I'll make this the last one."

Then she turned, smiled cheerfully at the demon, and gave the toy its final order.

"I'll be watching until the very end. Now, clean your plate!"

"*Damn you aaaaaaall!*"

"Ah-ha-ha-ha-ha-ha!"

"*Hee-hee-hee!*"

The doll plunged its cutlery into the demon's face and plucked out his eyeballs, feasting on them before tossing the head into the air and swallowing it down in a single gulp. The puppet belched and clashed its knife and fork together one last time for good measure.

The next instant, the toy began to change. Dark patterns swirled across the surface of its white fur like clinging shadows, dying it a deep black.

But meanwhile, an even more astonishing transformation was taking place before me.

"Huh? I feel warm... Hot, even... Mm...," muttered Shuria as a cloud of black mana enveloped her.

"Shuria?! What's happening? Are you okay?!"

I panicked. I didn't know what was going on, but any threat to her life was also a threat to mine because of our contract. Minnalis's, too.

"Hmm. I don't think it's anything bad," Shuria speculated. "It just feels like I'm burning."

She didn't appear to be in pain. Whatever this phenomenon was, it must not have been life-threatening. As I stood and watched, the eddy of black mana dispersed, and all was normal again.

Except...

"Oh, you're just full of surprises, aren't you?" I remarked.

"...Did I transform?" asked Shuria, looking down at herself. Her white porcelain skin, so soft that you could sink your fingers into it, was now an almost sensual tawny brown. On top of that, the color had faded from her beautiful blond hair, leaving it completely silver. Through the holes in her torn outfit, I could see that a black-inked tattoo of some sort was covering her stomach. The orange light of the candles illuminating the basement reflected off her hair as she ran her fingers through it.

This must have been a consequence of the doll regurgitating the demon's mana.

"A dark elf, huh?" I mused. "Ha-ha. How lucky you are. I couldn't make you a demon, but this is the next best thing, don't you think?"

"A dark elf?"

"That's what they call elves with dark skin like you. At least in my world, they do."

Elves were not an uncommon race. I had seen a fair amount walking around various cities. Many of them leveraged their superior talent for magic to make a living as adventurers. But an elf with dark skin... Well, I had never even so much as heard of one, let alone seen one.

That's why I had always assumed they didn't exist. But when I checked Shuria's status screen, I noticed that in addition to her new "Puppet Possession" ability, her race had changed from *Human (Elf Blood)* to *Dark Elf.*

Shuria   Lv33

Age 14 • Female • Dark Elf

HP: 292/332   MP: 780/780 (Assigned: 525)

Strength: 133   Stamina: 213

Vitality: 194   Agility: 288

Magic: 679   Resistance: 582

Intrinsic Abilities: Scarlet Eyes, Puppet Possession
Skills: Notice Lv 1, Stealth Lv 1,
Water Magic Lv 1, Wind Magic Lv 1,
Meditate Lv 3, Carve Lv 3
Status: OK

Shuria

- -

Hidden Statistics

Finesse: E

Reaction Time: E

Recovery Rate: F

Status: OK

Magic Affinity

Fire: 0   Light: 0

Water: 0   Dark: 0

Wind: 0   Null: 21

Earth: 0   Misc.: 154

Acquired Titles

Elf Blood, Hexed, Slave to Revenge,

Puller of Strings, Fallen Elf

"Well, it doesn't seem to be dangerous, at least," I reassured her.

"I'm a dark elf... I like it. I really feel as though I've been reborn," said Shuria, giving herself another once-over.

"Come on, let's go. The demon's dead, and I already used up a lot of MP getting through this place's wards. We need to leave before Eumis comes back, assuming she hasn't realized I'm here already."

As we walked over to the stairs, however, Shuria stopped in her tracks.

"Oh, wait. I have to set them free."

She turned back and gestured to the pussycat doll (which now boasted a marbled pattern of black-and-white fur), and the toy set about slaying the wretched undead that lay rotting in the cells. The undead were immortal, but without mana to sustain their bodies, they soon fell apart; even their bones returned to dust. Before long, there wasn't any indication that they had been there at all.

"Let's get out of here," I told her when it was done. "There's not much time, and we've got a lot to discuss."

"Indeed."

As we reached the base of the staircase, Shuria turned and took one last look around the cellar.

"I will kill Eumis if it is the last thing I do. I will take the pain she inflicted on others and return it to her tenfold."

Her words were wreathed in dark flames. There was nothing more for me to say. With the moans of the zombies now gone, the basement was silent. As she ascended the staircase for good, the black-and-white pussycat followed behind her.

==

Puppet Possession Skill Level: 2

Temporarily reduces max MP and turns an inanimate object into an unliving servant. The servant's abilities depend on the environment, the amount of MP offered, and the type and intensity of emotions expressed during casting.

Amount of MP donated cannot exceed max MP.

A number of familiars up to twice this skill's level can act autonomously, and the caster can exert manual control over as many as they can handle. While acting autonomously, a servant can absorb the mana of certain targets through ingestion. Each servant can only take on one type of mana at a time. If a servant obtains a new variety of mana that is stronger than what it currently possessed, the old type is replaced.

???????????????????????????????????
???????????????????????????????????

Absorption List:

Demon-Eater

==

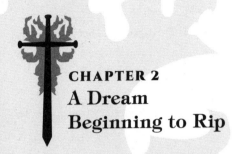

CHAPTER 2
A Dream
Beginning to Rip

Day xx Month xx

My research into magic items has hit a standstill. I simply do not have enough magical ability to continue. Without some way of increasing my power output, further progress is impossible.

This does not mean I am giving up. I will have my name carved into the stone monument. If I do not, then even my father, loving as he is, will refuse to accept my relationship.

Just you wait, Soriy. When our day comes…

Day xx Month xx

Today's experiment resulted in another failure. Even my area of greatest talent, Wind magic, is only slightly above average, and the insignificant monsters of this region do little to increase my level.

With careful training, it would yet be possible to increase the amount of mana I can handle, but this method is much too slow. Soon enough, Father will begin to speak of marriage. I must accomplish something before then.

Day xx Month xx

I tried adjusting my methods and succeeded in producing an effect.

However, it is still too weak. I am far from creating a magic item that will ensure my name is recorded on the stone monument.

They say that you must present a suitable item to the monument itself and that the spirits of dead heroes dwelling within will cause one's name to appear by magic if your offering impresses them.

What do I need to do to produce such an item?

Please forgive me, Soriy. I am weak. The moment we can finally be together grows further by the day.

Day xx Month xx

Today, some businessmen from the city came to see me at the academy. They were intrigued by a by-product of my experiments and wished to discuss bringing it to market. There was much money to be made in the enterprise, they said. I have no interest in becoming an inventor, nor are such petty discoveries enough to satisfy my ambitions, but maintaining my workshop requires coin, it is true, and it is better to have too much than too little. Thus, I sent some off to be sold in the city.

I thought nothing of it at the time, but now that I condense my thoughts into this diary, it strikes me as a rather good idea. If the townspeople know and respect my name, even just slightly, then surely, it will be more difficult for my family to object to my wish.

The wish granted to those who have their name engraved on the monument has long been a solemn tradition of my house, but it is always possible they will choose to defy it anyway. Better to be safe than sorry.

On another note, Soriy was particularly adorable today. I simply never tire of seeing her blush as she speaks my name.

Day xx Month xx

Today, a strange merchant accosted me in the street. The city of Elmia sees all kinds, so suspicious types like this fellow are not uncommon, and usually, I simply brush them off and go about my day. On a whim, however,

I heard him out. When he presented his wares, I found something of great interest to me nestled among them. A demon-summoning stone.

I managed to procure it from him for far less than it was worth. Perhaps the merchant was ignorant of its true value?

Day xx Month xx

I completed my research today. With the proper precautions in place, I succeeded in summoning and binding a demon. These spirits are able to bestow great power and wisdom, albeit at an enormous price.

I asked him if it would be possible to offer the life of a slave, say, to increase my talent for magic.

The demon said yes, then described a hex whereby I could seal a blood relation of mine within a magical circle for an extended period of time to transfer their aptitude into me.

Ah, it appears God is on my side after all!

The only thing I need is a subject. A relative who is both exceptionally gifted in magic and gullible enough to be locked inside a room for the entire length of the ritual.

Fortunately, such a person exists. A half sister of mine on my father's side, the abandoned product of an affair with a maid. Her name was Shuria, I believe. At long last, the end of this dark tunnel is creeping into view.

When I told Soriy my plan and explained that soon we would be together forever, she graced me with a joyous smile and asked if there was anything she could do to help. Oh, what a sweet and generous thing she is!

Day xx Month xx

The scheme is proceeding without a hitch. Lady Luck must surely be on my side for Shuria to require my assistance just as I sought her myself. I was able to secure her trust with promises and brought her back to the mansion.

After that, the demon took his price for his knowledge of the magic circle and the particular flavor of mana required to activate it, and I succeeded in securing several additional test subjects for my experiments. I told the authorities that a demon attacked the village, and they bought it hook, line, and sinker. Now all that's left is to ensure that idiotic half sister of mine never leaves that room.

Who knows the destruction she could cause with *my* power? If I gave her a reason, it would be a trifle for her to escape the magic circle or, at the very least, escape it and ruin the hex. I cannot count on finding another source of materials so convenient as that village. Even if I did, I doubt the same excuse would fool the authorities twice.

And so it seems that until the hex is 100 percent complete, I must continue to play the role of her kind elder sister.

Day xx Month xx

I have hit upon a momentous discovery. My doting upon Shuria appears to have struck my dear Soriy with the most bitter jealousy, and she seems quite keen on reasserting her possessiveness, particularly in my bedchamber. Though Soriy is no commoner, it is true that her noble house is subservient to ours, and so she has always adopted the meek attitude appropriate to her station. I am beginning to see a new side of her as of late, and her increased affections are very much welcome. Ah, how my loins burn even now!

Day xx Month xx

I received a letter from my parents in the capital. Though they were careful not to be direct about it, they clearly showed interest in my marriage prospects. I burned the letter thoroughly, until not even ash remained. Their probing has grown more pressing of late, perhaps due to my continued refusal to engage in such petty courtship. Ahhh, how I wish to be immortalized on the stone monument so that I may spend my life together with my beloved!

Day xx Month xx

Very soon now, the hex will be complete. I must start thinking about *what will happen afterward. Shuria's Scarlet Eyes have piqued my curiosity. Perhaps they could be used in the creation of a divination artifact of some kind.*

As for the girl herself, her temporary custody of my talents should make her a fine receptacle for mana. She will make a far better undead than those other failures.

Day xx Month xx

Finally, the day has arrived. The completion of the hex took far longer than I imagined. How much of my talents that pip-squeak of a girl has stolen from me! But by tomorrow morning, every last drop will be back in the possession of their rightful owners.

I think I will take her out tomorrow and show her a beautiful dream. In gratitude for all she has given me and everything she has yet to give. I am a kind sister, after all.

"I see. So that's what everything was for."

As I tried to keep my welling emotions in check, I slowly closed Eumis's diary and placed it back on the desk.

…How disappointing.

How utterly, utterly disappointing. *This* is the reason you wanted to create a new magic item? *This* is why you betrayed me?

She wanted a *statue* to recognize her achievements so she could marry her favorite maid. For that, she'd stabbed me in the back and thrown her own sister to the wolves. She'd built the ladder to her ambitions from the bones of the many.

"…Well, whatever. I thought that maid might be all you cared about, but I suppose you must respect your parents a fair bit, too, if simply killing them never crossed your mind. I guess that means they'll have to get up on stage as well, then."

I hid the diary back where I had found it and left the mansion, salivating at the delightful new seasoning I had discovered to sweeten my vengeance.

"Urk... Ahhh..."

Not this nightmare again. I knew it was a dream, but that didn't make the scene unfolding before my eyes any more bearable.

"Here is your medicine! Make sure you drink it all down, please!"

"Hrk! You might as well give up! I'll never give in to you— *Rrrh!*"

"Whether you submit or not is of no importance. You tricked me as well. That's the only thing that matters."

I was in a dark cave, illuminated by brightmoss. There, lying on a bed that was little more than a boulder split cleanly in two, was Soriy. Her arms and legs were cruelly bound with iron shackles, like what you would use on a slave.

In these visions, there was always a girl standing over her, wearing a peaceful smile. Though she resembled Shuria, her hair was silver instead of blond, and her skin was tan, like people who hailed from the desert. But her features were exactly the same, right down to her scarlet eyes.

Standing beside her, like usual, was a young man with dark hair and eyes whom I felt I'd seen somewhere before, along with a brunette Lagonid girl.

Shuria placed a contraption partially inside Soriy's mouth to force it open, then poured in some kind of pea-green liquid before forcing a gag over her mouth, as though she expected her to choke.

"Ngaaah! Aaah! *Cough! Cough!*"

When that was done, Shuria ripped off the gag and said, "Now then, we finished the arms yesterday, so we'll move on to the legs next."

"Here you are," said the Lagonid girl, handing her a black spike like she always did. It was apparently hollow, and the point on the end could open.

"Thank you," Shuria said in response.

I longed to look away, lest I be forced to bear witness to that terrifying spectacle once again, but alas, my dream offered me no such control over my own body. I could not even close my eyes.

"Hng?!" Rrrgh! Aaaaaagh!"

I could only watch as they drove that wicked prong into my beloved's beautiful leg.

"Aaagh! Hnnn! Uraaargh!!"

Her vile captors impaled three more spikes, and with each one, my ears rang with Soriy's screams. And yet somewhere in her voice were the soft, sultry tones she only used with me in the bedroom.

Shuria tittered. "What a deviant you are to be aroused by such treatment, Soriy."

"Mg... Ahhh... It's the fault of that tonic you fed me...!" she replied.

"Oh no, the tincture merely dulled the pain a bit. It only goes to show that a little is enough to bring you great pleasure." She gave a slight smile. "Now the easy part is over. Try not to pass out like you did yesterday, okay? There's no point in hurting you if you aren't awake to feel it."

"Eeek!"

She raised a large bottle containing a black, metallic liquid that moved and jumped at Shuria's command, as if it were alive. After bringing the bottle close to Soriy, she gently pulled the stopper free.

"Dinnertime," she announced. The black substance crawled up out of the bottle and slithered down into Soriy's body via one of the hollow stakes.

"Hgnah!"

As the end of the stake opened up inside her, Soriy let out another sweet yelp. But it didn't stop there.

"Mmmmmaaah! Hng! Oooh! Aaaah! Mmm! Mm! Ah! Aaah!"

"I really don't see how you can be enjoying yourself like that," said Shuria. "If it was *my* bones being dissolved, I think I'd scream."

"My lady… My lady! Miss Eumis!"

"Look, Master. The pleasure she feels is only slightly outweighed by the pain," the Lagonid girl remarked. "She must be quite conflicted over how to feel, the poor thing."

"Hey, it's your toxins doing that," the boy replied.

"I'd prefer if you referred to it as a 'tonic,' Master. It's helping her, not hurting her. After all, it'd be a shame if the agony broke her too quickly."

While my love lay tortured and bloody on the stone, her captors chatted idly among themselves. Yet as much as I yearned to burn the three of them to cinders, I could not so much as move a muscle, even in my own dream. All I could do was watch as the same terrible scene played out again, listening as Soriy cried out in a mixture of pain and passion.

"Hah?! Haaah…haaah… Ah…that dream again. What a terrible way to wake up."

Drenched in sweat, I sat up in bed and sighed. I glanced at the clock and found that it was a little later than when I usually awoke.

"That makes four days in a row. What is happening to me?"

The nightmares had begun shortly after my demon-summoning stone lost its power. They were the same every time I slept. The girl who looked like Shuria and her two mysterious accomplices would torture my dear Soriy. It all felt so real, and there was seemingly no end in sight.

"Perhaps that demon broke his contract and placed some sort of curse upon me."

After offering Shuria to the demon, I'd spent most of the morning after in wild ecstasy with my beloved. By the time I got dressed, I found that the stone I had used to summon him had reverted to a powerless old rock. I rushed to the secret cellar to find out what had happened, only to see that it was completely empty. There was no sign of the demon or Shuria. Even my host of test subjects had seemingly vanished into thin air.

Perhaps most surprising of all, though, was that the cage at the far rear had simply been cleaved open. I was at quite a loss on how to explain that. It was unthinkable that Shuria, what with her waifish figure, had done it, and any magic power she may have once possessed ought to be completely gone by now. Her elven blood would do her no good without any magic, so she should have been incapable of slaying a demon by every stretch of the imagination.

That meant the demon must have interfered. Though I knew not how, he'd broken our contract, taken off with both Shuria and my test subjects, and found a new stone in which to dwell. I had heard that demons often switched stones after completing their contracts, so it was not out of the realm of possibility.

"Oh dear, I cannot allow Soriy to see me like this."

I poured myself a tall glass of water from the pitcher by my bed and gulped it down before my beloved entered the room.

"Good morning, my lady," she said. "Breakfast is ready."

"Thank you," I replied. "Shall we take it together, then?"

"I—I could not possibly sit at the dining table, my lady. I am but a humble maid."

"Then we shall eat in my chamber where nobody shall see us. Prepare a large platter for us to share. I am not feeling too hungry this morning anyway."

I sent her away with a smile. Soriy seemed unsure, but she nodded and left the room, saying, "I shall bring it up, then."

I just wanted to be with her a while today. I had not mentioned my dreams to her, lest I make her unnecessarily anxious. Though no actual harm had befallen me, I could not help but feel a vague sense of dread. I longed for a time I could be at peace. Though my goals were in sight, there was still much work to be done.

"It is a shame, however, that I was not able to procure Shuria's eyes. They would have made fine ingredients for my research."

Eyes were a precious component of magic items, and plenty had been forged with dragon or fenrir eyes in the past. Perhaps an artifact made using the "Scarlet Eyes" would have won me a spot on the monument.

What a loathsome demon. Helping me to achieve my goals only to snatch them away just as quickly.

"Well, no matter. With my newfound magic power, it is only a matter of time before I succeed in creating a marvelous new artifact."

What's gone is gone. It was better to focus on where to go from here.

"I suppose I cannot wait any longer for everything to fall into my lap. I must travel to continue my study and collect even more valuable ingredients."

Though Elmia was a trade hub, truly rare items were sold in the capital or even in the empire, where they would fetch a higher price. My workshop did not want for supplies, but there was no telling how long it might take for another opportunity like Shuria to come along if I stayed put.

However...

I cast my gaze about the papers on my desk. There were requests for information on magic-item development from the capital, tax reports, and even a notice detailing a large amount of holy water stolen from a nearby church.

I would need someone to take my place while I was gone. As my father's only child, I could not simply abandon my duties.

"I heard rumors that the demon lord has been ramping up her assaults as of late. If a legendary hero was to appear once more, perhaps I could join their party somehow..."

If that happened, I would have a pretext for leaving the city that would not tarnish my good name. Instead of abandoning my domain to follow my own whims, I would be working for the good of the kingdom. My father, an aristocrat in the capital, could not possibly object to that.

Come to think of it, I had heard that the capital had attempted the ritual to summon a hero. I wonder what became of that?

As I was lost in thought, there was a knock at my door. In came Soriy with our meal perched atop a tea cart.

"My lady, breakfast is served," she announced, carefully transferring the plates to the dining table. "Today's meal consists of grilled pork sausages and boiled cluckbird eggs, with a side of bread and butter. For dessert, we have rawstberry and goat's milk pudding."

"Thank you, it looks delicious."

We proceeded to have a lovely breakfast, feeding each other spoonfuls of food before moving on to mouth-to-mouth. The juices of the dessert were so sweet that I wished to stay there forever, but eventually, I tore myself away and began changing into my outdoor clothes.

"Are you working at the office again? Good luck in your endeavors, my lady."

"Thank you," I said, getting up to leave. Just as I placed my hand on the knob, however, a thought occurred to me.

"Actually, could you do something for me, Soriy?"

"Hmm? Of course, my lady. What is it?"

"Could you roll up your skirt, please?"

"Huh?!"

Her face flushed, but she meekly did as I asked. I watched on in silence as she gripped the hem of her skirt and slowly lifted it to reveal her long, slender legs and lacy underwear.

"I-is this okay, my lady?"

Her legs bore no scars or marks whatsoever. Of course, since she'd been with me last night, right up until we fell asleep, there hadn't been time for her to sustain them.

...*I'm overthinking it. I must put it out of my mind.*

Perhaps it would behoove me to see a doctor or a priest about these dreams.

I tarried there awhile, taking in the precious sight of my dear Soriy, her face tinged scarlet with embarrassment, before leaving the mansion to take care of my daily tasks. As far as I could tell, everything was in order. I walked the streets thinking sweet thoughts about my future life together with my beloved.

The same dream again. How long are these going to go on for?

I had lost track of the number of times now.

...*At least it is about to end*, I thought. I had seen the exact same vision so frequently, I could recite it by heart. And yet tonight, it diverged from my memories.

"Now, everything is in place," Shuria said. For the first time, she turned to address me directly. "Sister? We're not done yet. My puppets will dance on the stage you prepared."

Huh?!

When she abruptly closed in, I could see that her eyes were not the brilliant scarlet I was accustomed to, but more of a deep crimson, like dried blood. Her unwavering gaze was unbearable, but as always, I could not so much as move a muscle.

"We can't stop now. We mustn't," she insisted. "We must continue until the final curtain falls. There is much in store. Please, please look forward to it."

Then a smile spread across her lips that made me shiver in terror.

A spine-tingling dread rushed up my back, causing me to shoot awake in bed.

Last night, Soriy and I had fallen asleep together. I shot a glance beside me, but she was nowhere to be found.

"*Khee-hee-hee! Khee-hee-hee-hee-hee!*"

"Wh-who's there?!"

As my troubled mind returned to wakefulness, I glanced around my room to find nothing out of the ordinary.

Wait, no. Something was different.

Atop a table sat a patchwork bear. Its design was quite memorable; I recognized it as one of the toys Soriy had bought for Shuria.

How did it get in here...?

"*Khii-hii! Khii-hii!*"

Astonishingly, the voice appeared to be coming from that stuffed animal. Not only that, but it also proceeded to unfasten a zipper I had thought to be a mere decoration and produced a letter from inside. It gave a neat little bow, as if mocking me, and placed the letter on the table before leaping out of my bedroom window.

"W-wait!" I cried. By the time I reached the open window, however, it had already fled out of sight. As questions whirled in my head, I tried to stay calm and analyze the situation.

The sealed envelope read "Invitation" on the front. On the back, it was signed "*From Shuria and your faithful avengers.*" I thought back to my nightmares.

"Soriy! Soriy! Where are you?! Answer me, Soriy!"

I shouted and shouted, but there was no response. The other servants heard my screams and came running, but none of them had any idea where she had gone. It was as if she had simply disappeared without a trace.

We turned the entire house upside down without finding her. Perhaps if she had been sleeping in the servants' quarters, the other maids would have some clue regarding her disappearance. As it happened, however, I had given her a private room to facilitate our illicit encounters on the pretext that a noblewoman should not have to sleep with the other servants, so none of them even knew at what time she had gone missing.

Wait, no. Soriy was with me that night. I remember seeing her fall asleep before me. In that case…

"…The only clue remaining is that letter."

I held the single sheet in my hand. Even disregarding the scarlet envelope, it possessed a deeply sinister aura. Nevertheless, it could serve as some sort of clue to Soriy's whereabouts. I rushed to break the seal. Inside was an audio message, recorded on my own light-blue paper marked with the family crest.

"My beloved sister," it began. *"The performance begins tonight after sundown. If you wish to see Soriy again, then I suggest you attend. Come to the eastern gate at sunset, and I will send for you. I look forward to seeing you there."*

It was Shuria, no doubt about it, and there was a sense of elation in her voice. Not like what I had shown while she was in my care, but pure, unfiltered joy.

This was proof that my sister yet lived and that my nightmares had been anything but ordinary.

"B-but how…?"

I had a hunch, but it simply defied all sense. How could Shuria, a completely powerless little girl, have escaped her cell and survived?

Had the demon allied himself with her? Impossible. There were certain rules that had to be followed when making a contract, so there was no way he and Shuria could have formed a pact, even if they wanted to. And without a contract in place, it would be impossible for the demon to take any action at all. He couldn't be helping Shuria. It just didn't add up.

But the fact remained that Shuria still drew breath and was retaliating against me for what I'd done.

I can think about that later. Right now, I have to save Soriy!

"Get me Lomberto," I demanded, and before long, a vulgar giant of a man appeared before me.

"You called, Mistress?"

Around fifty of the city's soldiers swore fealty to me. Together, they made up an elite force over which I exercised direct control. Since they were all former mercenaries or adventurers who had proven themselves in battle, they were very useful when I needed to get my hands dirty. My band of killers took care of people who obstructed my ambitions or got too nosy, and they had also aided me with the destruction of Shuria's village.

As long as I kept them happy, they did whatever I asked of them. At times like these, they were indispensable.

"I have a job for you, Lomberto."

"Yeah? And what about our pay?"

"Worry not. You shall all be given one gold piece each. Now gather the rest of the men."

"All of them?" Lomberto's eyes widened in shock. Assassinations or the like rarely required so many men; five or six at the most typically sufficed. Besides, their usual duties were espionage and intelligence. Today, however, I was not in the mood for that.

"Yes, all of them. This is not an assassination mission. Soriy has been taken hostage, and I need you to go rescue her."

"Why us, then? Hostage situations are the regular militia's thing."

"But they will likely make her captors face justice. I would much rather tear them limb from limb."

As I glared at Lomberto, infuriated, my mana began to seep out of my every pore.

"Just go and get every man you can find. We begin tonight."

"Yes, my lady."

Understanding when to keep quiet, Lomberto quickly left the room, leaving me to contemplate the situation alone.

"…"

There was too much I didn't yet comprehend. How had Shuria survived? What were those dreams? They had to bear some kind of relation to my present situation, but I'd seen for myself over the past few days that Soriy didn't have so much as a scratch on her.

I looked outside. The sun was still high in the sky.

Gritting my teeth, I set about planning how I would slaughter Shuria and the rest of her crew for taking away my beloved.

When all was in order, I arrived with my squad at the eastern gate, eager for battle. Our story was that we were headed to the northeastern forest for training, which explained why we were armed to the teeth.

Suddenly, something appeared before us.

"It's that thing again…!"

From out of the forest, walking down the road, came the cute little teddy bear that had given me the letter.

"*Khee-hee-hee!*"

It stopped a few paces from us and beckoned mockingly for us to follow before setting off the way it came.

"Follow that doll," I instructed the men.

"Got it."

We set off down the path, trying to keep the toy in our sights.

I was at a disadvantage. I didn't know the strength of my opponents, and they had Soriy. This puppet, which moved of its own volition, didn't appear to be a monster, but the men were already on high alert as they entered the forest. After walking for about an hour, we finally arrived where our enemies were lying in wait.

"Good evening, Sister, distinguished guests," came a soft, clear voice. "I offer you my most heartfelt welcome."

We had come to a clearing devoid of even grass. An empty, circular field. It was as though the forest itself had anticipated our battle.

In the center was a tall tree, barren of every last leaf, and in its branches sat three shadowy figures. One of them, a young girl wearing a black one-piece dress, gave us a cruel smile, her long silver hair gently drifting in the night breeze.

"Shuria… Is that you?"

"Yes, Eumis, it is. It seems I was unable to perish and find myself reborn instead."

She chuckled. I could see no trace of her former self in her visage. Her features, her clothes, and the very air around her were all different. Even her face and voice, which hadn't appeared to have changed at all, now seemed as though they belonged to someone else.

Bathed in moonlight, she peered down at me with burning red eyes and a seductive smile on her lips. The scene seemed so ethereal that it was almost as if I was still dreaming.

But those eyes were devoid of the light that once filled the Shuria I knew.

"What a beautiful night. The moon is clear and bright, but admiring it shall come later, when your crimson blood lies splattered beneath its glow."

A chill ran up my spine, like a frigid tongue of ice had licked my back. Shuria dropped down, as did her two companions, whereupon the enormous tree they had been sitting in quickly rotted and died as though flung forward through time.

The bear that had served as our guide gave another evil chuckle.

"Khee-hee-hee!" Then it trotted over to its mistress, who patted it softly on the head.

"Good work, Teddy," she told it affectionately.

"I thought I'd seen those other two before," I ventured. "Didn't I meet you outside the city when you were fighting the Black Orc?"

"Oh, you remembered us? That's a surprise. I wouldn't have expected you to deign to commit our faces to memory," said the dark-haired young man, and his female companion joined in.

"For someone with the brain of a flea, her memory's not half bad."

The pair shared a smug grin.

"...Utter trash," I spat. "It seems we cannot talk this through after all. Return Soriy to me."

Now I was sure that these two had helped Shuria escape. I had certainly seen their skill for myself in how they had occupied the physically resistant Black Orc without a shred of magic between them. But I couldn't allow myself to be unsettled, neither by them nor by Shuria's transformation. I still had the upper hand, and with my newfound power, I could bring this battle swiftly to a close.

But to my surprise, Shuria responded in the affirmative. "But of course, dear sister. I shall fetch her at once. Kitty, be a dear and bring her here, would you?"

She clapped her hands, and from out of the forest emerged the very last toy I had ever bought her. In place of its knife and fork, which were now strapped to its waist, the puppet instead gripped a chain in its paws.

"Hee-hee-hee!" the pussycat doll chuckled with its unchangeable face.

Groans rang out from behind. "Urgh! Aaagh!"

"Soriy!" I cried.

I watched as the frightful feline dragged my beloved along on all fours. Her clothes were ragged and torn, and her arms and legs were bound in iron fetters. Around her neck, they had fitted a sturdy leather collar, like the kind one might use to break in an animal. The pussycat doll tugged on the chain to lead her to me.

"Kitty, you can let her go now."

"Hee-hee!"

The puppet tittered and swiftly drew its knife, slicing apart Soriy's bonds in a matter of seconds.

"Eek!" she cried.

"Go on," urged Shuria. "Your work here is done."

"Oh, um…"

Soriy looked around in bewilderment before slowly making her way toward me. Then she broke into a run and embraced me with eyes full of tears.

"Miss Eumis! Miss Eumis!"

"Soriy!" I cried, hugging her back as tightly as I could. "My love, what have they done to—?"

But no, this wasn't her at all! No sooner had I realized this than I heard Lomberto's voice. "Get away, my lady!" he cried, swinging his sword at her. I tried to force her off me, but we were both a moment too late.

"Khee-hee-hee!"

The figure thrust a hitherto-unseen blade into my chest, a warped knife with eight multicolored crystals inset. Then the doppelgänger twisted its face and cackled. It was that strange teddy bear's laugh.

"Hrk!"

As I leaped back to make distance, the fake Soriy simply watched me go. Then Lomberto's blade sliced its arm clean off.

I quickly followed up with my own attack. "Witness the terrible shout of the wind spirits! *Lightning!!*"

"Khee-hee-hee, HEE-HEE-HEE!"

My blast of electricity sizzled the assailant, and it disintegrated away into nothing.

"Oh my. I should have known that you wouldn't be fooled by appearances alone," said Shuria, as though it was of no consequence, before she chuckled once more. "Tee-hee-hee! Now the real show can begin. It isn't only going to be yours truly up on stage tonight."

I was furious that she would use Soriy in this manner to get at me, but I set aside my anger as best I could and pulled the dagger free from my chest. When I did, it, too, dissolved into the air.

"What have you—? Ghaaah! M-my head...!"

Before I could finish my statement, a rush of memories came flooding back. I clutched my head in pain, but no. It wasn't my head that hurt. It was my very soul. It felt like part of me was being overwritten.

I wonder if it worked?

I had never expected to use it this way. I'd never tried this before, and to be perfectly honest, I wasn't even sure if it was possible. I had only thrown out the idea as a mere hypothetical because I knew how silly the argument sounded. Perhaps if I'd realized it earlier, I could have tested it on Zuily and her party. Oh well, too late now.

One of Eumis's hangers-on called out to her. "My lady! You bastards!" He scowled at us. "What have you done to her?!"

"What do you mean? We're simply jogging her memory a little," I replied with a smirk.

The blade the fake Soriy had stabbed Eumis with was none other than the Eight-Eyed Sword of Clarity, into which I had channeled as much of my mana as I could.

This soul blade has the power to view and record a person's status screen, after all. But what does that board actually draw upon? It can't be the body; if that's the case, it won't display the person's name. The brain, then? But that doesn't make sense, either, because the blade displays even the names of newborn, who don't have the language skills to understand them.

Which means it can only be the soul it draws upon. At the very least, it's obvious that something like a soul exists in this world, because undead creatures like wraiths exist.

So if status is recorded in the soul, then that means the information recorded in the Eight-Eyed Sword is a copy of a person's soul. Which means, theoretically, it should be possible to directly feed Eumis the information contained within her soul from my first time around.

I know, it sounds crazy. Too good to be true. I had been lucky enough to keep my *own* memories, let alone anyone else's. It would be nice if it worked, though.

And if it didn't, it wouldn't drastically change anything. I would just have to alter my plans a little. But if she did remember, if she knew why I was doing this, it would make her tortured screams all the sweeter.

That aside, it seemed to me that the dagger was indeed working.

"Haah… Haah…" Eumis panted. "Wh-what did you do…? What are these memories…?"

"I think *you're* best equipped to answer that question now, aren't you?" I shot back.

"…You're…Kaito Ukei. A hero from another world. I thought I killed you… Didn't I? These…these are *my* memories."

Her unsteady words were nonetheless proof that she had at last recognized me for who I was. An emotion bubbled up within me. Pure, unbridled delight.

"…Ah-ha! Ah-ha-ha-ha-ha!! Oh! …Oh! Oh! Oh! You don't know

how delighted you make me, Eumis! How glad I am that I can see you face-to-face once more! It's been a long time since you killed me, but now it's finally time to continue our dance. Lights! Camera! Action! The curtain rises on *The Foolish Hero*, act two! And you're to play the leading lady, witch!"

I didn't know whether her memories had replaced the old ones or were simply saved alongside them. It didn't matter to me. All I cared about was that she remembered.

"…I don't know what's going on, but it seems you are intent on opposing my dream," she said.

At any rate, the die was cast…

"That's right, I am! And now I shall fulfill my vow! I'll kill every last one of you! Starting with you, Eumis! I'll drag you down to the depths of despair, of grief, of agony, and there, you'll drown!

…and I would shatter that die to pieces, leaving no indication on which face it fell.

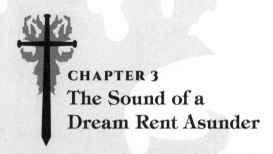

CHAPTER 3
The Sound of a
Dream Rent Asunder

At long last, the time has come. I am ready in mind, body, and soul.

First, I needed to overwhelm her with sheer force.

"What drivel! I do not need to see your status screen to know that I far outclass you! *Lightni—*"

Suddenly, Eumis froze, a terrified look on her face.

"It won't work," I explained. "The blade I stabbed you with was coated in a special toxin that prevents you from using magic. Even if your equipment can counteract it, you won't be able to cast so much as a Fireball until it finishes doing so."

"Hmph…"

Eumis scowled and retreated to heal. Now that she had all her memories and abilities, she would probably be ready to act again in about three minutes. More than enough time to complete the opening act.

"Now, let the slaughter commence. Be sure to watch from your box seat, Eumis. Your appearance is coming up next."

First, I'd give her a viewing of my warm-up—smashing her private army to pieces.

For this, I had prepared the Soul Blade of Beginnings and the Mystic Blade of Soulfire.

Like an exploding bomb, both our band and our enemies rushed into action.

"Stay calm, there's only three! We far outnumber them! Crush them all!" bellowed their leader, the man called Lomberto, as he guarded Eumis.

There were nearly fifty of them. That meant we got fifteen each. Then again, these were the men responsible for the destruction of Shuria's village. It would only be fair to give her the lion's share. I would have to exercise restraint.

"...Ha-ha-ha! Come on, what are you doing?! You'll have to try harder than that!"

We split off in three different directions, and like ants to sugar, a couple of the hired hands swarmed around me. They were too strong to go down in a single blow like those monsters the other day, but that was okay. I only needed to ensure they wouldn't be a nuisance later on. They could slowly succumb to their wounds as they watched the rest of the show.

"Wh-what the...? Graaagh!"

"He's too fast...! Gyaaah!"

"N-no, don't! Gblh!"

I scratched their eyes and sliced the tendons in their legs. As they fell to the ground, I bent their arms backward, so that the shattered bones pierced the skin and inflicted as much pain on them as possible. Before long, three mangled bodies lay strewed across the ground.

"Ah-ha-ha-ha! Hmm? Oh, whoops. Looks like one of you passed out."

And I'd wanted them to feel the life leave them slowly, too. Now he'd die from blood loss without ever waking up again.

Well, losing one was no problem. There were plenty more here, after all.

"What's the matter?" I taunted. "Scared already? I thought you guys were supposed to be ex-mercenaries?"

The soldiers' initial frenzy was already beginning to waver, and they found themselves hesitating to throw themselves back into the fray. Unfortunately for them, I wasn't so generous as to sit back and wait for them to rediscover their courage.

"Graaaargh!"

Leaping into the crowd of men, I impaled the front two in the elbows through the gaps in their plate armor. I tried not to sever their arms, as I didn't want them passing out from the pain again.

"Die, you little shit!"

With both my weapons "otherwise engaged," a third foe saw his chance and sprung on me. It was not a foolish move; to capitalize on your opponent's moments of weakness was a central tenet of battle, and everyone here understood that. He had erred, however, in recognizing what I had done as an opportunity.

I conjured a paper-thin, transparent wing-shaped blade with a red handle. The Wing Blade of Detoxification. With a single slice, I lopped off the man's nose, lips, and eyelids, leaving his face almost perfectly flat. His screams were most pleasing to the ear.

"Gyaaaaagh!"

"I don't want to hear that from you shitheads!" I retorted.

After that, I sheathed the Wing Blade and pulled my two other soul blades free of their targets. Sticking them straight through the wailing man's feet and pinning him to the ground, I gave his unguarded torso a mighty kick.

"Grghaaah!"

My mana-infused blow was nothing to sneeze at, and between my soul blades and his flesh, it was clear which was the weaker. Breaking apart at the ankles, his body flew backward while his feet remained in place.

Seeing this, one of the men broke formation and tried to flee, screaming, "No! He's a monster!"

Using "Air Step," I leaped high into the air to get a bead on him. "Trying to run, are you? Don't leave me all alone here."

I tossed one of my mundane longswords at him, which pinned his foot to the ground. "Gyaaagh!" he yelled out in pain.

The other lackeys around me were too afraid to even turn their backs to retreat.

"Dammit! Who is this guy? Can you cast your spells yet, my lady?" cried the one called Lomberto.

"Almost! Just buy me some more time!" replied Eumis.

"You must be joking! The only thing I'm gonna buy against this guy is my own headstone! I'm gettin' out of here!"

"What?! You would betray your employer?"

"Shut your trap, rug muncher! Money's no good if I'm dead!"

Yet still, there were those foolish enough to try fleeing. *I had better make an* example *of him*, I thought, flinging my throwing knife. It impaled the leader of the mercenaries right in the shoulder.

"Grgh! Gyaaagh! Aaaagh! It hurts! It hurts! It hurts! It hurts!"

The man's eyes went wide in shock, and he fell to the ground, wailing and screaming like a broken record. The knife had been coated in one of Minnalis's poisons, which I had made her prepare specifically for this purpose. The concoction ramped up its target's pain sensitivity until their whole body was racked with agony, but since it didn't obstruct proper blood flow, they wouldn't pass out. My partner in crime had specially crafted it to drain away the target's life more slowly than conventional toxins.

"Come on, don't run. You're harshing the vibes. If you want to survive, you're going to have to deal with us."

""""Eep!""""

I didn't even have to use "Intimidate" this time to get them scared.

"Now, come at me like you mean it. I'll slaughter the whole damn lot of you."

"Gyaaagh!"

"Please stop!"

"M-my arm! It's meeeltiiing!"

"Oh god, it burns! It buuurns!"

"Ah-ha-ha! Ah-ha-ha-ha-ha-ha! Come now, whatever's the matter? Surely, you big, strong men can have your way with one little girl, can't you?"

Their blades were slow. Their reactions were sluggish. Their movements were clumsy and easily dodged. The dirty work these men typically engaged in amounted to threatening shopkeepers or slitting people's throats in their sleep. Not exactly prime opportunities for honing their skills. They were no match for me. This was not even a fight. Like Master said, it was a slaughter.

Oh dear, I must not forget my place. I am merely a supporting actress tonight. I must rein in my desires.

"Die, you rotten bitch!" yelled one, swinging his sword.

"You should watch your tongue, maggot," I shot back, slicing off the hand holding his weapon.

"Hgyaaagh?!" As the man cried out in pain, the blood splattered from his wrist across my cheeks. I screwed up my face in disgust, for more reasons than just the mess.

Still, it was very difficult for me to avoid killing my foes. Master made it look so easy, but there was no way I could stab without hitting the vitals or flaying the skin of a moving target with just my sword like he did. I needed more training.

That's why I was targeting areas that would not prove fatal, such as the eyes, ears, and fingers, plus the genitals if they were men or breasts if they were women.

"You don't mind losing those, do you? You won't need them where you're going!"

"Ugh! Gyaaagh!"

"Oh, can it. Castration is supposed to help dogs calm down. Oh, but I suppose you're just a maggot, aren't you? Not quite as smart as a canine."

I kicked him to the ground, his mouth frothing, and moved on to my next target.

"I do hope you will keep me entertained. This may be the last time I get to cut loose all by myself! Hee-hee! Hee-hee-hee!!"

"What the hell is this doll...? No, my eyes! My eeeyes!"

This one killed the kind old man who'd always given me fresh vegetables.

"Sister?! No, it's a foul illu— Urk!"

That one had massacred the friendly neighborhood kids, smiling all the while.

"Stop! I'm on your side— Blgh!"

"I-it's not me! I can't control myself— Ghuh!"

And these two wretches had gleefully put Mother and Shelmie to death.

"Hee-hee! Ha-ha-ha-ha-ha! Ahhh, look at how terrified you all are!"

Kitty gouged out eyes, sliced off noses, ripped off ears, and cut out tongues before gorging on them, while Teddy transformed himself into people the targets knew, then attacked them in their moment of hesitation.

I, on the other hand, commanded their swords and armor with Puppet Possession to make them turn on their allies and even themselves.

In terms of level, I was very weak, but my new ability was quite effective against these humans because they'd all chosen to wear such perfect metal armor. Even if they were physically strong enough to fight back a little, I could slow them down enough for Kitty and Teddy to finish them off. Well, I say "finish," but I wasn't killing them just yet.

"Oh dear, does it hurt already? I'm afraid there's still a lot more to come if you're to feel the pain of those you murdered."

I could take my time and enjoy watching them perish. For three minutes, on this stage that Kaito and Minnalis had prepared for me, I would personally snuff the life out of everyone responsible for the slaughter and capture of my village's people.

"Ah-ha! Louder! Suffer! I want to hear you scream as loud as you can because my friends and family didn't ever get a choice!"

I commanded a corpse in full plate armor to slaughter the rest of them.

"Stop! Please! We were just doing a job!"

"Don't make excuses! If you had no choice, then what of those people just going about their lives, trying to make what humble livings they could?! What choice did you give them?!"

"Gyah! Aaargh! Stop! Gyaaagh! Ghhh!"

Consumed with rage, I sliced off the man's arms and legs one by one, before impaling him in the throat.

"…Oh, I'm sorry. I didn't mean to kill you so soon. Now we can't have any more fun…"

I ground my teeth. Three years. Three long years I could have spent back at the village, having fun with my family. Three years they spent as abominations locked in that underground cellar.

These insects would succumb to their wounds in less than a few hours, so I wanted to make sure they felt as much pain as I could get away with in that time. I wanted their minds to shatter.

"Yes, I want you to break. All of you! Ha-ha! Ha-ha-ha-ha-ha-ha!"

Kitty and Teddy joined in my laughter, as if resonating with my emotions.

"Hee-hee-hee-hee-hee!"

"Khee-hee-hee-hee-hee!"

"Eek! Gblh!"

"Grh! Gah! Gyaaah!"

"Hee-hee! Oh my, I'm getting wet just thinking about it!"

There's still lots more merriment to be had. Kaito and Minnalis had reassured me that I could have as much fun as I liked and they'd make up for any I lost.

There's not a lot of time. So I'm going to ensure I savor it slowly, like a lollipop, until the very last second.

The splishing and splashing sounded like footsteps in a field after the rain, but the scene before my eyes was nothing so tranquil.

"Ohhh god, it huuurts!"

"Gh… Ugh…"

"Waaaaah! Waaaaah!"

"My arm's gone…! Where are my legs…?"

The scent of blood wafted on the cool night air. Beneath the light of the moon, the earth was like a sea of crimson. In it, *broken* people twitched and spasmed, adding to the chorus of weak moans and wails. It was the perfect overture to Eumis's demise.

Though the corpses of those she had used in her attempts at power now lay around her, it wasn't like they had been anything more than pawns to her. Now that they were broken, she would merely throw them away.

"The lake of fire returns all to cinder. The wicked flame takes all! *Demon's Fire!*"

With a flick of her wrist, dark flames appeared and engulfed the fallen mercenaries.

"Oh god, it buuurns!"

"I'm meltiiing! I'm dyyying…!"

"Bbblblblbbl…"

"Oh dear, you finished them off. Well, they were going to bleed out anyway," I said.

I had taken special care to crush the wounds of the soldiers whose limbs I'd severed so that flesh and bone would seal in most of their blood. Minnalis and Shuria weren't yet skilled enough to pull that off, so their victims would only have lasted thirty minutes at most. Mine, however, could have gone on living in agony for another two, maybe even three hours. During that first hour, they could have even been restored to full health without any lasting symptoms.

Well, I suppose that just proved Eumis didn't want to save them if they were of no further use to her. In either case, their fate was sealed.

"That's not all," Eumis muttered. "My Demon's Fire can…"

"I know, I know. I guess that means you're still the second one at heart," I reasoned. If my record of Eumis's first soul had overwritten the second one—if she was now the Eumis I was familiar with— then she wouldn't have seen the need to explain powers I was already familiar with.

I had been thinking about the memory transfer in terms of data, like it was something from my world, but it wasn't as if the information I stored on my soul blade was a perfect representation of a person's soul, either. Perhaps I just didn't have right intuition for it yet.

Still, as far as my vengeance was concerned, it was good that

Eumis regained her memories, even if it did end up making her stronger; now she had access to the spells we'd developed together.

"Demon's Fire is a combination of Fire, Earth, and spirit magic that creates a chimera of a flesh golem and an undead called a Tenebris-Ignis Giant," I explained. "I knew you'd use that all along."

The dark flames incinerated the soldiers, leaving only charred bones, which started gathering together, assembling.

"Grr! But still, there's nothing you can do about it now! It seemed like I wasted a lot of my precious time tracking you down in that timeline. As recompense, I'll crush you where you stand, so that not even a speck of you remains!"

"Hey, you sure you want to do that?" I replied. "Kill me, and you'll never know where we hid your precious Soriy."

"That shall not be a problem," Eumis growled. "With my necromancy, it will be no trouble to extract the information from your corpse. As much as I'd love to experiment on an otherworlder's cadaver, I shall have to purge your horrid existence from this world immediately because you laid a hand on Soriy. The same goes for that beastfolk girl, and Shuria, too." She gave a fearless shrug. "The filth ought to be all eradicated in one fell swoop, don't you agree?"

But beneath her smug facade, she was evidently fuming at us. Good. That way, we could get maximum enjoyment out of torturing her.

"Grrrooooaaargh!"

"Grrraaaooorgh!"

With a pair of tragic wails, two golems lumbered up out of the earth, their very existence a blasphemy against all life in this world. The bones that composed their nearly six-meter-tall bodies were melted like black tar and cloaked in purple flames. The creatures looked less like constructs made to protect their master and more like the kind of unholy servants a demon would call upon. And owing either to the fires they wreathed themselves in or their overall menace, they appeared even larger than their physical size would suggest.

"Right. Follow the plan. I'll take these. You two, fall back and begin preparing for the next stage."

"Yes, Master," came Minnalis's reply. "Be careful not to overdo it."

"That's right, Kaito!" added Shuria. "If you kill her before I get a chance to, I'm never talking to you again!"

"You guys have no faith in me at all, do you…?"

""That's because we know how deeply you yearn for vengeance!"" they both replied.

Well, I suppose I didn't have a snappy comeback to that. As nice as it was that the Holy Sword of Retribution linked our hearts and minds to make us unable to betray or act against one another, it could be a real pain at times like these. I couldn't hide anything from them. I might as well have not even bothered.

"Just get on with it. I can still hold back. I'm not so hungry that I'd eat our main ingredient before the oven's even heated up."

I briskly shooed them away, and Minnalis and Shuria left to prepare.

"Now then, let's get this show on the road."

"Are you sure you want to ruin your chances like that? You finally had me outnumbered. Do you really think you're strong enough at this time to take me on all by yourself?"

"Of course I am. I'm not the only one who's weaker at the moment. Just because you've regained your memories doesn't mean your stats are any higher."

Well, her Finesse has gone up, I suppose.

Looking at her status screen, I noticed it had risen to B+. Also, with Shuria's magical proficiencies added to her existing training, all her skills ending in "Magic" advanced to their ascended forms, which ended in "Sorcery." Her skill levels were still low, but they were powerful nonetheless.

But none of that would help her against me.

"I suppose that's why you didn't go after the other two, am I right?" I teased. "You need every advantage you can get right now."

"...You talk too much. Now you will die alone at my hand."

"Will I? So how come after I made short work of that bloodthirsty assassin, Gordo, you only ever attacked me with at least three people to back you up?"

When I'd first arrived here, this marvelous illusion of a world ruled by stats and skills gave me some fanciful notions about the sanctity of human life and reinforced my wishful thinking. Alicia destroyed all that.

Soon after, Eumis, realizing she was not strong enough to take me on by herself, had decided to team up with Gordo and come after me. That way, he could keep me busy with his flurry of attacks while she prepped a powerful spell to wipe me out. If I'd still been averse to murder back then, perhaps that's exactly how it would have played out. I had been weakened by the stat-lowering curse embedded in Alicia's firebolts from when I escaped.

However, their plan didn't go so well. Even in my enfeebled state, I'd been strong enough to quickly dispatch Gordo.

Though I had the upper hand in terms of pure speed, his crafty feints and underhanded techniques placed him on about equal footing with me. But still, he could never hope to defeat me. All his clumsy swings and obvious tricks gave so many opportunities. I could read his intentions clearly, not just in the line of his sight and his breathing, but even in the twitches of his muscles and the way he applied his strength. And so I reduced his tricky swordplay to the mere fumbling of a drunken idiot.

Though I certainly didn't come out uninjured, it had been akin to a cat toying with a mouse. Even if the mouse got off a few good scratches in return, the cat would be in no risk of dying from them.

If I had been at full strength back then, perhaps I could have killed Eumis, too, but once she saw things weren't going her way, she used the mana she had built up to cast a powerful teleportation spell and disappeared. I could have taken a few more of them with me the first time if I hadn't let her escape.

Of course, then I wouldn't have been able to torture her as freely as I could now.

"If you're not the same Eumis I know, then I'll just have to teach it to you all over again. Impress upon you that you can never defeat me without hiding behind someone else."

I gripped the Challenger's Blade of Adversity in both hands.

"Grr! Such impudence!" Eumis seethed. "If you think you can kill me, then I welcome you to try!"

"Ha! Now you're starting to show your true self, Eumiiiiis!" I cried, lunging into battle.

While issuing orders to the two Tenebris-Ignis Giants, Eumis began casting her own spell. One of the golems took a few tentative steps before it broke into a run, then it swung a sword wrapped in deep-purple flames and composed of human bone like the rest of its body.

"Ughaaaaah!"

"Tsk!" I sucked my teeth as I caught the blade on mine. "They're as solid as they look!"

If I was to assign them a rank, they'd be in C tier easily. Their sturdy exteriors were about as resistant as the Blackhide of a Black Orc. In terms of pure strength, too, I was at a disadvantage, even with the Challenger's Blade in my hands. But the most threatening aspect of the golems were the flames that covered their bodies. They would drain my MP if I so much as touched them.

You'd think I would switch out my soul blade if it was dragging down my performance that significantly, but right now, it was exactly what I was going for.

"Tri-Lightning!"

"I don't think so!" I shouted, sneering as three separate bolts flew at me from different angles. Meanwhile, the other golem came at me from behind. This one wielded not a sword, but a weapon closer to a hammer. Relaxing my grip, I allowed my foe to launch me up into the air with its attack before using Air Step to create a thin rod in midair that I grasped onto. Then I swung myself around like I was using a gymnastics bar to evade the bolts. With all my momentum intact, I flew toward the golem's hammer, which was not yet in full swing. For an instant, I erected a free-moving Air Step platform between my feet and the oncoming weapon and perched on it like an acrobat.

"Gwuuuaaaagh!"

The blow knocked me back into the air; I did a single somersault and landed neatly some distance away.

"Ha," spat Eumis with contempt. "How unsightly of me. Usually, a single attack of this magnitude would be enough to defeat you."

"You say that, but that's not what you've been doing, is it? You've been hiding behind your golems because you know you aren't strong enough to command your old spells yet."

"Such impudence... I despise you. Golems!"

Realizing she could win if she kept this up, Eumis ordered the sword golem to remain nearby to guard her as the hammer golem lumbered toward me. Meanwhile, she began casting her next spell. I kept my distance from my slow-moving opponent without taking my eyes off it.

"..."

"O whimsical wind spirits, O Lord of Light, that which traces its bizarre locus..."

She was casting Multiple Lightning. Honestly, she was so predictable sometimes. I couldn't help but chuckle at her simplicity.

"I guess I'd better get serious, too…"

I began channeling mana into the Nephrite Blade of Verdure in order to use my secret technique. The one I'd honed against the goblin horde. The one that would allow me to go one step beyond and, in doing so, earn its name.

Eumis's chant continued. "…In a trice, deliver oblivion upon my foes. Unleash an inescapable tempest! *Multiple Lightning!*"

"…*Over Limit*," I muttered to myself, more out of conviction than necessity, and a pale-greenish light enveloped my entire body. As the world around me slowed down, growing dull and faded, I saw Eumis's incantation take shape.

Magic lightning differed from its naturally formed counterpart. While this was what allowed it to follow such contrived paths, it also meant that artificial lightning wasn't quite as fast as the real thing, despite it being swifter than other forms of magic.

I broke into a sprint, dodging past the bolts heading straight for me, then turned to face the hammer golem that Eumis had sent forward to attack.

The technique I'd just used allowed me to go a step beyond even my already perfect Finesse score while ignoring the toll it took on my body. I was not brushing up against my limits; for one small moment, I was surpassing them while continuously using the Nephrite Blade of Verdure to heal any injuries I took as a result. During that brief period, I was truly unlocking my full potential.

"What?!" came Eumis's cry of disbelief.

"Nugruuuagh?!"

"Try to keep up, you boneheaded dunce!"

One, two, three, four, five. I delivered slash after slash to the golem in its neck, upper arm, hip, thigh, and calf, all while it was still slowly dropping its hammer down on top of me. Though I was wielding my soul blade, it was really the blunt impact of my blows that was doing the damage, and they tore huge chunks out of its body.

"Raaaaargh!" I roared.

For a moment, Eumis hesitated. "Hrk! Go…! No, wait! Haah!" It seemed she had decided against sending the other golem after me and opted to launch a Fireball instead. It was the correct decision. Not only would the alternative have left her completely defenseless, but the other golem also wouldn't have been able to reach me in time anyway. Once I shattered the core that gave the one with the hammer life, it would stop moving and return to dust.

"You insignificant worm! Why won't you die already?!" shouted Eumis. As I dodged her attacks, I delivered one last strike to the teetering golem's leg, sending it completely off balance. As it fell to the ground, the deep-purple blaze that surrounded its body suddenly began to spurt forth more vigorously. It was going to self-destruct. Those flames were the golem's life force itself, and the brighter they burned, the shorter it lived.

"Pretty stubborn for a golem," I remarked, and with the flames licking away at my MP, I shattered its core.

Suddenly, Eumis spoke up. "You shouldn't have given me my memories back," she said. "Now I know Over Limit's weakness."

"…"

Indeed, my secret technique had a single drawback. It required a lot of MP to heal continuously like this, and the healing capacity of the Nephrite Blade of Verdure wasn't particularly high in the first place. What it couldn't take from my mana, it had to take from the rest of my energy reserves. That was why I felt so hungry after using it.

With a few more levels under my belt, I could increase my stamina and invest in the "Overeating" skill, which would allow me to load up on food beforehand. If I tried that now, though, I'd just get fat.

All this was to say that I couldn't use Over Limit for long. When I tried it out against the goblins, I hadn't even been using my full power, and I could only keep it up for about seven minutes. At full strength, it would be closer to three.

On top of that, the Tenebris-Ignis Giant had sapped a lot of my MP. I was sitting at around 30 percent right now, already feeling the effects of MP drunkenness. I wouldn't be able to call upon Over Limit a second time.

"Ha, but you're not holding up too well, either, are you, Eumis?" I shot back. For as fearsome an incantation it was, Demon's Fire didn't use a lot of mana. If the golems' cores were destroyed, however, the caster suffered severe pain and MP loss. Add to that the poison I'd stabbed her with, which was sapping her MP without her knowledge even now, plus the powerful spells she'd used earlier, and she would be feeling the heat. She wasn't holding up as well as she tried to project.

"Regardless," she said, "I still have about forty percent of my mana left, and there is one Tenebris-Ignis Giant remaining."

"..."

"You are as foolish as ever, hero. Had you not returned my memories to me, perhaps I would still exercise caution toward that power of yours."

She smiled, assured of her victory as she saw the pale-green light of my healing power fade.

"Now, my golem. Shift to maximum output."

"Rrrooooaaagh!"

Just as the other one had, the sword golem roared anew with intense flames. If I tried to fight it head-on with my soul blades now, my MP would be completely gone in a matter of seconds.

Eumis began prepping another spell while I stood in place. There was no chant this time, but I could see the Water and Wind mana swirling around her. I knew her well enough to predict what that meant.

"You really haven't changed a bit," I muttered, though the lumbering footsteps of the giant drowned out my voice as it ran toward me. "I may have been a fool once, but no longer. Unfortunately, I can't say the same for you!"

Thus far, everything had been going exactly as I envisioned, so my *facedown card* was exactly what I needed to counter her.

"*Suction Blade.*"

I conjured in my hand a soul blade I had reunlocked in case the plan to restore Eumis's memories succeeded. Though it took the form of an ordinary longsword, it was split down the middle into a red half and a blue half. It had the power to pull objects toward a particular location.

Noticing the weapon in my hands, Eumis stared at me quizzically. She recognized it, so she must have been wondering what I was planning to do with it. By now, however, it was too late. I had already won.

As the golem headed toward me, I stuck the tip of the blade into the ground at my feet.

"Wh-what?!" cried Eumis.

"*Brrraaaagh!*"

The golem gave an idiotic wail as the ground beneath its feet gave way. The giant tumbled into a pit about seven meters deep and landed with a splash in the water below.

"A pit?! Filled with water…?"

As Eumis spluttered in disbelief, I pulled out the Suction Blade and hurtled forth to deliver the finishing blow on the submerged golem.

"Huh?! You really *are* a fool!" she shouted. "Do you think that mere water is enough to extinguish those unholy flames?"

"You're the moron here, Eumis," I retorted. "Already forgotten what I said earlier?"

As the liquid settled, it was clear that the flames across the golem's body had gone out.

"I knew you'd use Demon's Fire against me from the start!"

"Y-you don't mean… No! Holy water?!"

Ordinary water was of no use against cursed fire. But water that had been blessed by the Church did the trick just fine. Unlike the golem, the flames that spurted from it were of an undead nature, which meant that the holy water was particularly effective against them.

I leaped into the pit and crushed the core of the struggling, frigid construct.

"Graaargh! Guh… Agh… Not yet!"

Eumis continued to weave her spell, even as the destruction of the core deducted all the more MP from her. As the golem crumbled into dust, she commanded it to stall me, just for a second.

"Now die, hero!"

Squeezing out the last of her power, Eumis unleashed her incantation.

"You still don't get it, do you?" I retorted. Everything I had planned had been leading to this moment. I activated the Suction Blade with my mana and flung it across the pit, where it embedded itself in the far wall. At the same time, Eumis sealed the mouth of the hole with a film of solid air, trapping me inside.

"I anticipated your every move. Just like how I knew you'd use Demon's Fire…," I said, chuckling before taking a deep breath and holding it. The water started to bubble almost immediately, breaking apart into hydrogen and oxygen. I was stuck inside an enormous hydrogen bomb; if it went off, I'd meet my end for sure.

Still, the smile on my face was genuine. "…And I also predicted you'd want to use the cheapest, most efficient spell you had access to right now…"

"…Hydrogen, be my sword! *Phlogiston Blast!*"

There was a spark of electricity, which gave birth to a flame. But that was all it was. A flame, not a blast, and after a moment, it fizzled out.

Eumis was aghast. "Wh-what? But I saw the flame! Wh-why…?!"

"Ah-ha-ha-ha-ha-ha! That's what you get, Eumis! You're working off borrowed knowledge! Power you stole from others! That's why you'll never be anything more than a worthless bitch!"

Breaking apart water molecules and setting alight a mixture of hydrogen and oxygen would result in an explosion. Eumis was aware this. But what she didn't understand was *why* it worked. All she knew was that running a current through water created two highly explosive products known as hydrogen and oxygen.

She didn't comprehend that an "explosion" was really a shock wave produced from rapid combustion, and she certainly didn't know what would happen if I separated the two gases using the Suction Blade. In that state, the only part that could burn was the place where they met in the middle, and that thin layer was not enough to cause the chain reaction that would lead to an eruption.

Soul Blade of Beginnings in hand, I leaped out of the pit and sprinted toward Eumis.

"Grr!" she grunted in frustration. "It's not over yet!"

"I'm afraid it is, Eumis. This is checkmate!"

I took out a pair of fetters, like what you would use to bind a slave, and slapped them on her while she was unguarded. Then with a low, sweeping kick, I tripped her over and plunged the tip of my soul blade through the back of her hand.

"Grargh! Gh… Aaaagh!"

She wailed in agony as I twisted the blade.

"Ha! What's the matter? Does it hurt? I'm so glad I can finally see that tortured expression of yours, Eumis. And I really must thank you for putting on such a show. Do you know how hard I've worked to reach this point? Do you?"

"Grh! Ugh… Aaagh!"

I impaled her again, and again, through the hands, the feet, the elbows, the knees, taking care to limit her bleeding as best I could.

"That was such a fun fight, too. Do you know how hard it was to hold back my laughter as you did everything I expected you to do, down to every last detail? I knew you'd resort to that spell once your little private army was of no more use to you! So how are you feeling now? I know MP drunkenness causes you nausea, and I bet me destroying those golem cores didn't help, either. I can see it on your face, even if you try to hide it."

"Grr! Uuuugh… Haah…haah…"

"Whoopsie-daisy. I'd better not start the meal before the others get back. Try to stay awake, would you?"

"Grah! Gh…ug…aaagh…"

With all her joints impaled, Eumis could only crawl along the ground. I stomped on her hard. That probably cracked a few bones, but I could be forgiven for that, couldn't I? It was okay if I just had a little taste of what was to come, right? Oh, and that thing where I twisted the blade? That was an accident. My hand slipped. Honest.

So don't go breaking on me yet.

"Now then, I'm all done over here. This is where the real fun begins, Eumis, so please try to last as long as you can."

"Ugh."

I gripped her jaw tightly in my hand.

"I've stripped you of your pride. Next comes your dreams, your ambitions, and everything you hold dear."

I could no longer control the glee on my face. The corners of my lips curled up into a twisted smile. She glared at me from her position facedown on the floor, but she couldn't run. I had already completely shattered her ankles.

"Gh...agh... You really are a rotten man, hero, to torture a help-less woman like this. I suppose that's why you hooked up with the demon lord, that bitch— *Hrk!*"

"Oh, is that right? Leticia was a fine woman. That's why you're not worthy to have her name cross your lips."

As I restored my MP using a potion, I thrust my blade into her wounds. Then I healed her and did it all over again. When my MP got too low, I downed another potion and continued. I had expected that Eumis, an important dignitary of the kingdom, would have under-gone pain-resistance training for national security, but by this point, it wouldn't matter anymore. In fact, it was a good thing she had some experience under her belt, or she would have either passed out long ago or be begging for death by now. As it was, I could enjoy toying with her while making sure not to cross the line into sneaking a bite ahead of time.

I decided to give the others a call. Minnalis still had some prepa-ration to do, but Shuria might be taking a well-deserved break by now.

"Minnalis, Shuria. I'm done getting ready on my end. How are things going with you two?"

I was using a skill called "Soulspeak." This means of instant com-munication traveled via our link with the Holy Sword of Retribution. I'd used it previously to relay Mouse #1's findings to Minnalis. It only worked over a limited range, but unlike conventional magical com-municators, our conversations through this avenue were impossible to intercept or listen in on.

"This is Minnalis. I'm sorry, Master, but there's about half of half of them left."

"That's fine. I was just curious. I'd be more worried if you *were* finished because I'd be wondering what pains you put yourself through to wrap things up so quickly. I know you're not the type to cut corners, after all."

Also, *"half of half?"* I suppose Minnalis isn't that great at math, being a village girl and all. It's easy to forget since she's whip-smart otherwise. I'll have to make some time to teach her fractions later.

"What about you, Shuria?"

"I have done everything you requested. I was just playing with them a little since there was nothing else to do."

"I see. In that case, come over here when you're done. I've got a way better toy for you to play with."

I heard a small gasp over the connection. *"Okay!"*

No sooner had our conversation ended than a circle of pale light spread over the whole of the field where I had just fought Eumis.

"A teleportation circle?" she grunted. "Is that ours?"

"Yup. I mean, we've got to use everything at our disposal, right?"

As its name suggested, a teleportation stone was a rock that allowed you to warp somewhere. Compared with my soul blade, however, they came with a few drawbacks. They didn't use up MP, but you couldn't teleport very many people at once or travel long distances with them. On top of that, they took some time to activate and were quite rare and expensive. Still, noble families tended to keep them on hand in case of emergencies.

The blinding light of the teleportation magic gave way to reveal Shuria, grinning from ear to ear, accompanied by a couple dozen men and women of all ages. Apart from my accomplice, they were all servants who worked at Eumis's mansion. In other words, they were people she trusted, confided in, and perhaps even cared about? Every single one of them was writhing in terror and agony.

I sighed. "Come on, now. *A little*, you said. Is that what you call this?"

"Aww, I don't think I did anything wrong," whined Shuria in response. "I just ripped off a few of their fingers, tore off their eyelids, bit off their ears, and pulled out their hair. Nothing that would *kill* them. I think I did quite a good job."

At what? I wanted to ask, but she had a point. They didn't look like they were about to shuffle off this mortal coil, so as long as they weren't broken yet, I supposed there wasn't a problem.

"Besides," she continued, "I see you've already had a go at my sister before I got a chance to."

"Well, I finished way earlier than I expected. What else was I supposed to do?"

Ah, the Japanese person's signature move. Hypocrisy.

Shuria instead turned to Eumis. "Oh, my dear sister, you do look wonderful no matter what it is you are doing, even when it's crawling facedown in the mud."

"Shuria…! You would bring my servants into this?"

Eumis glared up at her younger sister in disgust, but Shuria simply responded with a bewitching grin.

"Now then, Eumis," I told her, "it's time to begin. First up is *The First Annual Eumis-Pummeling Contest (There Won't Be a Second!)* Clap, clap, clap, clap!"

"Clap, clap, clap, indeed!" added Shuria.

The clearing was filled with nothing but the sounds of our fake clapping.

"Come on, you worms. The show's underway!"

"""Eep!"""

Shuria's faithful teddy bear chuckled, and the pussycat clashed his knife and fork together.

"No, no! Please don't bite off my ears!"

"I'm sorry, I'm sorry! You can shave me bald if you want! Just stop pulling out my scalp!"

73

The servants' voices filled with dread as Shuria turned her ice-cold gaze upon a man whose hair had been half torn out. He seemed to have taken the most punishment of all of them; the blood from his scalp had begun dripping down his face, lending him a rather dismal air, and one of his hands, which he clutched in the other, was also missing three fingers.

"Come along, now. You're the head butler," Shuria urged. "You should set a good example for everybody else."

"Eek! Forgive me ... Forgive me... I'm just a lowly, rotten, worthless insect... Forgive me!" The man repeated his apology over and over again as he stood up, quaking and sobbing.

"As for all you other maggots," Shuria continued, "you know what will happen if you don't do what you're supposed to!"

"""*Gasp!*"""

The rest of the servants all stood up when Shuria trained her scarlet eyes on them.

"Come on, Eumis," I said. "You stand right over here."

"Grh... Agh!"

I snatched her arm and dragged her before her faithful servant.

"I am so sorry, my lady..."

"What are you...?" she began. "Gah?!"

The head butler stomped on Eumis's back. His expression betrayed he was ruled by fear and confusion. At this, the other employees all followed suit.

"I'm so sorry! I'm so sorry," shouted one of them, "but I don't want to die! I have a sick little sister to take care of!"

"I have to protect my family!" wailed another. "Oh, god... Please forgive me, Lady Eumis. Please forgive me!"

"Gah... Urgh... Gh!"

The servants literally ground Eumis into the dirt as they voiced a chorus of regret.

"Ha-ha! Ah-ha-ha-ha-ha! How does it feel to be trampled on by those you trusted, Eumis? How ugly you look now! Ah-ha-ha-ha-ha!"

"Like maggots swarming a piece of rotten fruit. Aww, I suppose this is all they're good for. What failures."

Eumis was in another league compared with her employees, both in terms of level and everything else. Coupled with her pain resistance, it was likely their blows weren't hurting her at all right now. Nevertheless, she had trusted these people enough to let them work in the mansion alongside her and Soriy, so the humiliation factor could not be discounted.

"Grr! You cowards...!"

The face Eumis made was exquisite. I didn't know how long I gazed at it before I received a transmission from Minnalis.

"Master, everything's set up on my end."

"I see. Then I suppose we can bring the first act to a close." I switched off the connection and turned to the others. "All right, you can stop that now."

The servants slowly ceased what they were doing and looked at me. Eumis, too, glared up from her spot on the ground, her eyes filled with hate.

"Er...um...does that mean we can...?" the head butler ventured.

"I have no further use for you, so die."

"...Huh?"

Then with the Soul Blade of Beginnings, I lopped off his head. It fell to the earth with a soft *thud* and rolled along the ground.

"Wh-why?" asked a maid, terrified. "We did everything you— *Hrk!*" She was unable to finish her sentence before the pussycat doll impaled her in the neck with its fork.

"What do you mean?" asked Shuria, cocking her head quizzically. "Of course the actors must leave the stage once their part is played. That should be obvious."

"H-help—! *Guh!*"

"Stop, please! I'll do anything you want, just don't kill— Oh god, it hurts, it hurts, it huuurts!"

My aura was so threatening that the servants were too scared to flee. Shuria and I quickly and neatly disposed of them, and with that, the first act was over.

"You…fiends…!" Eumis growled at us through gritted teeth.

"Oh, my dear sister. Kind as ever. Even after the way they treated you just now."

"That's because you forced them to go along with your sick games!"

"Heh-heh," I chuckled. "Don't be so angry. We've still got a lot more to go. Act one was a trampling from those you trusted. Act two is to erase your past."

Saying this, I activated a magic item I had procured in town. It was a telescope-like object I had modified with the Tailor's Hook of Mending. It allowed me to peer in on things happening elsewhere, much like the alchemical life-form I had commissioned from Jufain. We had used one in my first life, so Eumis knew what it was.

"Is this…the city?"

As she cautiously peered into the spyglass, the stone spires of Elmia appeared before her. It was night, and the city slept.

"Now, it's time to begin the second act. *Whenever you're ready, Minnalis.*"

"*Yes, Master,*" she replied over our link.

Then an enormous explosion rocked the tranquil town.

"What?! What happened?!" cried Eumis. Through the device, she glimpsed a white-hot burst of flames, a raging inferno that lit up the night sky.

"Wh-what have you done…?"

"Ah, such beautiful fireworks," I mused. "What lovely flames your life's work ignites."

I had tasked Minnalis with blowing up Eumis's research facilities. All her notes, all the progress she had strived for, up in smoke. Across the city, people were coming out of their homes to watch, astonished, as the burning buildings crumbled, the books and ingredients inside reduced to ash.

It was the most beautiful blaze I'd ever seen.

The townspeople began trying to put out the fire with water buckets, but it wouldn't work. The inferno was augmented with a special poison Minnalis had created that burned at high temperatures, plus a healthy dose of oil for good measure.

Those unnatural white flames were like the fires of hell. By the time the city's spellcasters showed up to douse the conflagration with magic, all the fruits of Eumis's labor, the work she had poured her heart into, would be little more than ash, indistinguishable from dust.

Before long, only quietly rasping flames danced orange in the silent moonlight.

"Ah...ahhh...my workshops...the cornerstones of my research..."

"And that concludes the second act," I announced. "Next comes act three, where we erase your future."

The image changed. Now it showed the stone monument at the center of the city.

"Y-you can't mean...? No... Please, no...!"

Boooom!

As a devious smirk spread across my face, I brought my hands slowly together as if I was crushing something between them. At the same moment, the stone monument in the image crumbled into rubble.

"Im...impossible... The statue...," whimpered Eumis, her voice trembling.

"Ahhh, now that's a lovely face. However, this is still only the third act. We've seen your faithful servants, your accumulated history, and your long-awaited future all destroyed. Next comes act four: *what you have right now.*"

"Wha—?! Wait…what? What more do you plan on taking from me?!"

Eumis's face fell as Shuria leaned in and stroked her cheek. "Oh, dear sister," she said consolingly, with a smile just like the one Eumis had last shown her. "There's no need to be afraid. It's time to reap the fruits of your harvest. All you need to do is sit back and watch. This is our gift to you! ♪"

The image changed once more. Now it showed the ruins of Eumis's laboratories again. Amid the rubble, something stirred. An arm poked through as *something* tried to pull itself to the surface, and before long, dozens of undead goblins and orcs were crawling up out of the debris.

"Groooargh…"

"Broooagh…"

"Eeeek! Zombies! Zombies in the city!" someone screamed. The curious onlookers were soon running about making noise, like a disturbed wasp's nest.

"Wh-what have you done?" shouted Eumis. "From where did you procure such a large number of undead?"

"What do you mean?" I replied. "They're from Shuria's village. Don't you remember? You're the one who killed them."

In preparation for this day, I had paid a visit to that village myself. What I found there was an unimaginably large horde of undead, which was growing larger by the day. An entire village's worth of negative emotions of the people whose lives Eumis had unreasonably stripped from them, made only more powerful by the demon's residual mana.

"These poor friends were born of the suffering you caused, dear sister. What did I say? *It's time to reap the fruits of your harvest.*"

Afterward, I had spent a few days setting up a teleportation circle there that lead into Eumis's laboratories. This was also a way of helping those lost souls deal with their lingering regrets. Though I couldn't cast magic, I was able to channel mana into a magic circle just fine, as long as I had enough MP potions to keep myself going. After I made Minnalis mark the locations of Eumis's laboratories, the undead were now pouring through those portals to rise out of the rubble and attack the people of the city.

The color drained from Eumis's face once more. "No… What have you done?! The townsfolk are going to get slaughtered!"

"Yeah, I suppose a few of them will," I replied, returning her a joyous smile.

In reality, the explosions had immediately drawn the citizenry's attention to the undead horde. There were also holy men and women on hand, so rather than drawing innocents into my quest for revenge, the number of casualties resulting from my scheme might actually be lower than if I had done nothing. I didn't have to let Eumis in on that, though.

Still, a couple hundred people could very well lose their lives tonight, but that was how the cookie crumbled. I'd needed to do this to exact my vengeance.

"They'll die in the hundreds. This must go down as one of the most tragic events in the city's history. Do you think me evil for that, Eumis? It's all for the sake of my dream, though. I think you of all people would understand."

"Grr… You…," Eumis growled. I snickered at her with contempt before continuing.

"And might I add, you have some nerve for trying to pretend you care a single bit about the people of Elmia. Or do you just not want to admit it? You know what we're taking from you here, don't you?"

"Wh-what do you…?"

Suddenly, Shuria interjected. "Oh, dear sister? There's something I don't understand. Could you explain it to me? Who will the city blame when they see the undead rising up out of the ruins of your damaged laboratories? Whose fault will they think it is?" She punctuated her obvious question with a gleeful chuckle.

"D-don't be absurd! You would try to pin the blame for this attack on me?!"

"Ding, ding, ding! We've got a winner!" I smiled. "Ah-ha-ha-ha-ha! You're absolutely correct, Eumis. That's what you lot did to me the first time, after all. Just as I, the hero who saved the world, became the new demon lord and bore the weight of the world's sins, so too have you gone from the kind and gracious steward of House Elmia to a mad scientist who conducted illegal experiments on the undead. Only in your case, it's all true! Ah-ha-ha-ha-ha-ha!"

How ironic that the undead we had worked together to defeat the first time around would now be the weapon by which I brought her low.

"However, it won't be you they'll condemn. I mean, think about it. You're going to die here, and there's no way I'm going to let any of them know about that. So with you out of the picture, who do you think the blame will fall on?"

"Y-you mean…"

If the city of Elmia couldn't locate Eumis after all this happened? Why, her failures would fall on her house. Eumis's execution might have been enough to make up for that. The life of the lord's only daughter could outweigh a great deal of damage to the city. If she went missing, however, it would be her parents who would end up taking the fall. Everyone related to her house would be put to death. I didn't know *how* related that meant, but at the very least, it would include her parents, with whom Eumis had tried so hard to maintain an amicable relationship.

"You fiend!"

"Ha-ha-ha-ha-ha-ha! This is just what you did to me! You have your memories back, don't you? Then you know that every one of my family and friends were sacrificed to bring me here! After that princess bitch told me, you couldn't resist rubbing it in my face all the time! How does it feel to have that same thing happen to you? To have your family and friends, past and future, ripped away from you?! Ah-ha! ♪ Ah-ha-ha-ha-ha!"

On and on and on and on. I was having so much fun, I just couldn't stop laughing.

The anger and humiliation I felt when I recalled my miserable life as a fugitive. The righteous indignation that even now caused my hands to tremble. I had bottled it all up inside me. All in anticipation of this day.

"You…devil! You'll never get away with this! I'll see you rot in hell!" Eumis screamed in anger and humiliation, in fury that caused her hands to tremble. "Die! Die! You too, Shuria! Why are you still alive?! Go back to hell, where you belong, you…you specters!"

Her eyes flooded with hatred. In a way, it was proof of her suffering.

Shuria burst out laughing. "Ah-ha-ha-ha-ha! Oh, dear sister. You *do* say some strange things sometimes. Go back to hell? Why, haven't you realized? We're already there. And we're here to drag you down there with us."

"Ah-ha, nice one, Shuria!" I added. "Ah-ha-ha-ha!"

Indeed, we called the depths of hell home. We had chosen to stay there. Chosen not to climb our way out, bloodied and beaten, but to bring our enemies down kicking and screaming to our level. It was just as Eumis said. The moment we erased our path from the pit, we'd died and become ghosts.

"Wh-what is your problem…? You're insane!"

Shuria and I both burst into mad cackles at the same time. I would never get sick of seeing Eumis trying to put on a brave face.

"All right! All right, all right, all right! *Now* things are starting to get exciting! Pay attention. Next up is our final act. We're serving up your *dream*! Shuria, is everything ready?"

"Of course! ♪ Oh, dear sister. Wait until you see the final actress we've prepared for you!" She turned and called to her *third* pet. "Oh, Miss Metal! Bring her here, please!"

Miss Metal stirred into action, and soon, Soriy emerged from the forest once more—the real one this time. She was dressed in the same long-sleeved maid outfit she wore at the mansion, but what Eumis couldn't tell just by looking at her was that I had used the flamevenom emitted by the Pyrachnid's Claw of Kindling to melt away the marrow of her bones and fill them with a mithril alloy. This third servant, "Miss Metal," was none other than Soriy's skeletal structure itself.

"Another fake...? No! Soriy! It's really you!"

"My...lady..."

Her face was ghastly pale. Seeing her, Eumis went completely white with dread. The paint was beginning to peel on her brave facade. Her armor was beginning to crack, and Eumis herself knew it, too. This woman, Soriy, was her dream made manifest.

"Please... Please don't... Anyone but her... Please don't hurt her...!"

Eumis began shaking uncontrollably.

"The final act is called 'Dream Balloon.' We have filled your precious Soriy with one of Shuria's servants, just as you have seen these past nights."

"S-so that dream was...?"

"Teddy came into your room to show it to you while you were sleeping. Did you enjoy it?" asked Shuria with a sneer. Looking on Eumis's visage, pale as a corpse, she continued, "Aaah, torturing this bug of a woman was all worth it to see that look on your face!"

Shuria forced the maid onto her hands and knees, then stomped on her back.

"Eek! Gargh!"

"Soriy!"

"Now then, the rules are simple," I began. "When Shuria gives the signal, Miss Metal will expand. If she does that while inside your favorite plaything, then, well..."

I left the rest to her imagination and sneered at her.

"No... Please... I don't want to die...," Soriy pleaded, with tears in her eyes.

"..."

Eumis looked like she was about to cry, too. I suppose she could easily envision what I was going to say.

"But I'm nice," I added, "so I'll tell you how you can save her. That maid is infused with mana, and Shuria's servant is a magical life-form as well. If you channel your own mana into her, more than Miss Metal can tolerate, then she'll shut down, and you'll have your beloved back."

For a second, Eumis's eyes filled with the light of hope, before they returned to crushing despair. Obviously. She'd already expended all the MP she would need to free Soriy in her duel with me.

I released her fetters, and Shuria pushed Soriy to the ground with her foot.

"Your time starts now. Make sure you don't fill your dream balloon up so much that it bursts!"

"W-wait! Wait a minute...!"

"Nope! ♪ Go!" Shuria gave a sprightly cry, and the final act was underway.

"Aah... Aaaaaagh! Make it stop! It hurts! It hurts! It hurts!"

"Soriy!"

Miss Metal started to grow inside Soriy, who began screaming as the metallic rods pushed apart her bones from within. Eumis stumbled over, desperately channeling what little mana she had remaining into her lover.

"Krrrgh! Rrrrrrgh!"

"Grrrgh! Help me, Miss Eumis! It hurts so much!"

"Try to bear with it, Soriy! I'll save you!"

Eumis scrambled to infuse as much mana as she could, but Shuria's creation was sturdy. It would have been a tall order if Eumis was at full health, never mind now. She simply didn't have enough MP.

"Gaaagh! Urgh! Aaagh!"

She hit zero. But Eumis kept going, just as I had. Lacerations began appearing all over her body.

However, it still wouldn't be enough.

"Grh! Gah! Ah! Aaahhh!"

Soriy started twitching violently, her tears mingling with the blood dripping from Eumis. Though Eumis tried to push on, she was beyond her limits now, so she could only manage a small trickle of mana.

"No! No, no, no, no, no, no! Please! Hero, Shuria, I was wrong! I was a fool! Please forgive me, I'm begging you! Don't let Soriy die!"

Finally, she turned to us, with tears in her eyes. Eumis, the woman who had looked down on me, used me, betrayed me. Now I'd seen her at her lowest. An unsightly blemish on the world.

"Ha-ha-ha-ha! Me, forgive you? You must be joking! You said it yourself, Eumis—we're specters. And specters can't hear the words of the living!"

"Are you trying to mock me, dear sister?" added Shuria. "I chose to walk this wicked path so that I could get my revenge on you... That means you have to suffer! Ha-ha-ha-ha-ha!"

"You...demons! Both of you!"

I heard the creaking sound of her dream approaching its breaking point.

"Argh! Gah! Ugh...!"

"Soriy! Soriy! Soriy! Soriy!"

"Miss…Eumis… Ah…"

And then it was like a water balloon falling on the ground. A grisly reminder that the human body was mostly liquid. Just a wet-sounding splash as Soriy's body was reduced to moist chunks.

"…Huh? Uh? Huh?"

Eumis looked on in stupefied silence, her face stained with her lover's blood, either unwilling or unable to process the truth.

She simply sat there. I knew now that her heart had at last turned to sand. The slightest touch would cause it to all come crashing down.

And so I leaned over to her and whispered into her ear the words I longed to say.

"Now you're just like me, Eumis. A broken shell with broken dreams. Tell me, one last time. How does it feel?"

"AAAAAAAAAUGH! NOOOOOOO! NO! NO, NO, NO, NO, NO, NO, NOOOOOOOOO!"

"Ah-ha-ha-ha-ha-ha! That's right, that's right, Eumis! Let it all out! Let me hear it!"

"Ah-ha! ♪ Let us hear your cries, your shouts, your screams! Let Mother and Shelmie hear it up in heaven! Ah-ha-ha-ha-ha!"

One person's screams of dread, and two people's jubilant laughter.

This was it. Finally.

This was what I'd been waiting for!

This was what my second life had been leading up to! Seeing this!

"Now, that concludes tonight's program. I see you've enjoyed yourself quite a bit, Eumis," I announced.

"And so," Shuria chimed in, "the curtain is drawn on the play she began."

It was time to end this drama of fools.

Shuria and I reached into the Squirrel's Blade of Holding and pulled out a sword each.

"No. No! Nooo! This isn't happening! Tell me it's all a lie, please!"

Eumis scratched madly at her scalp, tearing at her hair and shaking her head, sobbing like a child, trying to deny it all.

"Ah-ha-ha. See you on the other side, Eumis."

"Good-bye, Eumis, my dear sister."

We raised the instruments of our vengeance high above our heads.

"Nooooo! G...blh..."

Our swords pierced her heart simultaneously, just as we had agreed on.

"Ah-ha-ha-ha-ha-ha-ha-ha! Ah-ha! Ah-ha-ha-ha-ha!"

"Hee-hee-hee! Hee-hee-hee-hee-hee!"

Again, and again, and again, and again and again and againandagainandagainandagain...

A strange warmth swept through the freezing night air. Our shrieking cackles sounded to me like an exquisite piano symphony I had heard somewhere before.

How long did we continue to stab our blades through that witch's heart?

Before long, all I saw on the ground before me was a misshapen mound of flesh. Tiny chunks of meat coated the sword in my hand, as though blood alone had not been enough for it.

The state of that place told all. In its center sat an otherwise unremarkable young man with jet-black hair and eyes, bathed in blood. A dark-skinned elven girl sat at his back.

Scattered all around them was flesh, blood, and shattered bone. A mountain of corpses so badly mutilated, they were an insult to even the word *waste*—it was impossible to discern any hint of their former lives.

"Shuria," the boy asked. "What will you do now that you've had your revenge? Will you stay here?"

"What a cruel thing to say," replied the girl, pulling a sulky face. "You know full well my vengeance is nowhere near complete. What about the hatred you and Minnalis have given me? It's mine now, too. All that's gone is what I had originally. What you gave me is still here. There's a long way to go, and I can't have you leaving me out of it!"

"I see. Yeah, I should have known. I guess that was a dumb question."

The anger lurking within the boy's heart had reached the girl and ignited a new flame. Even if that flame had been his to begin with, it was now hers as well.

"Perhaps I'm just getting a little sentimental now that we've taken our first step together," the boy muttered as he looked up at the sky. "Ahhh, that was fun. I can't wait for the next one."

The girl stayed silent but leaned against her partner just a little more.

The two were dreaming. Dreaming of the day when all those they hated would be swimming in the lake of fire alongside them, and they could finally rest in peace.

The moon shone down on them but said nothing. Then, as if it had seen all it had wanted to see, it slowly faded away as the sky brightened.

…Their vengeance was not yet complete.

For those dark flames still laughed with such intensity that they threatened to swallow up the sun itself.

The sun rose that day on a city in chaos. No sooner had worried citizens rushed to put out the fires from the smoking laboratories than hordes of undead had risen from their ashes. While monster attacks were not unprecedented, many of the townsfolk had never even *seen*

undead creatures before, so their appearance sent the community into total panic.

Still, the explosions had roused the citizens from their slumber, and adventurers, soldiers, and holy men armed with powerful Light magics quickly put the creatures to rest, resulting in surprisingly few casualties.

It could have been far worse. If the number of deaths had been much higher, the city would never have been able to recover, assuming it even survived.

After the dust settled, the authorities stormed the Elmia mansion seeking an explanation as to why the house had been inactive during all this, only to find that the lord and his wife had been away visiting the capital on business for some time. When they instead came to the doors of his daughter's private mansion, they found the place completely deserted, and neither the young lady nor her servants were anywhere to be found.

While the townsfolk began the task of treating the wounded and cleaning up the ruined workshops, the authorities sent a message to Lord Elmia demanding he take action.

A few days later, three facts gave rise to a new rumor in town. One, the fact that all the laboratories that had burned down had been under Eumis's direct control. Two, the fact that the undead had emerged from those very same laboratories. Three, the fact that Eumis and her retainers had disappeared.

The rumor went like this: Eumis, the lord's daughter, was so obsessed with her magical research that she'd turned to the dark arts and began experimenting on humans. These experiments angered God and thus brought down divine punishment in the form of destruction upon her laboratories, freeing the undead specimens. Eumis's servants disappeared because they, too, had been used as guinea pigs in her vile experiments, while the mastermind herself was killed in the explosions.

Other far-fetched modifications to the tale began to emerge, too, such as the notion that Eumis was brainwashed, that she was really a demon in disguise, or that Eumis had caused the explosion when she lost control of a magic item. Such tales circulated in town for quite some time after the event.

And what interesting tales they were. Truly a testament to the extent of human imagination. Personally, my favorite was the idea that a demon had killed the real Eumis long ago to impersonate her.

Eventually, satisfied with our handiwork, we put the city behind us. Four days later, we arrived at Shuria's old village. The magic circle we had been using to teleport the undead into the city had long since exhausted its mana, so there were still some zombies that remained here.

It was no skin off our noses if they were left to their own devices and attacked the city of Elmia once more, but we simply couldn't bear to see Shuria's dear home left in such a state. We'd slain all the undead we could find and were now standing in what was once the village square.

"What a curious feeling," remarked Shuria. "It has only been three years, and yet I feel as though I do not know this place at all."

The village had been laid waste to twice over. Once by Eumis's mercenaries, and again by the hordes of inhuman creatures that followed. Taking it in now, it was hard to believe that all this had once been a happy, peaceful hamlet. It looked exactly the same now as it would several years later, or at least it had when I'd visited it the first time around. In fact, it looked even worse now. The mana in this place was still rich with malice because there hadn't been enough time for it to fully disperse yet.

"That's because the negative energy created by undead causes things to deteriorate faster," I said.

"Then will this gravestone we have placed soon crumble into dust as well?"

We had placed a stone marker at what we had tentatively deemed the center of the village, though no one was buried beneath it. Around it, purple flowers had begun to bloom. Shuria had planted these when she'd lived here.

Stooped down by the gravestone, Shuria looked up at me inquisitively.

"No," I replied. "We've killed all the undead around here, so the mana should begin to fade."

"I see. That's good."

Shuria was wearing something *I* would have called a short kimono with long sleeves. It was covered in a subtle pattern of deep violet with crimson accents. The garment lent her a mysterious and bewitching air that very much suited her now. She had tied her hair up to one side with a flowery clip.

I had plundered the kimono from Eumis's mansion on the spur of the moment, and it could be infused with mana to raise the defensive capabilities of the wearer. Additionally, it came with several enchantments: Auto Don/Doff, Auto Fit, Regulate Temperature, and Disguise Race (Human). The last of these, as the name implied, made her appear to onlookers as though she was a regular human. It effectively worked the same way as Minnalis's illusions. I bet House Elmia had developed it so that the lord could keep his beastfolk and demihuman mistresses on full display.

The Japanese stylings of the outfit would raise a few eyebrows, but a dark-skinned elf would absolutely stand out in most circumstances, so it was still the superior choice. Shuria would rarely have to fight up close and personally regardless, but even if she did, the enchantments would fare better for her than most metal armors on the market.

Minnalis and I had also acquired new equipment. Trust a lord to have such nice stuff gathering dust in his storerooms. The armor we bought at the old man's weapon shop had been decent enough, but these were on a whole other level.

…Or so I'd thought, but for some reason, the item Minnalis had picked out of that trove of wonders was a frilly *maid uniform*. Her rabbit ears popped up out of the headdress, and she tied her long dark hair back in a high ponytail. The entire dress was covered in frills, and the blouse almost seemed designed to show off her sizable cleavage.

Somehow, it managed to expertly straddle the line between propriety and sexuality. My hat goes off to whoever designed it. Of course, it was no regular article of clothing, however. Turning my "Appraise" skill upon it revealed several enchantments, namely Defense Up, Agility Up, Augment Mana, Stealth Assist, Detection Assist, Resizable, Reformable, and Regulate Temperature. As much as I wanted to have her pick a different outfit, the enchantments were simply too good to pass up. I really didn't understand why it looked like a maid uniform, though. Nonetheless, its raw defensive power far outstripped any regular piece of armor, and so I had to admit it was a rare and valuable find.

Minnalis's and Shuria's new equipment were oddities on par with the legendary bikini armor, a staple of the fantasy genre, but I could hardly debate their existence given the reality before my eyes. Still, while I had grown accustomed to seeing such things my first time around, I never had figured out how they managed to offer better protection than real armor.

As for me, I'd picked out a decent set of regular leather armor. There were other good choices, but I had something else in mind for my gear, so I only needed protection that would tide me over until then. Besides, the other options for men had been ostentatious plate armor with all the trimmings. Weight aside, the stiffness of it would have obstructed my movements, and I didn't care much for the glitz anyway.

"Shall we get moving?" asked Minnalis.

"Yes," Shuria replied. "I am done here. There is nothing more to do." She slowly rose to her feet and gave Minnalis a nod.

"..."

"What is it?" Shuria asked at Minnalis's silence.

"Oh... I'm sorry, your village just reminded me of my own... I started thinking about what I wanted to do to them. How I'd like my hamlet to end up far worse than this... To morph it into a hellscape from which no one can avert their eyes. I just...got lost in a fantasy for a moment. I'm sorry."

Minnalis looked a little awkward bringing it up, but there was also a faint spark of joy in her eyes, and a trace of lust in her fleeting smile.

"Oh, do not worry about it," Shuria replied. "The only thing that matters to me is this place. The people who lived here. I do not wish to conflate them with the trash who live in yours. And so...," she continued, "...I am sure your revenge will be a great success. I will help you make it one, of course."

Her grin was a little different than Minnalis's. It was the seductive smile of a temptress reeling in her lover.

Ahhh, how beautiful and trustworthy my partners in crime are.

"...I have to make sure I'm good enough to keep up with them."

Eumis was dead. Yet the sweet, sweet nectar of revenge was only just beginning to tantalize the tip of my tongue. There was still much more to do. So many more enemies I had sworn to kill. Much more despair. Much more brutality. Many more fiendish acts.

"Master? Are you okay?"

"What's the matter, Kaito? You're smiling."

"Hmm? Oh, nothing. Come on, let's get a move on."

I had involuntarily curled my lips into a grin.

What would my next act of vengeance be like? The starved flame within me now burned with renewed passion. Most of my enemies were still going about freely, laughing and smiling without a care in the world, ignorant of what we had in store for them.

"Hmm, another beautiful day... Oh, I know! How about we put them in a hot, dry room until they're all shriveled up?" I suggested. "Then once they're about to croak, give them an empty jug."

"Master," responded Minnalis, "if you're going to do that, then why not really test their patience by making them think there's poison in it?"

Shuria butted in with her own ideas. "Oh, what if instead of that, we feed them animal dung until they get so used to it that they're actually grateful to be eating it…?"

Brilliant golden light shone down on us from above. It was perfect weather for another wonderful, revenge-filled day.

…When suddenly, there came a thunderous roar, and a huge black shadow appeared in the sky.

"Grrrooooooaaaaaarrr!"

""""Ah!"""" we all gasped in unison as our eyes flew upward. Overhead soared a gargantuan creature of legendary proportions, with crimson scales and wrings. The regal apex predator of the fantasy-land ecosystem: a dragon.

"It's him…"

"Master?"

"Kaito?"

I couldn't even respond to their puzzled voices. As the beast approached, I could make out its features more clearly.

"It's Guren."

That was the name of the baby Fire Dragon that Leticia always kept by her side. Usually taking the form of a dragon pup, you would often find him happily riding on Leticia's head or shoulders.

"Hrh!"

Feeling obligated to do something, I took to the skies using Air Step.

"Groooagh?"

"Ah…"

Once I was face to face with the dragon, I finally returned to my senses.

What was I trying to do?

Guren judged me curiously. It wouldn't be until a little later that he and Leticia would meet for the first time. Besides, even if he could recognize me, I was sure he wouldn't want anything to do with me after the way I'd treated Leticia. I had always been indebted to her, but I wasn't able to return the favor when it mattered most.

"*Grargh!*"

"Ah!"

It seemed Guren had decided I was just something in his path, and sparks flew about his jaws as he prepared to breathe fire. I didn't want to harm him, so I adopted a defensive posture, when...

"*Groah?*"

"What?!"

...all of a sudden, a blinding white light emerged from my chest. As it engulfed me, I felt something leaving my body.

"*Grah? Groah?!*"

"What... What's happening...?"

Guren seemed even more confused than I was. Then with a growl, he whipped his formidable tail, coated in scales not even a mithril sword could pierce.

"Hng?!"

I blocked the attack with the Soul Blade of Beginnings, but the force of the blow knocked me clean off my Air Step platform. I managed to land safely before I smashed into the ground, but my mind was reeling. My hands were numb from guarding against that attack, and it would take several seconds to heal them.

But Guren didn't capitalize on my moment of weakness. Instead, he gave a disgruntled snort and retreated into the skies.

"..."

"Master!" "Kaito!"

Soon, my two companions ran over to me. However, I just sat there gazing up at the skies in disbelief, watching as the dragon faded from view.

SIDE STORY
Minnalis's Plan: Operation Engulfment

It all started the day Master returned home with Shuria by his side. I was occupying myself with getting supper ready when the two of them arrived.

"Welcome home, Master. And you must be Shuria. It's a pleasure to meet you."

"A pleasure to meet you, too. I take it you're Minnalis?"

And thus went my first meeting with the girl, complete with smiles from both sides. It didn't seem like she'd totally missed what I was trying to get across to her, yet her eyes never strayed from mine. She was far more strong-willed than I had expected from what I'd heard about her. It seemed that betrayal had changed her, as it had changed me.

Still, I knew that she was of elven blood, but what was I to make of the dark tone of her skin? Her ears were certainly elven in appearance, but I'd been under the impression that all elves had fair skin, which was in fact a point of pride for then. Perhaps it had something to do with the fact that she was a mere human with elven ancestry?

…No, that couldn't be it. The Shuria I recalled from Master's memories was fair-skinned as well. Something must have happened to her.

As I pondered this, sparks seemed to erupt between she and I, but Master did not appear to notice. *"I do hope you get along,"* he told us blithely. I was a little disappointed in him, but lately, I had begun seeing the charm in those scatterbrained moments of his. Scary.

"Now then, I've prepared supper, so how about we all sit down and eat?" I suggested.

And so our first meeting ended in a draw.

We were all quite hungry and tired after supper, so we withdrew to our rooms, leaving the conversation for the following day. Master seemed to have grown quite fond of having a full and pleasant sleep, so we'd dipped into our savings to stay at the same hotel a little longer. Now that we had Shuria, we transferred into a larger four-person suite, with a bit of extra space. Besides, the next day, we would be leaving town, so we could afford to splurge a bit.

I had suggested to Master we share a bed instead, but he fiercely shot down my idea, saying, *"Then it'll be too cramped!"* From his blushing, I could tell it wasn't that he objected to the idea of sleeping with me, but simply that he wished to be able to stretch out and relax. Indeed, on a single-person mattress, we would lack even the space to turn over in our sleep.

Ugh... Still, it hurt for Master to tell me off, even though I knew he wasn't really angry. In the end, he told me, *"I'll never budge on matters of sleep! I don't care if it's a waste of money!"* It was my fault for not being more sensitive to his wishes. I shall have to repent.

Perhaps I had been laying on the womanly appeal a little too thick lately. *"Spoil men too much, and they'll run,"* a nice adventurer lady had once told me. Oh, if only she was here now to tell me what to do. The idea that Master hated me was too much to bear, even if I knew it wasn't true.

And so that was what led to Master snoozing peacefully and defenselessly in the room right now. That didn't mean it was safe for me to approach, though. If I harbored evil or even mischievous thoughts, he would sense them and wake up. It was agonizing, being so close and yet so far.

Normally, I would suppress my presence just enough to get up nice and close and watch him without leaving myself feeling tired the next day. Unfortunately, I had other things to do tonight.

"...Let's go," I said.

"...Yes," replied Shuria.

In the dead of night, as the city lay silent, the two of us nodded to each other and left the room.

Shuria had already heard about my past from Master, and I had already seen hers for myself when he'd recruited her. Now her dark hatred clawed away at the inside of my heart. There was no doubt about it; the strength of her anger put mine to shame. That's why I hadn't objected to Shuria joining us as our partner in crime. The moment I'd seen the world through her eyes, however, I knew that we needed to talk.

It seemed she felt the same. I had thought it a little unfair to do this on a night where she had already been through so much, but one glance in her eyes told me that I needn't have harbored such worries. There was not a shred of weariness or exhaustion in them. Only a fiery glint of anticipation for what was to come. Still, the spirit could be willing while the flesh was weak. Fortunately, though, she didn't seem about to nod off on me, either.

We went outside under the waning half-moon into the prickling-cold night air.

"Now then," I began. "This is all new to me, so I'm not quite sure where to start..."

"The same goes for me," replied Shuria. "Though, having experience in this respect is nothing to be proud of."

"Well, actually, I suppose I *have* been in a love triangle of sorts. That was how I ended up with Master in the first place." The mere thought of him sent a grin across my face. "Though, I doubt that's enough to make you stand down."

"Of course not. Besides, that was not a love triangle. That was simply other people abusing your kindness. A *real* love triangle is a passionate clash of pure emotion! Like in *The Ballroom of Love*, or *The Baron's House and the Garden of Flowers*…!"

"O-okay, okay, I get it…"

Shuria swept toward me in righteous fury, though precisely at what her anger was directed, I could not say. The girl proved far more intense than Master had told me. Perhaps that was also a consequence of the transformation he'd mentioned?

"Besides, I am not quite sure this is a love triangle, either. I don't think our feelings will bring us into conflict like that," she continued.

"I suppose you have a point," I conceded. This was not going to be a romantic showdown, more a mere confirmation regarding the rules of play. For neither of us could walk away, neither of us could harm the other, neither of us could ignore our feelings, and above all, neither of us could risk hurting one of the only true allies we had in this treacherous world.

Therefore, we had no choice but to join forces. And I had to put away any fanciful thoughts I had been harboring that not everyone who met Master would fall in love with him. Of course they would. He was the only one in this world who'd reached out to us. He'd granted us the power we so sorely needed, and it was with him we shared our dearest, burning desire. How could we *not* fall in love with him?

Well, even if she hadn't, I would need Shuria on my side anyway. I'll force her to help if necessary.

That was because I had an enemy whom I needed to be far more wary of than her.

"Our current rival is…," I began.

Shuria finished my sentence. "…The demon lord. It's not fair; she's been with Kaito longer than either of us," she whined, pouting.

"That's okay. It's like what the adventurer lady who came to my village said: 'Men will always choose the woman at their side over one far away.'"

"Then we must use our wiles!" Shuria declared. "We must make him fall madly in love with us! My books say that men are only after women's bodies!"

"But we must be discreet about it. If we're too bold, it shall only serve to push him away. That lady also told me that once a man rejects you, there's no coming back. So we must take care, play it cool, and gently lower the bar bit by bit."

"Be discreet… Now that you mention it, women in novels who are overt in their seduction often lose out in the end…"

"Our goal for now should be to reach the point where he won't shake us off if we hug him. Despite all we've said, Master is a boy at heart. He can't ignore our physical affections. We can use MP drunkenness as a cover. And it's not like he doesn't enjoy it; we just have to convince him he can't do anything about it."

Now Shuria knew the rules as well as I. No matter how cruelly he rebuked us in the moment, Master couldn't completely blame us for what we did while drunk. It would be one thing if he truly disliked it, but I could see the way he blushed despite telling me to settle down. His inexperience was so cute sometimes; it just wasn't fair.

"S-specifically, what sort of things do you do…?" ventured Shuria.

"Oh, stuff like pretending to trip and pressing my breasts against him, or kissing him while pretending to be intoxicated…"

"W-w-w… Oh my… Breasts…? And…ki-ki-kissing…?"

Her brown cheeks went slightly aflush with color. My, Shuria was quite an adorable little thing, but as a partner in crime, she seemed a little lacking. I would need to correc—I mean, instruct her.

"You must not blush so easily," I told her. "When Master finally swears off Leticia, the time will come at last to do far more daring things than that."

Also, by being her teacher, I can indirectly get a leg up on her and...

"Y-you are right. For eventually, I will have him _____ my _____, and I will _____ his _____ with my _____..."

"What?!"

I choked at what I just heard.

"Ahhh, we shall need ropes, and candles, and whips as well..."

"Huh?!?!"

"To tell you the truth, I think something awakened inside me today when Master stepped on me... My heart races whenever I think back on it..."

"WUUUHHH?!?!?!"

As Shuria muttered bashfully, I called upon my trusty "Iron Mask" skill. *What am I to do now? The darkness in this girl's heart far exceeds my own! N-no, I must not be flustered. I am the one who loves Master the most, and if he wants to do those sorts of things to me, then I am fully prepared for it.*

Shuria continued, "Master has the makings of a great sadist. I'm sure that he turns into a wild beast in bed."

"Y-you think so...?"

Now that she mentioned it, I had spied the occasional piercing look of wild lust in his dark eyes.

"I know it! The moment I saw him act, I knew he was a natural! He was born for sadism, I am sure of it!"

"I—I suppose I can't argue with that..."

I thought back on our relationship with Master. Though he was usually an upstanding gentleman, there were times when he laughed gleefully at my mistakes. And sometimes, he turned this mischievous smile on me—not the one he wore when taking revenge, but another thing entirely, and it excited me. But I couldn't really be... Could I?

Oh dear, I have to retake the initiative!

"L-let's leave it there for tonight. We have a very busy day tomorrow. We can continue this conversation afterward."

"Huh? Oh, okay!"

I returned to the inn. This was not a loss, simply a strategic retreat.

And so unbeknownst to Kaito, the two began their nights of studying "research materials" taken from Eumis's mansion, slowly raising their level.

Longing for a Faraway Hero

Why? Why? Why?

Until the very end, that demon held your heart.

But I was the only one who truly loved you.

The only one devoted to you.

The only one worthy of you.

And yet it was not me by your side.

And by mine, there was nobody.

Why did you cry for that demon's sake?

Worry for her?

Wish for her?

I would have given you my everything if only you'd asked for it.

And you would have been able to see that if that demon hadn't blinded you.

It was your destiny to slay her, just as it was mine to spend eternity by your side.

I still remember the joy I'd felt when I first learned that, and the despair I'd felt when I learned destiny had been perverted.

Hence why I'd thought slaying the cause of that perversion could bring things back to normal.

It should have gone perfectly. You sliced through the chains of his curse with your own sword.

…And yet, somehow, it all went wrong.

It was too late. The fragments of those chains had buried themselves deeply within your heart. Irreparably tainted your very soul.

After that, all I'd wanted was to liberate that soul. To set it free into the great arms of our Lady, that we might meet again in the life beyond.

Because I am a priestess, and you are a hero.

Then I learned that my wish had still come true. The world hadn't broken after all.

When I realized that, I was overcome with joy and relief.

I still had a chance to put things right. This time, there would be no mistakes.

This time, my soul would end up intertwined with yours. A perfect union.

Please wait for me.

My beloved hero.

After a long and bumpy stagecoach ride, I, Metelia Laurelia, was feeling the weariness of travel.

I must have grown too accustomed to the bump-free carriage that Kaito devised, I thought.

Kaito's previous world must have been a land of marvels. Unfortunately, I hadn't overheard precisely how it worked when he explained it to the merchant, Grond. How vexing.

Stuck in a plain old wooden carriage, my bottom felt every little dimple in the earth below, transmitted through the rigid wooden wheels. It was starting to sting.

I had been healing myself during our rest stops, of course, but it was crystal clear to me now that no matter how much I had improved on our journey, I was physically the same little girl trapped inside a birdcage, waiting for Kaito to come and set me free. All my skill levels in "Holy Sorcery" and "Water Sorcery" and the like had completely regressed, and the fruits of my training with Kaito had returned to zero.

But that was okay. There would be plenty of time to build everything back up again. With the information I possessed, the two of us alone would be enough to banish that demon. It had been a mistake the whole time for anyone other than the two of us to come along on our journey.

All he needed was me, and all I needed was him.

As I pondered this, the walls of the city of Orol, capital of the Orollea Kingdom, came into view.

"...*Phew*, it's been a while since I last came to this land," I muttered, lost in reminiscence.

"Huh? Has it?" asked one of my attendants, giving me a quizzical look.

Whoops. They thought this was my first time here. I must be more careful.

"It is nothing. I simply misspoke," I explained.

It was a little blunt, but I was simply asking them not to pry any further. The attendant, worried she had offended me, looked a little scared.

"Let us break for tea once we have concluded our salutations at the capital," I said with a kindly smile to set her heart at ease. "You are welcome to join me, of course. It is terribly lonely having no one with whom to enjoy a pleasant chat."

The attendant blushed and simply said, "Y-yes, ma'am," in a quiet voice. I returned my attention to the window, gazing out at the city ahead.

According to my informant, Kaito should presently be honing

his skills in battle in a new dungeon near the city called "The Goblin's Nest."

"Hurry… Hurry… Hurry…"

I clutched the hem of my dress in impatience, though I knew it would do nothing to hasten the horses.

This time, Kaito… This time, I will be by your side…

I couldn't wait. I just couldn't. I wanted to see him. I wanted to see my reflection in his eyes. I wanted to hear my name in his voice, see him smile at me.

This time, I wouldn't allow that base and contemptible woman to corrupt his heart.

"Leticia Lu Harleston…"

Merely the name of that demon brought me to anger. She'd taken advantage of Kaito's kindness to ensnare his soul and usurped the seat that ought to have been for me.

This time, I wouldn't let him fall in love with her. In the previous world, I'd met him only after his heart had already fallen prey to her. Now, however, things were different. This time, I would save his soul and stand at his side. That was how things had to be.

"L-Lady Metelia, are you feeling unwell?"

It seemed I had accidentally let my emotions slip.

"Perhaps I am simply nervous now that we are nearing our destination," I said. "I think the carriage ride has rendered me most poorly."

"Oh, that will not do! We must stop at once and…!"

"Tee-hee! Do not fret. I will simply rest once we arrive in the city."

I understood the attendant's worries. As a priestess of the Church, I received treatment on par with other countries' aristocrats and wielded not insignificant influence around the lands the Church controlled. Her response was clearly motivated by fear of offending me.

Still, I could not possibly reveal the truth to her, so I passed the time by retrieving my favorite doll from my magic bag. He was large enough to sit in both my palms, and with a robe pulled over his jet-black hair, he looked exactly like the real thing. I patted him as though I was really running my fingers through those dark, silken locks.

Wait for me, Kaito. I will be by your side soon.

This soothed my restless heart. A smile came to my lips, and for the rest of the journey, all I did was stroke that doll.

After enduring that bumpy carriage a little longer, I soon arrived at the capital. There were many people there, and the layout of the town was a little more haphazard compared with the holy city back home. Still, it was brimming with life, and there would be even more people coming here in a few months when Kaito finished conquering the dungeon.

Actually, with me by his side, it shan't even take that long.

As the carriage drove through the streets, I gazed up at the castle ahead.

First, I must speak with Princess Alicia. If I can't secure her cooperation, I'll have to confront her with the fact that she summoned a hero in secret, and that I know the price she paid to do so.

I squeezed the cheeks of the figure in my hands as I pontificated.

I must play my cards carefully. The only people who know the secret of the summoning ritual are the members of the royal family and the knights who make up the royal guard, led by Commander Guidott. I don't know what became of those rotten royals, but I must take adequate precautions or else there's a chance that my travels with Kaito will be interrupted.

This time, I would unite with him no matter the costs. I had the advantage now. And I would confound anyone who threatened to get in his way, that princess especially, with my knowledge of the previous world.

In fact, if we did that together, then my bond with him would be all the deeper for it…

"Tee-hee-hee!"

"I am pleased to see you have cheered up a little, Lady Metelia," said my attendant.

"Indeed. I am feeling much better now. Thank you for your concern."

"That said, the exhaustion could catch up to you at any moment, so be sure to rest well after your introductions with the royal family are concluded. I would hate for anything to happen to you."

After thanking the servant for her kind words, my heartbeat hastened. Kaito was so close to me now. It had been so very difficult for me to seek his death to attain his salvation. I knew it had been the only way to purify his soul, yet I will never forget the pain I felt as the blade pierced his chest.

It had broken my heart to see him look at me that way. My anger at the wretched demon who warped his heart grew stronger by the day.

But that world was behind me now.

Now, together, we could make the world what it was always meant to be.

"Hee-hee!"

I couldn't help but giggle as I tried to imagine what it would be like.

"How are you feeling, Your Highness?" asked the man in his thirties, covered in scars. This was Guidott, said to be the strongest among my royal knights. His appearance and bearing alone showed his wealth of combat experience, and his low, rasping voice sounded quite out of place in my chamber, all made up to befit a person of my standing. But of course, that did not concern me in the slightest.

"I am well, Guidott," I replied. "My injuries have healed, and there seems to have been no lingering effects after removing the necklace."

To get around the curse that prevented me from taking it off, we'd ultimately needed to destroy it through channeling a large amount of mana into it.

"And how is the repair proceeding?" I asked.

"We have the city's finest craftsman working on it. It should be fixed within a few days, but the enchantments..."

"That is unavoidable. Those enchantments were forged with ancient techniques, dating back to the early days of the kingdom. It would be impossible for us to replicate them now."

Still, I clenched my fists in anger. That necklace was more to me than a mere ornament proving my right to succession, and Kaito had forced us to break it. Even if the craftsman could bring it back exactly as it had been before, that wouldn't undo what that man had done.

"...Please tell him there is no rush. I want it back without a single blemish."

I tried to keep my feelings hidden. One slip, and I felt like I would to explode. Even if Guidott was one of my family's most loyal retainers, whom I had known since I childhood, it would not do to rely on him for emotional support. I was Princess Alicia Orollea, first in line to the throne of the Orollea Kingdom.

Besides, since Guidott was my elder sister's former knight, that necklace was no doubt significant to him as well. Surely, he felt the same way as I did right now.

He nodded. "Yes, Your Highness."

"Now, what is your business? You didn't come here just to check on me, did you?"

No matter how close we were, no one came to the princess's chamber for such a trifling reason alone. Guidott himself was surely busy with his other duties, and if nothing else, a bachelor visiting the princess for a chat would undoubtedly start rumors. He was not so foolhardy as to forget that.

"Indeed. I have a report to make. Unfortunately, we have lost track of the black-haired, black-eyed boy. You can rest assured we've turned this entire city upside down without discovering so much as a trace of him."

"What did you find out?"

"We had sightings of a boy matching the description you gave. Apparently, he's discarded his unique black garb, but we were able to track his movements for several days. He was spotted going in and out of the slums, before he disappeared at night from the inn where he was staying.

"And I suppose there are no records of him leaving the city?" I inquired.

"There are none. Presumably, he escaped through some other means. The knights in the chamber with you may have been ceremonial, but still, for a single boy to trounce them so thoroughly is quite unthinkable. He's no weakling, that's for sure."

"...The monster attack after the walls fell. That was the fault of a monster known as the Wall Eater, was it not? Maybe he took advantage of the confusion to escape during that time."

"The knights on the scene didn't report seeing him. But when you consider the fact that the wall collapsed at a dumping ground for scrap wood, and that the event occurred shortly after we lost track of the boy..."

"...Then perhaps even those Wall Eaters were part of his plan all along? He purposefully picked a place where it would go unnoticed for a while."

But for a city's barricades to collapse so suddenly, to say nothing of those of the capital itself… That was simply unheard of. I was not convinced he had merely been lucky enough to have been in the right place at the right time. In fact, this revelation only made me more convinced he was somehow responsible.

I shook my head. *But…that makes even less sense*, I thought. *There is only one explanation. The sheer power of the hero caused him to go berserk. He is but a mere otherworlder. A ghoulish beast in human skin.*

"Ahhh, how vexing. From the legends, I'd thought the hero drew power only from his intrinsic ability. He wasn't supposed to be this powerful by himself…"

"They are just tales, after all. It would behoove us not to believe everything we hear."

"…Quite."

And there is still some time before I next hear the voice of the Great Spirits. Perhaps if I was as adept in spirit magic as my sister was, I would hear them more frequently.

It would not be exaggerating to call my sister blessed by heaven for her genius.

"…There is much that is unclear. Continue your investigation. But ensure you are discreet. We do not wish to draw attention."

"Yes, Your Highness. One more thing. An envoy has arrived from the Church of Lunaria. Please prepare to meet with her."

Oh yes, I had quite forgotten about that.

"The priestess from the Lunarian See? I never expected her to come to the kingdom directly…"

The Lunarian See was a country ruled by the Church of Lunaria. Their goddess was named Lunaris, and their primary tenets were the slaying of monsters, the establishment of a heaven on Earth, and the salvation of the weak. There were many other pagan faiths, but only the Church of Lunaria had become dominant enough to establish a state for itself.

As a nation, however, it was inevitable that politics would follow, so no matter how pure the intentions of its faith, the people who made up the country could be as corrupt as any other.

"They say she maintains peaceful relations with the opposing factions of her nation," I explained, "but I am not sure I believe that. Her reputation as a woman of faith may precede her, but I have never heard of her possessing any particular talent when it comes to politics."

The priestess Metelia Laurelia was almost synonymous with the Church itself. She was upstanding and pure, beloved by the people of her country. However, not all her peers shared her virtues, and the See was rife with intrigue and struggle, which had only gotten worse after the archbishop collapsed. This wasn't the time for her to go gallivanting off to other kingdoms when she should be strengthening her support at home.

"But according to the message we received," Guidott replied, "the priestess herself is coming, and she has gone through the proper procedures to request a meeting. Though I am a little concerned she has not informed us what the discussion will entail, I think it's fair to say she has a grasp on the situation at her end."

"Indeed. Well, I suppose I can decide for myself what kind of person she is after meeting with her. Look into her for me if you get a chance between searching for that man."

"As you wish, Your Highness. It's almost time for your appointment, so please prepare to head to the audience chamber."

"Yes, I will need the appropriate attire for a meeting with a priestess of the Church. Please call a maid to dress me."

"Yes, Your Highness. Very well, then."

Guidott bowed neatly and exited the room. Soon after, there was a knock on the door, and an older woman called out, "Excuse me, Your Highness, may I enter?"

"You may," I replied. The maid came in and helped me change, my mind adrift the whole while, wondering why on Earth that priestess would come all the way here to talk to me.

"Pleased to meet you, King Eudrace Orollea. And the queen and princess as well."

We were in the audience chamber of Orollea Castle. Standing before us was an embodiment of purity, a gorgeous young woman with her long, silvery hair partially tied up in a braid slung over one shoulder. Her beauty far outstripped the rumors, and even her unflattering robe did nothing to diminish it. Her breasts were also oddly large despite being underneath her clothes, almost in defiance of her outfit.

However, while the soldiers could not help but stare, there was no lust in their eyes. She was an unattainable ideal, a single flower blooming at the peak of a tall mountain, a woman of such benevolence and love that it was impossible to harbor unwholesome thoughts toward her.

"My name is Metelia Laurelia. I humbly serve as our Lady's most unworthy servant. I thank Lunaris for Her guidance and request Her blessings upon our meeting."

As the priestess clasped her hands together in prayer, she practically shone with a heavenly light, though she was not casting a spell of any sort. I had heard that this girl was only two years my elder, and yet she appeared far more mature than that.

"Hmm." The prime minister took a step forward and addressed her. "Lady Metelia, I believe you arranged this meeting to discuss 'strengthening our bonds,' but could we ask you to elaborate on that? It was only last year that a trade agreement was signed between our two nations. Have you identified any clauses that are in need of amendment?"

Both my father and the prime minister were under the impression that Metelia's visit concerned the grain trade pact that we'd finalized a year ago.

"No. I am afraid I have not come for such a trifling matter," she replied, shaking her head. The prime minister was disappointed, both that he'd guessed incorrectly and at hearing an international agreement be dismissed as "trifling," but naturally, he prevented it from showing on his face. It was only because he had looked after me since I was very little that I could perceive his true feelings on the matter. His expression just screamed, *I expected more from a priestess.*

Metelia seized that awkward silence and continued, "I'm afraid I did not come here as a representative of the See. I come as a member of the Church of Lunaria."

Her words froze the room. Those who understood what she was implying fell silent, while those who did not pondered her mysterious choice of words. It was my father who spoke next.

"What might you mean by that?" he asked, beads of sweat forming on his forehead.

"Oh, are you sure you wish to discuss it out in the open?" she asked simply.

At that, we all realized the terrifying reason for her visit.

...She knew about the summoning.

Her earlier declaration, that she'd come as a member of the Church, could only suggest that she was visiting this country not for secular matters, but for spiritual ones, at least on the surface. But besides missionary work, the only religious reason I could think to journey here was if she knew the summoning ritual had been carried out. And if it was the former, she would hardly request to talk about it in private.

The hero occupied an important position in the Lunarian teachings. If word got out that we had conducted the ritual to use the hero for our own ends, the Church could construe that as an act of hostility.

And they would be right. We had performed the rite in absolute secrecy with the intent of raising the hero ourselves to manipulate him for our own ends. We had hoped that if anyone found out, we could simply claim that we'd kept things under wraps to protect him from the demon lord's armies.

But things had gone disastrously. The hero had turned against us, and it was obvious he bore some sort of grudge against the kingdom. If word about our botched rite got out, it would be a stain on our reputation we might never remove. Other countries would interpret this as not only evidence of us attempting to hide the hero's existence, but also that we were too weak to contain him.

"...Prime Minister, Knight Commander. You two stay. The rest of you, leave."

"Y-Your Majesty? Why...?"

"I said get out! I will not ask twice!"

At his bellowing voice, all those who were not in the know left the room. Metelia turned to her retainer and whispered, "You too. You're excused."

"B-but, Lady Metelia..."

"Do not worry about me, I shall be fine. We're just going to talk, is all."

"...If my lady says so, then so be it. I shall wait outside."

The priestess's retainer agreed to her request with frightening speed, then gave a quick bow before leaving the room as well. After the last person departed, the doors were bolted shut. The only people here now were Mother and Father, me, the prime minister Barath, the knight commander Guidott, and the priestess standing before us, Metelia.

However, my father seemed to have trouble choosing his next

words. No doubt he was still trying to deduce precisely how much Metelia knew. Was she only aware that we had summoned the hero, or was she also informed about what had happened to him after that?

Her next statement confirmed our deepest fears.

"Now," she addressed us, "I'm aware of everything you've done. Firstly, I know about the black-haired, black-eyed boy you summoned."

""""Urk!!""""

Everyone in the room sucked in their breath. I thought back to the hero, growing livid at the very thought of him. On the other hand, my father relaxed. Or perhaps it was more accurate to say he gave up. If this woman knew that the hero had black hair and black eyes, then it was safe to say she was privy to everything. At the very least, she must have realized he'd turned against us. There was no point in trying to lie to her.

"...In that case, Lady Metelia, what are your demands?" my father asked.

I winced at his rashness. It was still too early to give up. I knew my father had no talent for lying, but at times like this, it was important to remain sure of yourself, even if all was lost. We might have yet salvaged something from this.

"I would like to court him unopposed. It is my duty as priestess to be by his side."

Metelia's face grew bright and cheerful, like a flower. As relieved as I was that she hadn't asked for anything unreasonable, I couldn't help but feel a little creeped out by her as well. How could she smile at the thought of that if she knew what the object of her infatuation had done?

In the Lunarian faith, the priestess was supposed to support the hero in bringing compassion to the world. Personally, I couldn't comprehend how someone could simply stand there and spout such sappy nonsense without a hint of irony.

From what she'd said, however, it seemed like she didn't know where the hero was, either.

"I apologize," said my father, "but he seems to have simply disappeared. We were tracing his movements within the city for some time, but then we suddenly lost him."

F-Father! You and your big mouth!

I bit my lip in frustration as he so casually handed over classified information to someone from a rival state. However, the most unexpected reaction came from the priestess herself.

"...What?"

She stared back in blank amazement, as if she hadn't been expecting to hear anything close to what he'd just said. Father, however, failed to notice and kept on talking. No doubt he was still feeling guilty for being found out and wished to smooth over any potential for poor relations with the See. Rebellious factions had been causing domestic troubles lately, after all. Though we had tried to summon the hero precisely to quell such discontent, our efforts had ended in failure.

"Immediately after the summoning, the hero attacked my daughter and many of our knights. When I saw their wounds, I assumed he must be a wicked brute with no capacity for intelligent thought. However, his ability to outwit our spies disabused me of that notion. He left a note behind declaring his intent to strike again, so all we can do is wait for that to occur. We are, of course, continuing our search, but with nothing else to go on than his hair and eye color, progress is exceedingly slow."

"He left a note behind?" the priestess asked.

"I will not follow your orders." Father recited. *"Let the scum I send you be a warning. Your punishment will be many times more painful. Prepare to lose all you hold dear. The Revenant."*

Though they had completely healed by this point, I almost felt as though the scars on my back still burned. Fury boiled inside me, but I was not so foolish as to let it show.

"Perhaps you know more, but it seems clear to us he is not going to stop there. We may be able to capture him when he returns to enact this 'punishment.'"

My father heaved a sigh of relief, but for some reason, the priestess seemed even more disturbed than me by this. She muttered something just barely audible, not even responding when my father called out to her.

"...Revenant? ...N-not be... Could...? ...But..."

"Lady Metelia? Are you quite all right?"

Did the fact that we had lost track of the hero really come as that much of a shock to her?

"...If... Then maybe... Leticia Lu Harleston."

"Hmm?"

From where I was sitting, I saw the priestess grit her teeth in anger. Her single moment of weakness sent a strange chill up my spine.

"Lady Metelia? Lady Metelia? Are you feeling unwell?"

"...No, it is nothing," she replied, looking back up again with another big smile on her face. "I believe the long journey has simply left me wearier than I'd expected. Perhaps we could continue this conversation some other day?"

It was plain to see that something had frightened the priestess, however, for her current grin was altogether different from the flowery smile we'd glimpsed earlier.

"I—I see. Well, we would hate for anything to happen to you while you are in our care, Lady Metelia. Maybe it is best you rest for now. We can speak again later."

The priestess placed her hands together in prayer once more and, with a bow, left the throne room.

Leticia Lu Harleston?

That single name was all I had been able to make out from Metelia's murmurings. It was an unfamiliar name, and yet it filled me with a very faint sense of dread.

☆

"AAAAAAAAHHH! Aaahhh... UUUUUUUGH! AAAAAAAH!"

Once she arrived at the castle bedroom, Lady Metelia seemed to lose her senses. She was currently taking out her anger on the bed that had been made for her.

"Why?! Why?! Why?! Why...do...you...keep...getting...in...my...waaay?! You demon! Demon! Deeemoooon!" she screamed, repeatedly beating her pillow against the bed in anger.

Before I'd become the priestess's retainer and accompanied her on this journey, I would have said I knew the lady better than anyone. But I had never seen her as incensed as this. She was downright furious.

"Why?! Why do you still hold sway over his soul?! There was supposed to be time! I was supposed to be able to save him!"

"L-Lady Metelia? What has brought this on...?" I asked, my heart trembling in fear. What could have infuriated my lady so? I knew I should never have left her side.

"Stay off him! You witch! He's mine! MIIIIIINE! RRRGG-GHHH!"

It was no use. She couldn't even hear me.

"Lady Metelia..."

I could only watch her tempestuous rampage, unable to do anything to soothe her troubled soul.

CHAPTER 4
Welcome to the
Maze of Doom!

"..."

After putting both the city of Elmia and Shuria's village behind us, we set off toward our next destination. The sun was dipping in the sky, so we stopped to make camp. We had borrowed some things from Eumis's mansion beyond just equipment. One of those things had been a barrier that repelled monsters and detected living things passing through it. Now we no longer had to drink that disgusting fuzzyweed concoction just to make sure we didn't all die in our sleep.

"Er... Master?" asked Minnalis.

"Hmm? What is it?"

"Er... Nothing. Never mind."

"Okay."

Minnalis had grown strangely reticent as of late. I could tell why. She wanted to talk to me about Guren...or to be more precise, about Leticia. They'd gathered a little about her from my memories, but what they had seen focused primarily on the motivations for my vengeance, so most of my memories with her had been pleasant ones. Apart from where *that one person* was concerned, my partners probably didn't know the full story.

They must have been aware that Leticia was special to me, as I made no pains to hide it. Though Minnalis and Shuria were my partners in crime, they were also young girls, no doubt eager to hear about other people's relationships. My sister had been like that, too.

Besides, both were kind and considerate at heart. They probably didn't want to ask me about Leticia when it was very likely I'd never get back together with her. Still, they needed to be aware of her in case it was important for our future revenge, which was why Minnalis kept trying to broach the subject.

The only reason I hadn't brought it up myself was that I was too embarrassed. You can call me a coward if you like, but come on! There's no way I could look Minnalis in the eye and tell her the story about how I met the girl I loved... No, the girl I still love! Anyway, we were never really a proper couple or anything like that; we hadn't even gone further than kissing. And also, how would it sound if I just started talking about it out of the blue...?

And also also, it was just embarrassing!

As I laid down excuse after excuse to nobody in particular, Shuria spoke up as if to change the topic.

"I'd like nothing more than a nice hot stew tonight, with lots of meat if possible," she remarked.

It was about time anyway. "Yeah," I replied. "Let's use up that Grateful Boar we hunted earlier. I'll cook."

"Huh? Y-you will, Master?" asked Minnalis in surprise. "You need only say the word, and I will take care of it. Or are you trying to say...?"

"Don't look at me like that. I'm not trying to take anything away from you. It's just, I'd like to make this."

I patted her reassuringly on the head. Minnalis took pride in being the one to prepare supper every night, and that was fine. She was an excellent cook.

I took out the pot and stove and prepared the water along with a broad selection of vegetables. Then I retrieved the body of the Grateful Boar from my Squirrel's Blade of Holding and began using my soul blade to slice it up, bones and all.

Though it faced stiff competition from its boar comrades, the meat of the Grateful Boar was far and away the foulest of its species. Cooking it only caused it to get stringier and tougher, on top of removing what little flavor it might have initially had.

Minnalis had to have been aware of this, for she'd suddenly gotten into a tizzy. But I knew something about an ingredient she didn't. Simmer the meat in the wine of unripe ricolle fruits, and it would transform into almost something else entirely. I didn't want to let the cat out of the bag just yet, though. I was kind of enjoying watching her squirm.

I added a fair bit of seasoning and the wine, then let it boil.

"Now, we wait," I declared. "I bet it won't be as good as Minnalis's cooking, but let's have a chat in the meantime. Do you want to hear about Leticia?"

"Er...er...yes," Minnalis ventured.

"I want to hear as well," added Shuria. The two of them still looked a little hesitant but nodded.

We couldn't go on like this forever. I had to bring it up sooner or later, no matter how much heartache the memory brought me. Otherwise, I could just imagine her calling me a "pathetic fool" or something again.

"There's not really that much to say, though," I admitted. "That Fire Dragon—Guren—he was sort of Leticia's pet. She picked him up shortly before we met, but given how he just acted, I don't think that's happened yet."

That was all I really had to say about the dragon. They would have already seen his abilities for themselves in the vision. What they needed to know was that the more new experiences I had, the more the few tender moments I'd shared with Leticia felt like an unnecessary hindrance. So if I was going to talk about her, then I would have to start there. Right from the beginning.

"It happened on a bright clear day, much like this one. It had been about a year since I'd arrived, and I was in a remote location in the northern regions of the empire, not far from the border with the beast lands. Back then, I was about equal in ability to an A-rank adventurer. I had a couple of tricks up my sleeve, but I wasn't so strong that I didn't have to be cautious, so I kept my power under wraps."

It was after we cleared out the dungeon near the capital and fought off the undead horde at Elmia. We had secured the emperor's blessing to use one of their legendary artifacts, the Teleportation Gate. That had shaved weeks off our journey, so we were traveling around visiting a bunch of dungeons.

Back then, I had been struggling with feelings of homesickness, coupled with an anxiety over my future. I tried to bottle them up, but I could ignore them no longer, so I threw everything I had into leveling up as fast as I could to distract myself.

"I was tired of being in this world," I told them as I stirred the pot. "I was still excited about getting to be the hero, and I cared about the people I had met here, including those I still thought were my friends, but I couldn't go on denying how I felt any longer. My initial hope that this place would be just like a video game was turning to despair."

I had consumed tons of games and books about people getting sent to other worlds, so when I arrived here, all I could think was how much everything seemed like a game. In fact, perhaps I thought it *was* a game, and that I could finish it just by going down the preplanned railroad.

The whole time, I allowed the glamorous heroics to blind me to the fact that I didn't *know* when I'd be able to go back to my world. And yet if I'd just thought things through for a few seconds, it would have been obvious. The demon lord and her dark kingdom were a power on par with a state. Back home, could a ragtag band of misfits ever hope to bring down an entire nation? Obviously not. Even a child knew that.

I was like a solitary beetle stuffed inside a clear plastic box, and the more time passed, the more it felt like I was suffocating. I took to doing anything and everything I could to attain the power to free myself of that cage, all while I tried to avoid reflecting on the impossibility of that aspiration. Because I knew despair would claim me the moment I did.

Somewhere, deep down, I'd wanted it to be a game. That was all the agency I could exert. But after a year, the truth was finally starting to dawn on me. I was learning how to survive in a world where murder was as natural as drawing breath. The scales couldn't stay over my eyes forever.

"I snuck away from my party at night just so I could slay more monsters. The only thing I cared about was getting stronger, by any means necessary, so I could get everything over with and go back to my world."

While we were in town, I trained. When we were on the road, I prayed for monsters to ambush us. When we came across dungeons, I devoted myself to slaying everything that moved, continuing even after the rest of my party had gone to bed for the night. I relaxed less. I ate less. I slept less. Day after day, I stripped away everything that made me human, convincing myself I was making good progress the whole while.

And yet I could never sit idly by when I saw someone in trouble. I would always step in, leaving less and less time for myself. My life became a contradictory mess of wanting to help people while simultaneously getting rid of anything that made me a good person, all for the sake of nurturing my power.

"Then one day, a hole opened up beneath my feet that sent me falling headfirst into the bowels of the earth. I was in a new dungeon, a really obnoxious one, too. It was there that I first met Leticia."

The way I saw it, that had been where my life in this world truly began. That was the moment I stopped worrying about how I could die here and instead started thinking about how I could live here.

"In my world, we refer to the garment Shuria is wearing as a kimono. They're the national outfit of my country."

"These clothes?" asked Shuria, wiggling her sleeves.

"Yeah, and Leticia was wearing something similar when I first saw her. I was shocked. I had never expected to see a kimono here."

I tried as best I could to calmly relate the story, but the warmth in my heart was sullied with envy as I recalled my first encounter with Leticia.

Kill. Kill. Kill.

"Gugyaaa?!"

"Boguh?!"

"Gweeeh?!"

I tore through the pack of monsters, healing my wounds with the Nephrite Blade of Verdure.

"Gh... Sheltering light: *Verdant Healing.*"

Still too slow. I need to be faster. Faster...

"Haah...haah...haah..."

I sliced, skewered, severed. Over and over and over again. Kill enemies, farm experience. No different from the RPGs I'd played after school with my friends. The more I trained, the more powerful I grew, seemingly without limit. And so I kept going.

My reactions? Always too late. My strikes? Always too weak. My movements? Always too slow. I needed more. More, if I was ever to return...

"*Groooargh!*"

"Grh?! Grraaargh!"

...I had been lost in thought and didn't see the bite coming until it was too late. The pain spread through my shoulder, and I devoted all my mental faculties to battle once more. I wheeled around, slicing apart the Beogarm. Once its jaws relaxed, I kicked its lifeless body away.

"*Groooooargh!*"

"*Gyaragh!*"

"*Garh! Garh!*"

"*Phew...* This still isn't enough. I'm still too weak. I'll never go home at this rate. O sheltering light, guardian of the forest: *Verdant Healing.*"

I used a longer chant to cut down on the mana consumption, healing my bite wound as the pack of monsters eyed me with hungry looks.

"Mom, Dad, Mai—I'll be back. Just you wait."

I downed an MP potion from my bag and sprinkled an HP salve over my light wounds. Tossing the pair of empty vials aside, I charged once more into the horde.

After dispatching the Beogarm pack, I rid myself of the bloodstains using the Clean enchantment on my robe, then checked my status screen.

"Still only level 125..."

At this level, some attacks didn't even damage me anymore. My maximum HP and Recovery Rate had both increased, so it was well within my ability to hunt monsters night after night like this. The actual value for HP was more involved than I had originally anticipated; it not only tracked wounds, but also seemed to decrease when you got tired or fell ill.

"I restore more HP per rest now, so I think I can keep going a bit longer...," I muttered, sipping on a cup of fuzzyweed decoction.

Potions were not perfect. The amount of HP or MP they restored was underwhelming, and drinking more only gave you diminishing returns. That was why it was important to take a break every now and then to give your body a chance to recover naturally. That being said, I could get better results by taking fewer breaks if I resorted to repeatedly healing myself with potions instead.

I'm getting a bit tired.

My level was one of the highest in the world, but there were still other people who were just as strong. That level wasn't enough to defeat the demon lord; if it was, they wouldn't have needed me.

How long was this going to go on for? I stood up and sighed, shaking my head as if to exorcise that haunting thought from my mind. Mulling it over was just a waste of time. The only thing I needed to concern myself with was how I was going to improve.

"I need to hurry up and find more monst— What?!"

That instant, the earth opened up, like a great, gaping maw beneath my feet. I reached for solid ground, but it was already far beyond my grasp.

"Wh-whoooooaaaaaaaa!"

There was a moment where time seemed to slow down, almost to a halt, before I felt the sensation of free fall lifting my stomach and plummeted down into the depths below.

Oh shit, oh shit, oh shit!

The wind howled in my ears. The first thing I remember thinking was that I had to make sure to land on my feet, so I adjusted myself midfall. Unfortunately, my panicking mind was unable to come up with any other ideas, so I collided feetfirst with the fast-approaching ground in an impact so shattering, it ought to have had *Ker-ash!* written above it in block letters.

"Graaaaaaargh!"

I opened my eyes and saw the opening of the pit high above me. It brought to mind looking up at the skyscrapers of Tokyo. There was no way I could climb back out. As if to confirm that thought, I watched as the hole slowly contracted shut as though alive, before it finally disappeared without a trace.

"Uuuurgh, what? What now?"

I was so shocked that I could barely even move. When I calmed down enough to scan my surroundings for a way out, I discovered I was now in a white rectangular room. It was clearly unnatural and had three exits—one in front, and two to the left and right. The area was illuminated despite the lack of any obvious light source, and the whole setup chilled me to my very bones.

"What is this, a dungeon?" I muttered to myself. Certainly, the mana that hung in the air *felt* like the kind you'd find in dungeon, but there wasn't supposed to be one here. It must have been a new one. Just my luck.

"Still, just how powerful can I get? Am I even human anymore?"

As I walked, I carefully looked myself over, finding no injuries from the fall of any kind. I had effectively just bungee jumped without out a cord, and by any reasonable metric, my guts should have been decorating the place right now. But I hadn't so much as sprained my ankle.

"Am I going to get even stronger when I go back to my world? ...I'd better watch out for that."

If people back home learned I was some sort of super-soldier now, I'd never hear the end of it. I couldn't be having that.

"Wh-whoa!"

Suddenly, the floor gave out beneath me like a giant trapdoor. Luckily, I was on guard this time and managed to leap aside at the last moment.

"Not this way, then, I guess."

I watched as the hole immediately resealed itself, then retraced my steps back to the first room. However, the next path I chose also ended in a similar trap. Once more, I leaped back just in time, and once more, the pit closed back up like it had never been there.

"*Tsk*, not this way, either," I grumbled, returning to my starting point again and picking the final path. As I walked carefully down that final passage, a worrying thought occurred to me, and my hunch proved to be correct when the floor dropped out from under me for a third time.

"You have got to be kidding me…"

Suddenly dumping you in a random dungeon that punished you no matter what you did. This was like one of those obnoxious trap-filled browser games.

"Okay, I suppose I can still leap over it if I get a running start."

It was about a ten-meter gap. Even a world-record long jumper wouldn't be able to close that, but it was no problem with my current abilities.

"Who the hell's gonna fall for a trap hole these days? Here we go!"

I built up speed and hurled myself through the air, but just as I felt like I was going to make it, I collided with something.

The far wall?! Wait…was this just a painting?!

Once again, I had simply no words for what I was seeing.

I've gotta wall jump and save myself!

"Nrgh?!"

But as if the dungeon itself was reading my mind, an enormous flyswatter-like thing appeared above my head and swatted me down into the hole.

I could only scream, "What sadist designed this game?!" as I fell down into the perfectly engineered trap. The emotion I felt at that moment brought me back to late nights sitting at my computer, slamming my keyboard against the desk in frustration.

"God...damn it!" Cursing my big mouth that so magnificently sealed my fate, I conjured up a soul blade and jammed it into the wall to slow my fall.

"Come on, stop!" I yelled as the blade carved through the stone of the pit, slowing me down bit by bit. Letting out a tremendous scream, I stabbed the sword in even deeper. I learned from the first pit that as long as I didn't fall too far, I wouldn't take fall damage, so I didn't really need to go to such lengths. But at this point, it was more of a battle against this dungeon's designer than anything else.

"*Phew.* Just about managed to stop," I said as I came to a complete halt, hanging from my sword by one hand.

"Hmm? And who might you be?" came a voice.

"..."

I couldn't respond. Standing there below me was a petite young lady with skin as fair as snow, dark eyes that glimmered like pearls, and hair colored a deep crimson. She looked innocent and beautiful in equal measure, more than a girl, but not quite a woman.

I'll admit it, at that moment, I thought she was the most beautiful person I had ever seen. Had this been a more peaceful world, I might have fallen in love with her right then and there. Alicia and Eumis were beautiful in their own right, but this girl was just my type.

But as she sat stirring the cauldron before her, it was not her beauty that captivated me. What she was wearing was something I had never seen in this world before. Something I thought I'd never lay eyes on again. A *kimono*.

Or rather, something that very much resembled one. It was too

short to conceal the legs, and only came down to above the knee. It was more like a dress in a kimono style. Still, it was the first thing I'd seen here that made me think of my home country. I felt as if my world was calling me back, and I wanted nothing more than to answer.

"Huh? I don't know who you are, but if you have come to deprive me of my precious pot, you can move along and find your own! This one is mine!"

After giving me a suspicious look, the girl raised her hand and cast a spell, launching a Fireball toward me. Her casting was so utterly flawless that I only managed to react to it by the skin of my teeth.

"Wh-whoa?!"

The Fireball whizzed past my head, just singing my ear, then hit the wall of the pit, where it exploded. It had only been a warning shot, and so it wasn't enough to hurt me, but the blast dislodged my blade from the wall and sent me plummeting down.

"Uh-oh."

"Wha—?! You idiot, fall someplace else!" the girl shrieked up at me, raising her hand once more.

"More, huh?" I braced myself, preparing for whatever spell she would fling next. Another Fireball perhaps? Or would it be Water this time? Wind? Earth? It didn't matter what; I would slice my way through it!

"Wha—?!"

But the spell she cast wasn't any of those things. It was something I didn't expect at all. A clear protective dome appeared above the young girl, perhaps some kind of Wind magic. It didn't feel like an attack. It was likelier that she was just trying to defend herself, which made it all the more unfortunate that sadly, I had already begun my swing, and there was no stopping it now.

"What?! He's atta—?!"

Oh no. I'm really sorry about this.

I saw terror flash across the girl's face as I swung my soul blade, slicing her barrier apart. Gravity took over, delivering me right into her boiling cauldron.

"Aaaaaagh!"

The metal pot tipped over, sending scalding hot soup over my arm. I quickly took out a canteen of water from my pouch and doused the wound before sprinkling an HP potion over it to heal the burns.

"Aaahhh! I spent ages making that!" she screeched. "I was finally about to have some decent grub, too!"

"Ah, uh… I didn't…"

The tragic scene left me without a rebuttal. I simply kneeled down and hung my head like a scolded puppy.

The room around me looked quite similar to the one I had just fallen from. The only differences were the small spring at one end, and the large pile of strange-smelling mystery meats rotting in a corner.

From the state of this chamber, I could more or less tell how the girl had been living and what she had been eating. For the sake of her honor, I decided not to comment on her idea of "decent" food. Besides, I needed to offer her an apology first.

"I'm so sorr—"

"Look at what you've done, you absolute fool!"

"Gabluh!"

Her iron fist came down on my head, and it was clear that the word *mercy* was some sort of foreign concept to her.

"You don't like to go easy, do you? But well, I guess we're even now— *Gugh?!*"

Just as I thought I could let down my guard, the girl swung again, screaming, "Like hell we're even! Take this, you flatfish-face!"

"Grrr… I'm *trying* to be apologetic… Listen!"

"Shut up, baldy!"

The girl hurled another baseless insult, along with an upper-cut this time. Somewhere inside my head, the rope holding me back snapped. After everything I'd been through, all the traps, the reminder of my home, getting attacked…but not only that. My duty. Whether I would ever return. My own weakness. All of it was simply too much to handle, and that punch finally opened the floodgates.

"I'm not even bald, you stupid girl!"

The only rational part of my mind left was the one saying *Never punch a woman*, so I conjured up the Slapstick's Blade of Many Folds and struck her over the head with it.

When activated, the Slapstick's Blade could harm and banish nonliving entities made of mana. Otherwise, though, it was just a normal pleated paper fan. While it made an *extremely* satisfying noise, its damage output was near zero, so it wouldn't hurt her at all. That meant I could hit her as hard as I liked without feeling guilty about it.

"It's just food, tomato-top! Besides, what're you calling 'decent'? I bet the slop in that pot's no better than the biohazard you've got lying in the corner over there!"

"O-ow! How…how dare you insult my meal! And this beautiful hair my mother gave me!"

"I just call 'em how I see 'em, pip-squeak! How did you even make that crap? It's all sticky and bubbly, and I don't know *what's* going on with the colors! No human's gonna eat that! And where's the lie about your hair? It's red, isn't it?"

"You said it in a mean way before! And I am not a pip-squeak! I am compact and cute! You must be blind if you cannot see how per-fectly my size complements my beauty!"

"*Pfft!* My sides! You think you're cute? Get over yourself!"

"Say! That! Again! Now you've done it! You think you can get away with such mockery?!"

"Huh?!"

I stepped back to prepare myself as I detected her warming up a spell. Based on the Fireball earlier, I could expect the attack to come immediately. However, this time, it was taking longer. Only two seconds longer, but still.

Then I was flabbergasted for the umpteenth time this night, because the incantation she cast was not an offensive spell at all. Before my very eyes, Tomato-Top disappeared...and reappeared a short distance away.

"A short-range teleport?!"

She raised her hands above her head, and five different orbs of magic appeared around her. I had never seen such control over one's mana before.

Water, Earth, that one's Dark, and the one that looks like a coconut—must be plant! But what's that last one that's all red and gray?

"W-wait a second!" I cried.

"Never! You shall pay for your slander!" the girl screamed back, thrusting her hands downward. The five orbs shot away in all different directions at unimaginable velocities and spiraled toward me.

I couldn't believe what I was seeing. The speed of her casting was simply unparalleled, especially considering she was juggling multiple attributes at once, including some strange mixture or anomaly I had never even witnessed before. Eumis was the best spellcaster I knew, and even she wasn't capable of this.

"Tsk!"

I already knew I couldn't dodge them all. I would have to tank one of them before making my counterattack. Through the barrage of spells, I spotted Shortstack Tomato-Top grinning back at me.

That coconut one looks like the weakest. I'll dodge the Water, Earth, and Dark balls, and as for that last one...

"I'll swat it back! Rrrraaaargh!"

I channeled mana into the paper fan in my hands, turning it a deep metallic color, and swung it at the fifth mysterious spell, flipping its trajectory backward.

"H-hwaaah? You can reflect it?! Th-that's nonsense! Mweaaahhh!" the girl screamed.

I watched as my return shot flew toward her and exploded into a cloud of smoke. However, I didn't have time to see any more than that, as the one that looked like a coconut struck me and cracked open on impact, splattering me with a strange liquid.

"Gah?! Blegh, what the hell is this? …Oh god, it's so itchy! Itchyyyy!"

It was like I had mosquito bites all over. Meanwhile, the girl's eyes had gone bloodshot red.

"It buuuurns! My eeeeeyes! My nooose!"

"Aaaaargh! What the hell did you do?" I screamed at her.

"H-heh! You're in for it now! The sap of the uyl tree makes your skin itch for up to an hour!" she explained, trying to put on a brave face before collapsing in pain. "It buuurns! Oh, it stings all over!" Tears streamed from her eyes, and her nose had gone red as a clown's.

"Th-this lasts a whole hour?!" I cried in disbelief. I almost hoped the shock would cause me to faint, so I could spend this whole time unconscious and unfeeling, but the itchiness prevented me from doing even that.

"So itchyyyyyy!"

"It buuuuuurns!"

And so the next hour consisted entirely of the two of us rolling around on the floor in discomfort.

"Hurgh…hurgh… I can still feel the itchiness…"

"Haah…haah… Uuugh…my eyes and nose still sting… I cannot stop crying…"

A little while later, the two of us had plunged into the spring in the corner of the room in desperation. After thoroughly scrubbing ourselves all over, we both dragged ourselves back out onto dry land, dripping and miserable.

"I can't believe you did that, Tomato-Top."

"Heh. Serves you ri— *Iiiiiie!*"

"Don't talk like that with tears in your eyes. You sound like your nose is clogged. Damn, it still itches."

There wasn't a rash or anything, but the feeling of irritation nevertheless persisted.

The effects of magic decreased with the defender's Resistance attribute. That meant that she had to be on the same monstrous level of strength as me, at least. Furthermore, it was already vanishingly rare for a spellcaster to command *any* attributes other than the basic ones, and yet this girl had been using Fire, Wind, Water, Dark, plant, and smoke attributes—seven of them. Eight, if you included teleportation, which wasn't an element, strictly speaking.

I looked over at the girl to see her blinking repeatedly, her eyes as red as her hair. She had already dried her sopping wet clothes with magic. As for me, I sat cross-legged, flapping my shirt to get it to dry out quicker. It had the Quickdry enchantment, so it shouldn't take too much time. It would be uncomfortable until then, but I'd live.

Now, how long are we going to keep up this childish feud, I wonder?

Somewhere inside, I knew I was only doing this to vent, and I already felt a lot better. I was starting to see just how much of my frustration I'd been bottling inside all along, without even having time to complain. I felt like I finally had room to breathe.

Her whining shattered my meditative silence. "What are you staring at, you creep?!"

"Don't call me that, you snake!"

"Snake?!"

"Yeah, you're a snake! If I hadn't reflected that one shot, I'd be rolling around in itchiness *and* stinging! You're pure evil!"

"Shut up, baldy! Baldy, baldy!"

"I keep telling you, I'm not bald! Can't you see my luscious locks?!"

"I hope it falls out!"

"What a terrible thing to say! You really are a snake!"

She was still pissing me off, so I was under no obligation to apologize at this time. However, there was something I wanted to know.

"…Hey, can I ask you something?"

"No," she said flatly and turned away.

"Ugh! How old are you?!"

"Shut up!" she screamed, launching a Fireball.

"Whoa! Stop flinging spells! Somebody could get hurt!" I shouted as I leaned aside to dodge the attack. While the casting speed was short as ever, the Fireball itself didn't seem quick or strong enough to do any serious damage to me, so it fizzled out as soon as it hit the far wall.

"Ugh…fine," I relented. I had ways of getting children to talk. If words weren't getting through to her, then perhaps I could appeal to her stomach instead. I was getting hungry, too, and surely anything I made would be better than that slop of hers.

"Hmm? What's that?" she asked as she spotted me setting up my portable stove. I lit the fire and placed a small pot atop it, before slicing up some vegetables and stewing them in water.

"Now, what to do for the meat…?" I pondered aloud. "Oh, I know."

I still had some Grateful Boar meat left over. It tasted awful cooked on its own, but by boiling it whole in overripe ricolle wine, you could get the flavor to come out of the bones, turning it juicy and tender. A dwarven weapon-shop owner in the capital had taught me that trick.

I skinned the beast and channeled mana into my knife, slicing through the bones so that I could add it to the stew in large chunks. Then once all the ingredients were in the pot, I put it to a boil.

The girl looked over curiously, both at the ingredients I'd chosen and the soul blade I used to cut them up before making it vanish. I could tell she wanted to say something but found it too humiliating to speak up after all she'd done.

I found her amusing, like a small animal, and so I watched her as I stirred the pot. This continued for about twenty minutes, until the whole room filled with the scrumptious smell of the stew. Tomato-Top was casting glances in my direction with a higher frequency than ever before, and she was sitting a lot closer, too. Her greedy eyes were plain to see, yet whether because of stubbornness or pride, she still sat on the floor, hugging her knees and facing away.

That is, until a soft rumble echoed throughout the chamber.

"N-no!" she floundered. "You did not hear that! Nothing happened!"

"*Pfft!* Ha-ha-ha!"

It appeared her stomach had usurped her pride and thrown up the white flag in her place. Red-faced and teary-eyed, she made her excuses while clutching her belly. It was hilarious.

"Whatever do you find so funny?! I'm not hungry, you know! Don't go thinking I am!"

"Sure."

I poured out some of the soup into a wooden bowl and placed it before her.

"Wh-what? You think you can win me over with this?"

"I didn't say anything like that."

"B-but if you insist…I suppose I wouldn't mind eating a bit…if that is what you really want…," she murmured, hands slowly reaching for the bowl. I swiped it away and held it high out of her reach.

"Hey, are you deaf as well as blind? Say *please* when you're asking for something."

"Hwah? Grrr... You're the snake here, not me!"

"Then here's my proposal. You can have it if you answer me one question," I said, grinning.

"M-mrrr..."

If only I could see the majestic battle between hunger and pride currently taking place within her. Soon enough, however, her stomach rang out in resounding defeat. She was so easy to understand. It was as easy as dangling candy before my younger cousins.

"Fine," she said at last. "Ask your questions. In return, you shall serve as my cook while we are in this dungeon. I'll hear no objections."

"...Fair enough. It'd be animal cruelty to let you live off that stuff anyway," I remarked, eyeing the toxic waste in the corner. How long had she been subsisting off that junk? Surely, that wasn't what she normally ate, right? Surely, that was just because she was stuck here, right?

"I-it's not cruelty, and I'm not an animal! I was doing my best, you know! I was trying!"

"Okay, calm down, don't cry. Here, eat up. I'll have some, too."

At least the fact that she was eating my cooking showed she was willing to work together. I'd seen from our fight earlier that she was plenty capable, too. She'd probably survive on her own, but as a Japanese person, the thought of leaving someone younger than me in trouble was bad for my mental health.

We hadn't exactly made the best first impressions, either, so I wanted to avoid revealing that I was the hero if at all possible. This whole situation was shaping up to be another massive pain, like what always seemed to happen when I tried to help. Another problem was that I wanted to keep my abilities secret while I was in the dark about what she was capable of. So far, she'd only seen me use the Slapstick's

Blade of Many Folds, so I would have to keep it that way for now. Well, that wasn't too much of a problem. I had never used it that much because its strange appearance drew people's attention in battle, but it was pretty versatile, so I should be able to make do.

"Grr, how come this loser-face can whip up such good food, while a super-ultra-mega cutie such as myself can toil and toil and it still comes out bad?!"

"What did you just call me? Would it kill you to show a little respect?!"

I was also planning to add, *So you* do *know how awful your cooking tastes*, but after seeing the tears in her eyes, I refrained out of respect for what must have been an arduous test of her stomach's fortitude.

"More!"

"Already?!"

Tomato-Top polished off her plate in an instant and began serving up a second helping from the pot without even asking. At this rate, I wasn't going to get another serving!

"Don't you know how to slow down?!"

"Don't be silly! This all belongs to me now, as we agreed!"

"I don't remember saying you could have all of it!"

"Well, I let you have—*om!*—one bowl, didn't I? Mmm! This stuff is so good!"

"How arrogant can you get?! And don't talk with your mouth full!"

As I sat dumbfounded by her brazenness, the girl just laughed at me.

"What are you—*om!*—babbling about? Food is the foundation of life! *Glug! Paaah!* To put it above all else is a primal instinct! It's the law of the jungle! Let down your guard, and soon enough, you'll have nothing left to eat!"

"What war do you think you're in…?"

"The war of the dining table! It's first come, first served out here, and while you've been listening to me, I've been pouring myself a third helping!"

"What? Hey! That's mine!"

"Hwa? Hold it! You can't just take it out of my hands! That's not fair!"

"All's fair in love and war! And this is the war of the dining table, you said!"

I had wanted to ask her about her kimono, but now it was starting to look like I wouldn't get the chance. I quickly wolfed down my second helping before she could steal it back.

Meanwhile, the girl patted her stomach, full. I'd made quite a lot of soup, but now the pot was completely empty. "Ahhh, it's been a long time since I've felt this good," she said. "You're not a bad cook. The meat was quite exceptional; I've never eaten such soft and tender flesh before. I'm guessing it's from a monster?"

"Yeah, from a Grateful Boar."

"Hmm? Do you take me for a fool? I have tasted Grateful Boar meat, and it's the most stringy and flavorless in all the land. You think me unversed in the ways of meat, and you say such things to taunt me, is that it?!"

"Yes, you're absolutely right. Well done."

The girl looked at me dubiously as I gave a noncommittal shrug. I didn't feel like telling her the secret if she was going to be like that. I didn't really have a good reason to hide the recipe, particularly since it hadn't cost me anything, but since I'd begged and begged the old dwarf to teach it to me, I felt a little reluctant to give it up so readily.

"Look, can I ask my question yet?" I asked.

"Oh, yes, I'd forgotten about that. What did you wish to ask?"

"I wanted to inquire about those clothes of yours," I said, pointing. The girl lifted her sleeves and wiggled them side to side.

"You mean these? I thought for sure you would ask, *What can you tell me about this dungeon?* or *Whoever might be this super-ultra-mega cutie standing before me?*"

"I'll get to those. Also, stop calling yourself a super-ultra-mega cutie; it's kinda cringe."

This girl ought to come with a warning label. What a waste of good looks.

"You sure are petty, aren't you? Fine, I'll tell you about my clothes. Cute, aren't they? They come with Auto Don/Doff, Auto Fit, Regulate Temperature..."

"Er, no, I don't really care about the effects. I was more wondering where they came from, who made them..."

If someone in this world was making kimono, it was possible they also hailed from Earth, just like me. Perhaps they'd even come through some other mechanism—fiction was filled with examples of people stumbling across portals or dying and getting reincarnated into different worlds.

However, Tomato-Top lacked that context for my question, so she interpreted it quite differently.

"You *do* understand these are women's clothes, do you not? Is that the sort of thing you're into?! Not only bald, but a sexual deviant to boot! What an unfortunate soul you are...," she said, watching me with reproach.

"What's with you and the bald thing anyway? And I'm not a cross-dresser! I just want to know who made them! I'm not gonna steal 'em off you, so don't give me that look!"

"I—I don't think it's anything to be ashamed of. Be true to yourself, okay?"

"I appreciate the support, but I'm telling you, you've got the wrong idea. If you don't cut it out, I'm not cooking for you again."

The vein on my forehead twitched. The girl simply shrugged and sighed. "Seriously," she said, "do you not know how to take a joke?" Oh boy. Hold me back.

Just as I was contemplating bringing out the Slapstick's Blade again, Shortstack continued talking as if nothing had happened.

"Anyway, regarding the origins of these clothes. Unfortunately, I do not know who made them. I just found them in the storeroom at home and put them on."

"...I see."

"However, I have seen similar garments for sale. I believe it was in a village somewhere in the beast lands. Now, what kind of beast-folk were they again...?"

Beastfolk? No chance of them being from Japan, then. Hmm, though saying that, if the last hero was summoned here two hundred years ago, I suppose the kimono design could be something he left behind. I did remember them saying that he had black hair and black eyes like I do. Oh, but then in that case, wouldn't it have gotten popular in the capital instead?

As I thought about it, I realized I didn't really know what was normal for this world. Ever since arriving here, all I'd focused on was getting stronger and helping people. I'd never had time to explore. Though I'd been here a whole year already, the only thing I'd really learned about was how to fight monsters. It was a little surprising.

Oh well. I figured I could ask Eumis about it once I got out of here. Or perhaps Guidott would be more familiar with faraway lands—he'd been to many kinds of places, after all.

"Even that's a great help," I reassured her. "I see. The beast lands, huh..."

The beast lands of Gilmus were the opposite of the kingdom in that beastfolk supremacy was the prevailing ideology. As such, Orollea and Gilmus shared a rocky relationship, and Alicia had even said there had been endless wars fought on the border before the empire was established between the two realms.

So even if I was the legendary hero, it was not hard to imagine what problems might arise if I just casually sauntered into hostile territory. I wished Alicia could exercise her royal authority to help in some way, but she had rebellions to deal with at home, too. It was complicated.

Even just the fact that we were dungeon-crawling near the Gilmusian border had apparently sparked off furious debate. After all, Alicia was supposed to stay in the castle. The only reason she was with us was to avoid the troubles brewing among the anti-royalists back home. It was decided she'd be safer traveling in a party alongside the legendary hero and the peerless knight commander. The life of a princess sounded rough.

Fortunately, she was well trained as a healer, and her father, the king, hoped she could practice these skills so she would be more likely to avoid injury during her travels. As long as we stayed out of enemy territory, of course.

"Whatever. Let's just get out of this dungeon first," I said.

I had fallen down a hole to get here, so logically, I should be able to escape by going up. What worried me was that there was no information regarding this dungeon, which meant that nobody had ever successfully beaten it before.

"My, you're feeling confident. *Let's just get out of this dungeon,*" she repeated in a singsong voice.

"It's not about confidence. I just don't have time to be dallying here."

Every minute away from my party was another I was falling behind. Another minute away from going back home. I stood up and took a look around the room again. To use a familiar point of reference, it was about two classrooms in width. If I stood facing the wall with the spring, then there was a doorway to my right, and a staircase behind me.

For now, it would be best to head up the staircase and leave the dungeon. I could always come back with the rest of my party if I wanted to complete it.

"Hmm. Very well. Down that hallway is a room where edible monsters appear. When the time comes, I shall expect you to feed me again. I'm retiring for now, as eating makes me sleepy. I warn you, though: Time starts to feel odd down here. Do remember to pace yourself."

With a yawn, the shortstack tomato-top produced a pillow and blanket from her bag and laid herself down on the floor. I stared at her in bewilderment.

"Wait, what? You're going to sleep? I'm going to be out of here in no time, and I ain't coming back to wake you up. If you think I'm gonna keep watch for you while you doze off..."

I had assumed with her calling me her cook that she planned on us working together, but I saw now that I was mistaken. She had no intention of doing any work whatsoever, and I sure as hell wasn't giving her a piggyback.

"You shan't need to keep watch. This place is safe. Even if something does approach in the night, then my sharpened senses will warn me of the danger."

She extended a hand out from under the blanket and made a shooing gesture, as if to say, *Get on with it already.*

I looked around, and sure enough, the room was furnished with what were called "safety torches," mysterious items unique to dungeons that marked rooms where monsters could neither spawn nor enter. The watering hole, too, meant this room must have been a "Safety Zone."

"Besides," the girl continued, "I am certain you'll only end up back here anyway. The corridor is a dead end, so that stairway is the only path out of this dungeon. Now do as you please."

"Hmph, what's wrong? Think I'm going to be so scared of a few monsters that I come running back?"

After a year of leveling, the creatures in this area were no threat to me. In fact, it was precisely *because* they were so weak that I had to spend all hours of the day farming them for experience. Ironically, though, that's exactly what had gotten me into this mess.

I was a little peeved at her slight against my year of hard work, but whether she realized that or not was unclear.

"There's no need to yell. You'll see what I mean."

"Fine, whatever. I'm going. See you never. Hope you enjoy making your own lunches."

"Yes, ta-ta. When you get back, I'm expecting another dinner, with a little more pizzazz this time!"

"I told you, I'm not coming back!"

I didn't ask about her level or stats, but from what I'd seen, she would be in no danger if I just left her here. Annoyed that she'd made fun of me, I set off up the stairs.

Soon, it curled in on itself and became a spiral staircase. I walked and walked; I must have ascended close to two hundred steps, two at a time, and there was still no end in sight. As I did, my head started to clear.

"...What the hell was that? Am I a kid?"

As I reflected on what had happened, it dawned on me that I'd been acting like a spoiled brat. What asshole leaves a young girl all by herself in a dungeon, simply because she was 'pissing me off'?

Just I was considering turning back, I took another step...

"Huh?! Wah!"

...and with a *click*, the entire staircase flattened beneath me into a steep slope. I stumbled to get a grip, but some sort of slick oil suddenly came out and coated the entire surface. I could do nothing but fall head over heels back down the way I came.

"Grh! Naaaaaaargh!"

There was nothing to grab onto, and even my knife found no purchase on the oily surface. Drenched in the mysterious fluid, I slid down to the bottom of the staircase, bounced off a bump that wasn't there before, and ended up deposited unceremoniously in the very doorway through which I had made my bold exit not five minutes earlier.

"Ow!"

As stars practically circled my head, a paper globe that *definitely* hadn't been there before came down from the ceiling and popped open, showering me in confetti. A banner reading WELCOME TO T.K.'s MAZE OF DOOM! in large, mocking letters also unfurled from the orb.

"Wh…wha…?"

"Hmm, it allowed you to climb higher than I thought it would," came the voice of the red-haired young girl, looking back over her shoulder as she lay. "Lucky you. So what happened? I thought you said you weren't coming back? Hmm?"

I just let out a grunt of frustration. "Grrrrrrrgh!"

"*Pfft!* Imagine making all that fuss only to be so swiftly proven wrong! I couldn't have done it better myself!" The girl put her hand to her lips, pretending to stifle a laugh. How obnoxious. She was like a demon. No, given what I'd seen, she probably *was* a demon.

"You knew that would happen, didn't you?"

"I tried to warn you! Anyway, like I said, when next I wake, I'd like something to eat. And I want it made with a little more oomph next time, *cook*."

Then with one last shrug, Tomato-Top pulled the blanket over herself and turned away.

"You...little...! Grrrr!"

My face was red with anger, but I couldn't say anything back, and I wasn't going to throw a tantrum like a child. So with nowhere else to go, my rage settled down within my heart, and I swore:

One day...I'll get my revenge on you...

I withdrew my earlier reckoning of her being a child. There was no need to hold back on somebody so insufferable! Make fun of me, will she? Well, we'll see who gets the last laugh!

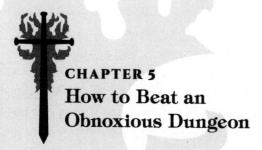

CHAPTER 5
How to Beat an
Obnoxious Dungeon

A while later, when my clothes had finally dried, I set off exploring the other corridor Tomato-Top told me about.

"Oh, there they are."

The room it led to was large enough to contain multiple school gymnasiums, and it was filled with creatures of various kinds. I wasn't sure that *all* of them were edible, though. There were various bugs and lizards that I'd never even seen before.

They also didn't seem able to leave the room, as they had noticed me standing in the corridor but weren't attacking. That must have been thanks to the safety torches that lined the hallway. That in itself wasn't strange, as many dungeons employed a similar setup, but it still felt very unnerving to have so many monsters staring at me. But even when I cautiously entered the room, they still kept their distance. Hopefully, they would stay like this so long as I didn't make any sudden movements.

"That one'll do," I decided, spying a Grateful Boar positioned near the entrance. I took it out with a single swing, before bundling it into my bag and retreating back to the safety of the corridor out of fear that striking one might bring the wrath of the whole herd down upon me. Luckily, that didn't appear to be the case.

At least one thing was certain: We weren't going to starve. Far in the distance I could see a Gigas Giant, Multihydra, Paralyze Moth Kingler, and Darkblood Tarantula, monsters that in any other dungeon might have served as the final boss. To fight even one of them meant embracing the fact that you might not come out of it alive, so taking on the whole pack would have been suicidal. Despite the great distance, when I slew the Grateful Boar, I felt a hint of their displeasure... Or perhaps to them, it was something more on the level of *What's that racket over there?*

As much as it pains me to say it, those monsters could skin me alive before I had time to lace up my boots. I was still too weak. If there'd been a room like this at the top of the staircase, I really *would* have had to run all the way back. How embarrassing.

In any case, so long as I still had the boar meat in my bag, I wouldn't need to come back here again. I turned and retraced my steps. As ridiculous as this dungeon was, it was beyond S-class in difficult. Clicking my tongue in frustration, I soon arrived back at the safe room.

"You fool! Where did you disappear to?!" yelled Tomato-Top, firing a Sandball as soon as I arrived.

"Stop casting random spells at me!" I shouted, knocking it away toward the ceiling with the Slapstick's Blade, where it broke apart and rained sand down on both of us.

"Pleh! What the hell did you do that for, oil-head?!"

"This is all *your* fault, Tomato-Top!"

"Whatever! Just make me something to eat!"

"Are you serious? You just ate! What kinda mileage are you getting outta that thing?!"

...I know she told me she wanted to eat when she woke up, but it hadn't even been three hours yet. Is she keeping a black hole inside her stomach?

*   *   *

"Nrgh? I never knew that pig could be so delicious! How could it taste so good compared with before?"

"Well, of course it would. I worked on it longer this time."

The only way I could make the exact same meal with more "pizzazz" was to take longer preparing the meat. All I'd ended up doing, though, was cutting out the sinewy bits more carefully and scooping the scum off the surface of the broth. I wasn't trained in the culinary arts or anything, so I wasn't sure what else I could do.

"That is not what I mean. The Grateful Boar meat I have eaten in the past tasted most foul indeed."

"Did it, now?"

"What did you do? Is it because you boiled it? The way you lit the fire? Or perhaps the way you cut it? The spices? Hmm, I can taste something alcoholic in there as well... No! I am sure the answer must lie within these vegetables!"

Well, some of those guesses were right. The secret to making the meat tender was just to boil it on the bone in overripe ricolle wine. Tomato-Top eagerly spooned herself a second helping, casting furtive glances at me the whole while.

"H-hey. Just so you know, I am rather interested in your recipe. How did you make that awful meat taste so good?"

As if done with the buildup, she finally asked me outright. Considering how reluctant she'd been to give me the time of day, it must have been weighing heavily on her mind.

I looked over at her. She had just finished her second bowl and was perched forward, eagerly awaiting what I had to say. I, on the other hand, was still on my first. How fast did this girl eat?

Her eyes glimmered in anticipation. I put down my bowl and turned to face her.

"There's a very special way you have to prepare this meat…," I began.

"I—I knew it!"

"And that is…"

I paused, the crucial information on the tip of my tongue…

"…Psych! Not gonna tell ya! Ha-ha!"

"…"

Tomato-Top stared blankly as I roared with laughter. I never expected to get my revenge so swiftly. It felt sweet.

"You…! How dare a mere cook humiliate me in this way!"

"Huh?! What country are you from where chefs give out recipes to their customers?!"

Not to mention everything I'd gone through to learn it in the first place. Who would tell it to a girl like this after that whole ordeal?

"I'm gonna burn your hair off!" she screamed, flicking a Fireball in my direction.

"Whoa!" I cried, dodging the blast. "How about you? How on earth do you cast magic so fast?"

"All I do is channel the mana super quickly, construct the spell super quickly, and release it super quickly… If you teach me your recipe, I'll tell you!"

"You just did, Tomato-Top! And it sounded like a scam! I want my money back!"

"Grrrrr! Stop calling me that!"

"What am I supposed to do?! You haven't told me what your name is!"

When I said that, the girl looked taken aback.

"I—I don't need to give my name to a rude man like you!"

"Huh? What the hell does that mean?"

She seemed to be losing steam and turned away from me in a huff.

"Don't ask a girl about her secrets! Yaaah!"

"Whoa! Stop casting spells at me!"

In the end, she never did tell me her name. That was a shame because I was looking forward to calling her "Tomato-Top" regardless. Instead, she just returned to her meal, grumbling under her breath.

"Grr, you balding, loser-faced cook…"

"You wanna start a fight?"

"Hmph!"

"What's that 'hmph!' for? God, you're such a kid."

Showing my own trademark hypocrisy, I returned to my own bowl as well.

"I see. They really are laughing at us."

After our meal, I had asked Tomato-Top what she knew about the dungeon. Apparently, she had been trapped down here for three days now, and every time she tried to advance, more traps like those sliding stairs had forced her back to this starting room.

It appeared that this chamber was the true starting point of the dungeon; from here on out, it only got more difficult. Also, there wouldn't be any monsters farther in.

If you're wondering how I knew all this, it's because we'd found a note explaining it all on the back of that ridiculous banner.

On it were nine points:

1. From here on out is a maze. No cheating.

2. There are no monsters in the maze.

3. If you shout *I give up!* then a hole will open up and take you back to this room.

4. You can return to the surface by clearing the maze.

5. If you spend six months here, then the dungeon will automatically spit you out.

6. The monsters at the back of the room beyond the hallway will not attack unless you approach them

or stay there too long. That means it's safe to hunt there as long as you stick to the monsters near the door.

7. If you run out of creatures to hunt, then you can subsist on the water from the spring in this room indefinitely.

8. The water in the spring will change color every day.

9. If you clear the dungeon, you win a prize.

"So I guess this really is a dungeon," I remarked. "But it's like no dungeon I've ever seen."

Dungeons were naturally occurring phenomenon that followed a simple pattern: Fight your way through hordes of monsters, defeat the boss, and claim the treasure. This dungeon, however, had been very obviously *designed*. The explanation, the obnoxious traps—someone had put all this here. It was simply unheard of. At the very least, no dungeon *I* had ever encountered looked anything like this.

Well, I won't get anywhere just wondering about who made it and how. I'm no dungeonologist. All I can think about is how I'm going to beat it.

I could leave the academic side of things to the experts. Once I escaped, I'd report it to the empire and let them deal with it.

"The first thing we have to get past is that staircase," I stated. By now, the slope had reverted back into a staircase, and even the oil had disappeared somehow. As I stroked the first step with my fingers, I felt nothing beneath them but cold, hard stone.

Most likely, some of the steps had switches on them that activated the trap. The problem, then, was figuring out how to get to the top without pressing any of them.

"What do you think?" asked the girl. "I can take you to the top myself if you'd like."

"What does that mean?" I replied. "Do you know which steps trigger the trap?"

"It's nothing like that. I'll reveal all if you teach me that recipe…"

"No. Never. I'm not telling you a damn thing."

You think I'd give up my one advantage that easily?

"Ugh! Grumpy, aren't we?"

"I don't need your help. I'll think of something myself," I swore to her. With that, I broke into a sprint toward the staircase and leaped into the air just before I reached it.

"Hiyah!"

I clung to the side wall and kicked off toward the opposite side.

"Hup! Hup! Hup!"

A wall jump. Leaping side-to-side between the walls, I began to ascend.

"Hah, hah, hah! I ain't afraid of no slide!"

I couldn't slip down the stairs if I wasn't using them in the first place. When I was a kid, I'd told people I wanted to be a ninja when I grew up. Now I finally had the skills to make that dream come true.

"What a fool… An incorrigible fool…," muttered the girl in disbelief. But I failed to hear her over the ninja-jump sound effects I was making to go with my awesome stunt.

"Mm… Mai…move over… You're hogging the bed…"

"What are you mumbling in your sleep about, moron?!"

"Guh! Ow! Don't hit me like that!"

The sudden shock to my cranium brought me out of my slumber like an old TV switching off. As my mind settled, the dream I'd been having quickly faded into mist, before disappearing entirely. All I could remember was the feeling of safety and family.

"Well, you said to stop casting spells!"

"Stop hurting me at all, you freak! Just wake me up normally!"

"What did you call me?!"

Any sentimental thoughts I might have had were purged from my mind as I settled back into the old abuse-flinging routine.

"Come on! It's time to eat!" she demanded, dragging me out of bed and immediately sitting down expectantly at the table.

"All right, all right, keep your socks on."

She had been conjuring the table and chairs out of thin air every time; she claimed it made the food taste better than sitting on the floor. Personally, I wouldn't have wasted the MP like that, but she seemed to have plenty to spare.

"Let's have that Grateful Boar meat again," she demanded.

"Again? I mean, we still have some left, but aren't you sick of it?"

She really did have a black hole for a stomach. She took five meals a day and ate more than I did each time. It violated the laws of thermodynamics.

"That Black Orc wasn't bad, either," she said, "but I can eat that any time. Let's go back to basics." She licked her lips and smiled.

"As for the soup, I'll have tomato today, and make it snappy," she demanded, smacking her palms on the table. So that gesture existed in this world, too.

"Yes, Your Majesty. Though, I can't make it cook any faster."

A while later, I placed the finished meal in front of her, which she polished off in an instant. She reminded me of my little sister somehow, even though her looks, personality, and everything else about her were completely different.

"Come to think of it," I mused, "if you fell down into this dungeon through a hole in the forest like me, then you must have been traveling somewhere. How did you survive by yourself if you can't even cook? Did you only eat rations?"

"Hmph. I don't like the way you said that, but I was not traveling alone. My partner is most likely outside waiting for me. She's really taken with how lovable I am, after all."

"I see. Now that you mention it, I suppose that makes sense."

I deftly ignored the part where she seemed to be bragging.

"Yes, I was traveling with my big sister," she revealed.

Oh, so I guess technically she is a little sister. That explains a lot.

"Two sisters out on the road in times like these?"

"Well, there's a reason for that. Hmm, I guess I don't mind explaining…"

I thought for sure the girl would refuse to elaborate like she had with her name, but for once, she actually seemed to think before she spoke.

"What is it?" I asked. "Now you're hyping it up. Were you on some epic quest or something? Off to defeat the demon lord?"

"Ha-ha! Defeat the demon lord? That's your best joke yet! I didn't realize you could be so amusing!"

I wasn't sure why she found that so funny, but whatever.

"The reason for our journey is…a secret. A cute girl needs to keep an air of mysteriousness about her."

"Huh? What's the matter? Didn't you say you wouldn't mind talking about it?"

"I don't, but it's still classified," she teased, holding out her finished plate. "More!"

"The only mysterious thing about you is where all that food goes. You'll get fat, you know."

"Drop dead."

"Gyagh!" I shrieked, narrowly dodging her Windball. "Are you trying to kill me?"

Unlike the Fireball and Waterball spells she usually used, the Windball spell was especially hard to see coming. It was like she'd wanted it to hit me for once.

"Huh? Yes, obviously. The punishment for telling a cute girl she'll get fat is death. Didn't you know that, you nincompoop?"

"Oh, I didn't. So where is this cute girl you speak of? I only see a pip-squeak who ought to come with a warning label."

"What?! You must be blind as a bat if you can't see me!"

Our noisy mealtime continued. How long had it been since I'd had such a lively bite to eat? When had fueling up started to feel like work?

...*Oh yeah. It was after I came here.*

The last time I'd enjoyed a meal like this had been back in my own world.

"F-finally... We're nearly there..."

"What an obnoxious dungeon this has been..."

Through sheer trial and error, we had evaded hallways full of traps and gotten covered in mud, oil, and some strange white powder (flour?) along the way. But at long last, the end was in sight as we arrived at another one of the many Safety Zones we had encountered among the traps. Like the others, the floor was painted yellow, and from here, it was a straight path to another similar zone, complete with a hanging banner that read, CONGRATULATIONS! THE EXIT IS RIGHT HERE!

Still, the path there was a long one, and I had only been able to read the banner from here because of the mana I was channeling into my eyes. If I had to guess, I'd say we still had about eight hundred meters to go.

"After you," I motioned. "Ladies first."

"No, no. We are friends. There is no need to be polite. It is a woman's duty to play a supporting role."

At that moment, both of us were thinking the exact same thing:

""You're just planning on using me as a stepping-stone!""

We both grabbed on to each other, trying to shove the other

ahead of us. There was no way the homestretch wasn't filled to the brim with dangerous traps.

"You would make a helpless little girl go ahead? You should be throwing yourself in the way to protect me!" she squealed.

"Sorry, but I'm all about that gender equality! Besides, what kind of 'helpless little girl' are you supposed to be?"

"Don't you see how dainty and cute I am?"

"Ohhh myyy gaaawd! Shut up! Shut uuuup! Don't give me the cutesy look! Is this some kind of new psychological attack? Because if it is, it's working!"

"I really pity you for being blind to my charms! This always worked when I tried it on Father!"

"Father! Oh, Father! Your daughter's being a little brat! How did you let her turn out like this?!"

Wait, what am I doing?!

I was acting like a complete buffoon. I felt like I'd been regressing back to childhood ever since I got here.

No, wait. I *was* a kid. This is how I'd acted back at school with my friends. Messing around, telling jokes... Now I was in another world as a hero who needed to defeat evil and fend off attacks from monsters and bandits... I'd had to learn to kill. I couldn't act so immature any more.

"Hey...," the girl started. "All this fighting is just a waste of energy. Why don't we take a break for now?"

"Y-yeah... That's a good idea. Okay. I'll count to three, and then we both let go of each other."

"O-okay. On three, right?"

"Yeah. Okay. One, two..."

"Wait! Is it on three or after three?"

"Huh? Oh, er... Let's do on three."

"I prefer after three."

"Then you should have said so earlier! Does it even matter?!"

Ahhh, what a pointless argument. You know when you're messing around with your friends, and everything that pops into your head feels like the greatest idea ever? Until the dust settles, and it's just like, *Was I drunk then, or plain stupid?* I felt like that right now. Just empty-headed.

"Whatever. I don't care," I snapped. "We'll do it after three, then. One, two, thr—"

Right then, the ground shook.

"What?!"

"Hyah?!"

It wasn't an earthquake. The floor beneath our feet sank, as though it had been waiting for that exact moment.

It was then that I realized something very important.

The note never specified there weren't any traps in the yellow zones!

The floor dipped down and sprung back like a springboard, catapulting the two of us down the (obviously trap-filled) far corridor.

"Not again, dammiiiiiiit!" I screamed, my mind racing in confusion. There was nothing we could do now. We couldn't take back what we'd done. The die had been cast for us.

"Aaargh! There's only one thing for it now!" cried the girl.

We booked it as soon as we hit the floor. It was a reflex at this point. If you stopped moving, the traps would get you. Perhaps once, we'd been foolish enough to believe that nothing would happen if we just stayed still, but those days were now just a distant memory. As we ran, great stone stairways rose up out of the ground to block our path, but we were used to this by now.

"Hng! Hup! Rah!"

"Hup! Hah!"

We grunted as we hopped across the stairs. All we did was run. Barrel straight forward with our superhuman speed.

"Hup!"

We ducked to avoid pillars flying out from the floor, walls, and ceiling. Seven hundred meters.

Suddenly, a host of cannons popped out of the ground and fired a volley of glue balls at us. "Out of the way!" yelled Tomato-Top as she cast a Water spell to wash them away. Six hundred meters.

Then a strong headwind began to blow. Anticipating that more traps would come once the gale knocked us over, I rolled forward like I'd learned in gym class to reduce my air resistance. Five hundred meters.

Just then, the ceiling, which had been stuck on with glue, began to collapse on us. From either side, a series of glue-tipped spears came at me. I heard Tomato-Top shout, "You owe me one!" beside me, before a vast wall of water rose up to protect us. The traps in this dungeon were well-made, so even the most ridiculously powerful spells we had access to would only stop them for a few seconds. Still, that was enough for us to escape the danger zone. Four hundred meters.

"Urk! Not this one again!" she groaned when she saw what was up next.

"The invisible block!" I cried. This was one of the most devious traps we'd encountered yet.

Despite the fact that invisible blocks of solid mana were easy to detect with magical senses, this trap mixed in several blocks where the flow of mana was interrupted, which rendered them imperceptible. For Tomato-Top, this meant her excellent magical senses were actually a drawback here. Because she would get so focused on figuring out the locations of the normal invisible blocks, she was much likelier to gloss over the nonmagical ones. Since we couldn't rely on our magical senses, the only way of spotting them was to pay attention to slight diffractions in the air.

"Time for me to pay back my debt!" I yelled. I took out the

Slapstick's Blade and channeled mana into it, causing it to shine with a metallic glint. At my command, it spread out into its fan form.

"Scatter on the wind: *Unraveling Gale!*"

I swung the fan with all my might, sending out a mana-infused gust that dispelled the illusions on the blocks.

"I don't need your help!" yelled Tomato-Top. "I was fine on my own!"

"Yeah? Well, so am I! You don't need to help me, either!"

Three hundred meters.

"Nrgh! Whoa!"

Suddenly, it felt like my stomach was yanked upward; gravity had reversed. Suspended below…no, *above* us was another flyswatter, ready to activate once we fell into the patch of glue on the ceiling. We could already see the grisly remains of some now-unidentifiable insect that had fallen into the trap before. Obviously, we simply leaped off the flyswatter to avoid it and were on our way. Two hundred meters.

As if to punish us for how easily we had cleared the last one, there came an unimaginable barrage of traps. Pillars of water shot out of the walls, gusts of wind blasted in all directions, the ground beneath our feet turned to quicksand, and floating stone blocks sought to impede our progress.

"Hrh! Hrh! Hrh!"

Drenched in water, deafened by gales, slowed by sand, and grazed by the blocks as we ducked past them, it took all our powers of concentration to make it through.

Then we were in the final stretch. Just ten meters left.

As soon as we neared safety, the floor and ceiling started to close in on us. By some miracle, both Tomato-Top and I were still neck and neck, so we sprinted side by side toward the safe haven beyond. Desperate to make it to the far platform before the trap crushed us, we jumped.

"Come…" "Ooooon!" we both screamed.

Just a little farther, and we would be free.

Come on, come on, come on!

At that moment, however, my frenzied mind spat out a short calculation. At this speed, I wasn't going to make it. One of my legs was going to get caught. It had happened before and sent me right back to the start.

"Dammit…! …Whoa?!"

Just as it all seemed all hope was lost, a powerful gust suddenly kicked up from behind, pushing me on. As it lifted me through the air, I heard the girl's prideful voice. "Heh-heh, now you owe me one again!"

"*Tsk.* How come you got to do the best one?" I grinned. At least we'd finally cleared the dungeon.

Or so I thought.

We'd forgotten the simplest of things, even though it had been impressed upon us mere moments ago: The yellow-marked zone between us and the far door was not necessarily free of traps. We had only assumed that. In fact, this area was the perfect place to spring a trap on us, just as we'd let down our guard.

""Hrh?!""

As we fell toward the ground, gravity normalizing again, the yellow-marked floor beneath us suddenly vanished before blistering hot air rushed out to scald our skin. It was a trap the likes of which we had never seen. The floor had opened up to reveal a roaring pit of flame.

Damn! That'll kill us!

Up until now, the traps we'd come across had never caused us any serious injury. Even if they completely caught us off guard, the worst we'd get was covered in bruises and glue. But this one was different. Even with our superhuman abilities, it was obvious these magical flames would roast us alive. The only reason the traps hadn't killed us already was because they hadn't been trying to. But they *had* been strong enough that we couldn't simply destroy them all. And now it seemed they were finally showing the true depths of their fearsome might. The flames licked at us, ready to devour us whole.

There's gotta be a way…!

Contrary to how it had appeared when we were farther away, the exit was too far for us to reach, even with the tailwind at our backs. It was too late to turn around, too, as the hallway had already clamped shut behind us. As impending death loomed, the whole world turned black-and-white. Time slowed to a crawl, like we were swimming through tar.

Suddenly, a burst of inspiration cut through my muddled thoughts.

Wait! If I can just do that again…!

I couldn't cast spells, but I was able to manipulate my mana.

Before I stopped to second-guess myself, I put my plan into action. The name of the skill flowed freely from my lips, as if on instinct.

"Air Step!"

"Mrh? That fire— Gyagh?!"

Tomato-Top didn't have time to finish her thought behind me before I wrapped her beneath my arm and leaped off the floating platform of mana I'd created. How ironic that a cruder version of the invisible blocks that had tormented me so many times before had saved me.

As I propelled myself forward, the blue-hot flames leaped up to give chase, like a dragon opening its jaws.

"Come ooooon!"

We tumbled into the doorway without letting up. However, I had given little thought to how we would stop, so we carried on rolling straight through the open door. Fortunately, there was a wall beyond to stop us, but unfortunately, such a service came at great cost.

"Nraaaaargh!"

There was a dull *thud* as Tomato-Top's head collided with the stone wall before she screamed out in pain. At least we were still breathing, though.

"Now we're even again!" I told her.

"Like hell we are! Thanks to you, I bumped my noggin!" she yelled, leaping to her feet in rage. "And wipe that stupid smirk off your face! You fool! You incorrigible fool!"

"Well, I couldn't help it!" I shot back. "You should be glad we're not both piles of ash!"

"What?! Are you seriously telling me you didn't realize?" asked the girl, rubbing her bruised head and glaring at me.

"Realize what?"

"This!"

Tomato-Top walked over to the door we had just come through and stuck her hand into the roaring inferno.

"Whoa, what the hell are you doing?!" I cried out in surprise and leaped to my feet. Flames that rich in mana would vaporize her flesh in an instant. The girl, however, just gave me a mocking laugh.

"*Pfft!* Calm down, you bumbling oaf! Look, nothing is happening to me."

"Uh... Wha?"

She withdrew her hand from the flames. Sure enough, it was completely unscathed. The blaze hadn't even singed her kimono.

"Errr...what? What's going on?"

"These flames are nothing more than an illusion done up with a tremendous amount of mana to make them look more fearsome. They're completely harmless," she explained, a gleeful smile on her lips. "Well, I suppose they could hurt a complete nincompoop who tripped over running for his life."

"Ah... Grr... Er..."

"*'Now we're even again!'*" she mimicked. "*Schwing!*" She struck a cool-guy pose to mock me.

"Y-you little…!"

"I do declare, never have I seen a face so undeservedly smug as yours was then. It's going straight into my top five. Have you ever considered giving up the adventurer life and settling down as a comedian?"

"Rrrrrrrgh!"

She's a demon! A true demon! It took the full potential of my rational mind to stop myself losing it right then and there. I had to be the better man. Unfortunately, as she continued to laugh at me, I could find no other reasonable outlet for my wrath. More for the pile, I guess. What difference did a little more pent-up anger make at this point?

"Heh-heh-heh. Well, I suppose we can move on for now," she announced at last, just as I was about to give in to the voice telling me to snap. "At least we are finally done with that insufferable passage."

I wanted to beat her silly with my fan so bad.

When I finally calmed down, I looked around. The room we were in looked worryingly similar to the starting chamber, but it was only about a quarter the size. In one corner was another spring of water, and even the walls and floors gave off the same unnatural warmth despite being carved out of stone.

The only other difference to speak of was that the hallway leading to the monster room was gone. Instead, there was a huge set of metal doors. Presumably, they led outside.

"You'll regret laughing at me like that… Anyway, it said this door was the exit, so I guess that means we made it through the maze. Finally. At long last, I don't have to look at your stupid face anymore."

"What? Are you going to be lonely? Huh? Huh? I suppose I could always hire you as my cook full-time if you really insist…"

"Gee, self-centered much?" I chuckled. Unlike usual, though, she wasn't responding to my taunts. I guess she was happy to be getting out of here as well.

"Ten days we've been down here." I sighed. "I don't even know what time it is up top, but I'll just be happy to breathe clean air again."

I stood up and approached the door. Tomato-Top walked up beside me.

"I believe it is just about suppertime," she remarked.

"How do you know that?"

"Because I am expecting supper. Make something nice for me after we get outside," she demanded, sticking her tongue out.

"...About half of what I've done in this dungeon is making meals for you," I said. When I agreed to cook for her, I didn't know what I was getting myself into. I didn't think I'd be cooking five meals a day for a week and a half. Hell, I didn't even think we'd be down here that long.

"Truly, the world is a mysterious place. How can a nobody like you know how to cook, while a cutie like myself possesses no talent whatsoever? It just does not make sense. You didn't put anything strange into it, did you?"

"How many times are you going to ask me that? And of course I didn't. How rude."

The two of us stood before the double doors and grabbed a handle each.

"Whatever. I suppose this'll be the last time. I'll make you so much food, your belly'll fall out."

"Now I like the sound of that! I've been starving myself so far!"

"What?! How much do you normally eat?!"

"Food is the truth of this world! I can eat twice as much as that when I really want to! For the last one, I am seriously going to pull out all the stops, so think long and hard about what you are going to make me!"

"What's wrong with you? Is your stomach the size of your entire body? Or did you get your stomach acid from a monster?"

Well, I guess I'd better whip up something really special, then, I thought as I pushed open the large metal door...

Scuttle, scuttle, wriggle, wriggle, swish, swish, squeak, squeak, crawl, crawl.

""..."""

Then without saying a single word, the two of us pulled the door shut.

""Hmm... No, that's not right,"" we both muttered to nobody in particular.

"Huh. I wonder what that was," I said. "Guess I must be getting tired."

"That cannot be, can it? I mean...surely not."

I rubbed my eyes, hoping it would help me wake up. Then we looked at each other once more, nodded, and opened the doors again.

But no matter how much we denied it, the same scene awaited us. Beyond that door was not the smell of fresh air or the clear sky, but...

Slither, slither, scuttle, scuttle, scurry, scurry, chitter, chitter, squirm, squirm.

...cockroaches, centipedes, slugs, rats, mosquitoes, and moths. Each about the size of a small dog.

""No, no, no, no, no!""

Individually, they were disgusting, but a whole room full of the creepy-crawlies cut straight to our primal instincts. We couldn't even bring ourselves to look directly at the sight.

We closed the door again.

What. The hell. Was that? Had I finally lost it and started hallucinating?

I could barely even think. I just stood there in stunned silence, until Tomato-Top's voice brought me back to my senses.

"What in the blazes is going on?" asked the girl, crouching, head in her hands. "I thought it said there weren't any monsters in here!"

"...I'm not even sure if they *are* monsters or not," I remarked, checking the note again. "That being said, it only specifies there aren't monsters *in the maze*."

Technically, we had reached the exit, so we weren't in the maze anymore.

"But if we're out of the labyrinth," asked the girl, "how come we have not reached the surface yet? Didn't it say if we beat the dungeon, we get to go free?"

"Well, yes, but... I guess we've cleared the *maze* but not the *dungeon*?"

Now that I thought about it, these double doors looked awfully like the entrances to boss chambers in other dungeons.

"Ah."

"What is it now?"

"Look up there," I said, pointing above the door. "It's kinda hard to make out, but doesn't it say 'Guardian Room'?"

The text was almost the same color as the wall and located so far up that it was almost impossible to read, but sure enough, that was what it said.

"" ... ""

Another awkward silence reigned.

"N-no! No! No! No! You mean we have to *fight* those things? I cannot! I simply cannot! This is too much!" she screamed, shaking her fists in denial. "Hold on. Boys like bugs, do they not? And girls hate bugs, do they not? So..."

"Don't give me those puppy-dog eyes! I don't like vermin any more than you do! Besides, those aren't bugs, they're something else entirely! They're not even remotely the same as the cicadas back home!"

"But I do not want to go up against something as loathsome as that! I know! You still owe me one, remember? I'm calling in the favor! Right now! Fight those creepy-crawlies for me!"

"No! I...I let you make fun of me without saying anything, so now we're even!"

"Wha—? You would shirk your debt? Have you no shame? What kind of man refuses to pay back his favors owed when the time comes?"

"What are you talking about?!"

I didn't want to do it. Absolutely not. I think my mind would be in more danger than my body if I did. I could handle monsters that were a little creepy, but insects freaked me out at the best of times, let alone at this size. I needed bug spray. Extra-large.

"Besides, it should be a crime to force a cutie like me to go against those monsters! You're a scoundrel!"

"How dare you call me that when you're way worse than I am! Why do I have to fight them when I'm close-range?! I shouldn't have to get so near that I can smell what they had for breakfast when you can just blow them up from far away with your spells and not have to worry about it!"

"Just close your eyes!"

"Are you crazy?! How am I supposed to fight like that?! If I go in hacking and slashing, I'm gonna get drenched!"

"And what is the matter with that? You could do with a bath."

"It ain't gonna be water I'm drenched in!"

Honestly, the thought of getting covered in guts and fluids made me want to take a shower right away.

"I can't do it! I just can't!" she screamed. "They're all scaly and slimy and glisteny and squishy and creepy and crawly and wiggly and jiggly! It sends shivers down my spine!"

"Yeah, well, I don't want to do it, either! No one in their right mind does!"

We were like a pair of kids, squabbling over who had to do the housework. It went on like that for a while. Then finally...

"I told you, I don't wanna do it, either! Why can't you just use your magic to blast them or bury them from a distance?!"

"That's not the problem! And why can't you just dodge their guts?! If you're so unwilling to get close, then just throw monster bones at them!"

At each other's suggestion, we suddenly both fell silent.

""Actually, that's not a bad idea...,"" we both said at once. Suddenly, I felt exhausted. Geez...why didn't we think of this earlier and avoid this entire argument?

"You're right. It's only because we're still thinking in terms of *fighting* them that we're getting so worked up."

"You are right. This will be no brawl. It will be an extermination."

Once again, we pushed open the doors.

What had I been so afraid of? Vermin were vermin, no matter how large they were, and arguing in front of the door wouldn't change anything.

"I ain't afraid of no bugs!" I yelled, kicking open the door.

"I shall exterminate the lot of you!" screamed Tomato-Top as we plunged into the boss fight.

"Cheeeee! Sksksksk! Blblblblblb!"

""Noooooooooooooooooooo!""

For all our fearless talk, our courage quickly fell apart like damp paper when we entered. Thus, our despair-inducing battle began.

"Get crushed, bugs!"

"Kyukyuu..."

"Checheee..."

The scene was even more gruesome now than when we'd entered.

I had been hurling horns, bones, and shells from my bag, so now the dry, scuttling creatures were coated in gelatinous goo and smushed insect bits. One look at the grisly arena was enough to tell you just how messed up whoever designed this dungeon was.

"Ha-ha-ha! You worthless insects! You're like ants to me!"

I wasn't even sure what I was saying. I was trying to avoid staying too sane because I thought I'd faint on the spot if I understood what I was looking at. Praise be to the Confusion status! Merciful and benevolent savior!

Yeah, I don't really get what I'm thinking anymore.

"Aaaaaagh! Gross, gross! Stay back, foul creatures! Insects taste the worst!!"

Huh. So Tomato-Top's actually eaten insects, has she? Sounds like she hates them even more than me.

"Checheee!"

"Bibiii!"

"They're so creepy and crawly! Make them stopppp!"

Tomato-Top was so scared that she wasn't even aiming properly, just casting spells as fast as she could. It looked like she was also confused, just like me... Wait, if she was crying, then did that mean it wore off? Maybe her resistance to Confusion was so high, the status effect never stuck in the first place.

"Well, whatever. Who cares?! Just die already! Ah-ha-ha-ha!"

"Dammit! How come you get to go insane without me? Grr! I've never been so vexed at having good magic resistance!"

"Sorry, I can't hear you! I'm craaaazy!"

"Shut up, baldie! Stop your eyes from spinning and come back to reality already!"

"Whoooaa?!"

Just then, a ball of water doused me. Now I was sopping wet and cured of my Confusion.

"What are you doing?!"

"Making up for your subpar resistances! How long were you planning on staying loopy?"

"Forever! It was on purpose! If I wanted to heal it, I would have done it myself! How am I supposed to go up against these things without losing a few marbles?!"

Now that I was looking at the scene again, I found it was truly a horrifying spectacle. It would have been bad enough in a movie or TV show, but the sheer destructive power of being here in person was unequaled. Even the air itself seemed heavier than before. I didn't know if the Confusion had stopped me from realizing this before, but now the mucus, the strange bewildering spores, and even the breath attack of a bizarre earthworm-like creature had all combined to give rise to a truly awful smell that made me want to literally lose my lunch. Fortunately, I was quite a high level by this point and had access to several status effect–preventing skills, but they couldn't fix the stench.

"Damn, it's getting so hot and humid in here… I thought bugs were supposed to be cold-blooded. What gives?"

Now that I was back to normal, my superhuman senses were flooded with information. My eyes took in every minute detail of the gory scene, a deeply unpleasant buzzing of wings filled my ears, and the visceral smell I just described filled my nostrils. On top of all that, it was sweltering, probably due to all the Fire spells Tomato-Top had been hurling around.

As for the girl, she had cloaked herself in a semispherical Wind barrier and was blissfully ignorant of the temperature outside.

"That's not fair, Tomato-Top! Let me in, too!" I yelled, running toward her. As I did, I hurled two more projectiles, the first taking out a centipede-like creature crawling toward me, while the second knocked two flying ants out of the air.

"Nrgh? Stay back, you fool! You're bringing the gross ones with you! Plus, you reek!"

"But I just had a shower, thanks to you!"

"Well, it smells like you need another one! Take this!"

"Whoa?!"

Another huge sphere of water appeared, but this one formed around me like a bubble and began to swirl.

Whoa… This must be how a car feels at the car wash…

While I watched Tomato-Top fire spears of rock that pierced the wings of several more flying ants and brought them down to the ground, the bubble scrubbed me clean from the neck down for about ten seconds before collapsing into a puddle with a splash.

"You just gonna leave me dripping wet?! You did that last time as well!"

"Deal with it! A little bit of water never hurt anyone!"

"Yeah, now all those weird fungal spores and moth scales are gonna stick to me! That's a disaster!"

"Oh, I wouldn't worry about that. I'd never let those disgusting things anywhere near us."

During my short soak, a few of the vermin had approached me, so I crushed several of them under the three-meter corpse of a Stone Golem. It had once served as the boss of a low-level dungeon that I'd defeated fairly easily. I was holding on to it because Eumis had mentioned wanting to study its corpse, as golems were relatively scarce in the Orollea Kingdom. We'd originally planned to send it back to Elmia once we reached the next town. I'm sorry, Eumis, but this is an emergency. It doesn't matter if I give it back to you covered in bug guts, does it? …Okay, if it does, I'll hunt you a new one.

"Urgh, my clothes are sticking to me. This sucks!"

The textile quality in this world was worse than what I was used to, so my outfit caused me mild discomfort at the best of times. Now that my clothes were wet, this issue had gotten only more pronounced. At least it should dry out quickly in this heat, I suppose.

"*Shashashashaaa!*" came the shrill cry of a sluglike creature as it rushed toward me.

"Don't give me that '*Shashashashaaa*' crap, you stupid insect!" I shouted, continuing to throw things once more.

The fight dragged on. After a while, the immeasurable number of insects had somewhat abated. A little longer, and we would have exterminated the lot of them. Now the room was clearer. We could see another door directly across from the one we entered, this one colored bright green. That was the true exit, surely. However, there was something else weighing on both of our minds...

"Hey," Tomato-Top asked amid the fighting. "What about that thing...?"

I had been trying not to think about it, and evidently, so had she, but we could ignore it no longer.

"Don't say it," I said. "I know."

At one end of the room was a large, sticky, egg-like growth with veins across its surface that pulsed intermittently. Now that I had a clear shot, I took one of my few proper throwing knives from my bag and hurled it toward the mysterious object. However, before the knife could reach his target, a wall of insects lined up to receive the blow, as if protecting it.

"*Tsk.* Still nothing, huh?"

The egg was blocking the path to the exit, too. It was basically lodged right in the doorway. We'd known there was something foul about it, even before it grew darker in color and began to swell in size.

"I am getting a most unpleasant feeling about that thing, you know."

"Oh, I'm glad it's not just me, then. What a relief."

"I fear that relief will do you little good before long."

Tomato-Top continued flinging her Fireballs at our foes with little trouble. She seemed to be holding up much better now. Fire was usually a good bet against any kind of enemy, and against it, these bugs fell like...well, like flies, I suppose. In addition, the room was filling with smoke, and while it was still easy enough to see and breathe, it looked very much like some kind of apocalyptic landscape.

Should I just go up and try attacking it directly? I don't really want to leave this shield...

Tomato-Top's Wind barrier was keeping it at bay, but if I left, I'd have to smell that awful stench again. In fact, it was probably even less pleasant by now because of the heat from all the Fire spells. I was impressed at Tomato-Top's casting speed and MP reserves, but the power she was putting into each individual incantation was relatively low. That wouldn't be enough to get through that wall of meat...and whatever else bugs are made of.

"Nrgh... These creatures are quite resilient against my magic," she snarled, grinding her teeth. Meanwhile, the egg continued to grow. It seemed defeating the enemies only caused it to become larger and darker. Although there were very few insects left in the room now, they all crowded around the egg, seeking to protect it from damage at any cost.

Then at last, my fears were realized as the egg's transformation suddenly sped up. The veins on the egg pulsed faster and faster.

"Grr!"

We were so close to defeating the whole lot, too. I should have known it wouldn't be that easy. In desperation, I flung my last five throwing knives at it, hoping for a hit. All but one of them were intercepted by the bugs, while that last dagger somehow evaded them and hurtled on toward the egg.

Bull's-eye! ...Oh crap, I tempted fate...

The second the knife was about to make contact, the soft, flabby shell of the egg burst open in an explosion of yellowy goo that struck it midflight and sent it to the floor.

"Goddammit! I knew I shouldn't have said anything! ...And that's hella gross!"

"Eeeeeeek! Th-th-that's disgustiiing!"

What emerged from the egg was an enormous insect that resembled a creature called a giant isopod, which I'd seen in a documentary. Its body glistened with slime as it curled and uncurled its dozens of crab-like legs, and it identified its prey with a twitch of its centipede-like head. It was an alien. Unmistakably an alien. It made my stomach lurch. The masses of insects we just slaughtered were like cute puppies by comparison. You could even glimpse its organs through its semitransparent body.

"*Khakhaaaaaa!*"

Its...roar (?) was like a low rumble and a high-pitched screech combined. That alone was enough to disorient me. Then as if to signal that the true fight was only just beginning, the boss began crunching up the corpses of its underlings—shells, wings, and all—and scooped them into what could only have been its mouth. It bit into the slug one, sucked out its juices, and then gobbled up the desiccated remains. Soon, the few living bugs that remained had become food for the boss monster's belly.

So this was the real last trial of the dungeon. Even the psychic damage from its appearance alone was leagues beyond anything I'd ever faced.

"Curses! Who created this dungeon?! Nature could not possibly come up with something this cruel...!"

"Aaah... Aaahhh... Aaaaaahhh..."

Before I could even work up the courage to speak, I heard something to my side snap.

"Oh, for crying out loud! I can't take it anymore! Just DIIIIIIIIE!"

"Whoa?!"

Giving up on keeping herself together, Tomato-Top began weaving a spell quicker than any I had ever seen before. In just a few seconds, about a dozen balls of flame floated in the air around her. I dived to avoid being caught in their trajectory.

"Watch it! You can't use explosive magic on an enemy that big! *Guh!*"

I choked back my words as the heat emanating from the girl became too much to bear. It was clear she was only thinking about ending this fight as quickly as possible. The protective Wind barrier was gone now; whether that was due to the explosion or simply because she no longer cared enough to maintain it, I didn't know. In any case, a mixture of burned proteins and boiled bug juices rushed up my nostrils and made me gag. She wasn't going to listen to anything I said now. The die was already cast.

"DROP DEAAAAAD!"

"STOPPPP!" I screamed in vain as what must have been close to a hundred Fireballs all descended on the foe.

"Khakhaaaaa?!"

Individually, they were no stronger than the ones she'd been casting previously, and of course, the enemy was bigger this time. However, the sheer number of flaming orbs and the precise control with which the girl targeted her spells made the outcome orders of magnitude more destructive. In the end, the poor Giant Isopod was blasted to smithereens without even getting a chance to attack.

And then the downpour began. A literal shower of surprisingly gelatinous body parts about the size of a man's fist mixed with mucus that made me want to spit up my stomach. The force and speed of the explosion, coupled with the extraordinary size of our foe, meant that it was only possible to do one thing as the hail of soggy bug bits splattered us from head to toe...

""AAAAAAAAAAAAAAAAAAAAAAAAAAAAAAAAAAAAA
AAAAAAH!""

"Hurh... How mortifying...," grumbled Tomato-Top, drying herself off with a blast of Wind magic that fluttered her shimmering crimson hair. We had returned to the previous room to wash ourselves off in the spring. However, her exasperated attitude was really starting to tick me off, so I charged up to her.

"Listen, you. That was *your* fault, and you know it! Don't you think you should show a little remorse toward me?"

"Very well, very well. I am sorry. I do apologize. Is that better?"

"Oh? Is that weak-sauce apology really the best you can muster after this disaster?"

Disaster was the only word for it. It wasn't like we hadn't been coated in all manner of strange substances by the previous traps, but even the oil was surprisingly smooth and rather pleasant-smelling, like camellia oil. It had made my hair nice and silky, and I think Tomato-Top over there had actually set off a few of those traps on purpose. However, this substance was far less pleasant. It had the consistency of vomit. Puke with little bits of shit mixed in. It was like the contents of a college bathroom. And the *smell*. It had the harsh stench of stomach acid, only ten times more pungent, as if it had been left to ferment for a month. You could feel the bits of undigested insect flesh mixed in, like pebbles in corn syrup. Their color was a mix of shocking pink, purple, and baby-poo yellow, and they still twitched as if in rigor mortis. Even a certain spiky-haired lawyer would have no objections if I passed down the death sentence right here and now.

"I can't believe you'd make a drenched little girl get down on her hands and knees and apologize! You're on the fast track to a life of crime!"

"You already *are* a criminal with what you've done!" I shot back. "You're going away for a long time!"

Besides, *I* was the only one standing "drenched" now. The nerve of that girl!

"Anyway, I did apologize. You sure are petty. Look, I'll dry you off. Will that make things better?"

Suddenly I was blasted by a rush of warm air as if from a giant invisible blow-dryer.

"There you go. Happy now?"

Not really, but I didn't want to stand here quibbling any longer, so sure. We were almost out of here anyway. Now that the Guardian was defeated, we only needed to pass through those doors and we'd be free... We *would* be free, right? Surely...

It wouldn't be, like, the real Guardian was actually in the room beyond, right?

As we picked ourselves up and approached the boss room doors again, the very same worrying thought popped into both of our heads. But surely, we were just overthinking it, weren't we? They wouldn't do that to us. Not after all this.

"C-come on. Let's just get out of here."

"M-mm. Very well. Let us be off."

We had just grown too weary. The dungeon wanted that. It had trained us to mistrust everything. We couldn't let it win...and yet it had managed to subvert our expectations every single time.

And this moment was no different. For when we pushed open those steel double doors...

"Cheeeee! Sksksksk! Blblblblblb!"

...without a word, we smoothly pulled them close once more.

""WHYYYYYYYYYYYYYY?"" we both screamed.

Sure, we knew that a Guardian would regenerate if the Core was left alone for long enough, but a few minutes?! In fact, now that I thought about it, we hadn't even seen the Core yet. What was going on? Unfortunately, thinking about it wasn't going to help. There were no two ways about it; we would have to fight those insects again.

""DIIIIIIIEEE, YOU LOUSY BUGS!""

For what it was worth, we exterminated the boss twice as quickly as before.

""COME ON, WHAT'S NEXT?!""

Save for our screams, the room was silent once more. We had exterminated the vermin with all the swiftness of an overpowered Chinese warlord, mowing down the legions of buzzing flies and chopping the egg in half before it even hatched. Then we marched to the double doors, ready for anything the dungeon could throw at us.

Beyond it was another square chamber, like the many we had seen before.

"It's not the exit!" I cried, my fears confirmed.

"What's next? A pitfall? Falling ceiling?"

"Where's the trap?! Where is it?"

We searched the area with bloodshot eyes. By now, no trap was safe from our keenly honed senses.

Just as the door quietly swung shut behind us, a glowing magic circle appeared on the floor. Particles of green light filled and brightened the room.

"Huh?!"

"Ngh?!"

We could only glimpse what was happening for a second before a sea of white washed the whole world away.

"I can sense teleportation magic!" yelled the girl. "What is going on?"

"Is this another trap?" I asked.

There were no markings or anything. Just endless white that played games with my vision.

"This is not a trap," came a voice.

"Wh-who's there?!" I asked.

The girl looked at me. "You heard that, too, right?"

"Hello! Well done, guys! You've beaten the shortest time!"

"" ..."""

"You did a really good job. I've never laughed so hard in my life!"

"" ..."""

"Especially that fight you two had at the start. I didn't even plan for that! I thought for sure I was going to die chuckling! Ha-ha! Even just remembering it now is giving me the giggles!"

As we simply stared in shock, a woman in her early to midtwenties materialized before us, wearing a broad grin on her face. Her shoulder-length hair was tightly curled at the ends, as though it had been permed. She had on a habit like those worn by Lunarian nuns, but her mischievous smile was that of the devil himself.

However, there were three even stranger things about her.

The first was that she seemed to be levitating. Her feet were off the ground, yet I could detect no magic about her. It wasn't exactly easy to determine where the ground was, though.

The second was that although she appeared to be standing right in front of me, I couldn't sense her presence at all. I could hear her voice, see her face, but it was like there was nobody there. Not even investing many levels into Stealth could make you undetectable in plain sight; for that, you would need a powerful intrinsic ability.

And then the final point. I could see right through her. No, I don't mean she was a poor liar; I mean she was literally transparent. Although, there was only white behind her.

Right now, though, I didn't care about any of that.

"Might you be thinking what I am thinking, oil-head?"

"I believe I am, Tomato-Top."

We shared a glance and nodded.

""DIE, YOU EVIL BITCH!""

I grabbed whatever I could from my bag, hurling item after item as fast as possible. Meanwhile, the red-haired girl conjured balls of Fire, Water, Wind, Earth, smoke, plant, and lightning, as though it didn't even matter what element they were. And yet even in the face of our barrage, which was far more frenzied than when we'd faced the Giant Isopod, the lady flitted from side to side like a leaf on the breeze, deftly avoiding every last blow.

"Pfft! Not likely! Hardy-har-har!"

"Goddammit, stay still!" I shouted as I emptied the contents of my bag at her.

"Hup! Hah! Whee! Oop! You're going to have to do better than that!"

"Y-you dare make fun of me?!" shouted the girl. "Just die already!"

"No, thanks! Har-har!"

The woman chortled as she twirled and spun, eyeing the two of us with glee.

"Now, it's about time to reward you for completing my dungeon! I wonder what to give you...?"

Tomato-Top and I had some ideas.

"How about letting me punch you in the face?!"

"How about letting me burn you to a crisp?!"

"Hmm... Nope! ♪"

And with that, she disappeared.

"Wha—?!"

We next heard her voice from right behind us.

"How about this? Here you go!"

"Rrgh?!"

"Waaah?!"

We had no time to react before the woman plunged her hands

into each of our torsos. Then came a tingly sensation; it felt like she was caressing something very precious within us and smearing something over its surface.

System Message: "Mystic Blade of Soulfire" unlocked.

"Huh?"

"Nrh? I see, so that's how it works…"

In a flood of logical connections that seemed to come out of nowhere, we were made to understand that our attacks had little effect on beings without a body.

"And also, I think you ought to lay off the fuzzyweed," the woman added to me. *"Work yourself too hard, and it'll come back to haunt you. Take it from me, okay? Well then, see you! This was fun!"*

Then the woman took a step back from us.

""Wait right there, you…!""

We turned to see the world changing color once more. Even though I knew it wouldn't affect her, I couldn't live with myself without at least trying to land one good hit. Given where we were standing and the time we had left, I was the only one close enough to try.

"Hrah!"

However, at the last moment, something in her face stayed my hand. She looked lonely. Then…

"Bleh," she taunted, sticking out her tongue.

"N-not again!"

I cursed myself as the dungeon spat us out to the surface. She had been toying with us to the very end.

CHAPTER 6
Their Thoughts

When I came to, I was sitting beneath the stars and the moon in a small clearing nestled among thick vegetation.

"That bitch!" I yelled. "I'll tear her head off next time!"

"You idiot! You should have punched her when you had the chance!"

"Shut up! Don't you think I know that?!" I retorted, cradling my head in my hand, distraught.

Then as if to change the subject, both of our stomachs rang out in unison.

"Oh, food first! Let's have something to eat!" said the girl.

"Yeah. Me too, I'm starving."

My willpower was running at an all-time low, so I simply filled the pot with salt and water, then added in the overripe ricolle wine and slabs of Grateful Boar meat I had sliced up previously.

"I-is it done yet? It has been stewing for quite a while..."

"Not yet. Just wait. I'm hungry, too."

"Urgh... I don't wanna..."

Tomato-Top fiddled impatiently with the bowl in her hand, looking up at me like a waiting puppy while I stirred the pot. After a little more simmering, the meal was done.

"Okay, it's re—"

"Gimme!"

"Whoa, calm down!"

"Never!"

The girl snatched the ladle out of my hands and poured herself a bowl before wolfing it down greedily.

"Cripes. Don't come crying to me if you…"

"Ng?! *Cough!* Hurk!"

"…choke. See? What did I tell you?"

"More!" she exclaimed, steam still coming from her mouth.

"Okay, okay." I sighed, doling out a second helping. "Here, eat up." Then I downed the contents of my bowl, keeping an eye on the rapidly lowering level of the pot.

"Aaaah! That was mighty tasty!" said the girl, after we (mostly she) had polished off two pots' worth. Then she laid down, rubbing her belly contently.

"Seriously, how do you pack so much in?" I asked her. "If you fall asleep now, you'll turn into a cow, you know."

"What? I've never heard that before!"

I was sitting against a tree, turning the stove into a bonfire.

"…I don't know where we've ended up," I said, "but we can figure that out tomorrow. I'm tired."

As far as I could tell from the vegetation, we were still in the northern part of the empire, near the border with the beast lands. Once the sun came up, I could at least get my bearings. I don't know if it was due to that soul-smearing devilry, but my senses seemed a lot sharper than usual, and I could even sense a highly populated area off in one direction. Perhaps there was a city or a road that way.

"Hey, seriously, how do you get Grateful Boar meat to taste so good?" asked Tomato-Top.

"Why—?!"

Just as I was about to ask, *Why would I ever tell you that?!* I paused.

"…You boil it on the bone in overripe ricolle wine."

"Hmm? What?!"

"That's the secret to getting Grateful Boar meat so tender. That's what you wanted to know, right?"

"Ahhh, so that alcoholic taste was ricolle wine! Very good. I shall have my sister make it when we meet back up with her! Listen well, oil-head. The food my sister prepares is the tastiest in all the lands. It was she who taught me everything I know about magic, and there is no fairer beauty than she. I may be a super-ultra-mega cutie, but she is something more… A super-*duper*-ultra-mega cutie!"

"Yeah, yeah, she's pretty, great at cooking, talented at magic. I've heard it all before." I shrugged. Whenever Tomato-Top wasn't arguing with me, she'd barely stopped talking up her big sister.

"Anyway, I told you, so now you have to tell me."

"Hmm? Tell you what? You want to know my body measurements? What a creep."

"I don't need those to know you've got less curves than a trigonometry textbook."

"Drop dead!"

I leaned aside to dodge the Rockball that came flying toward my head. It lodged itself in the tree behind me, scattering splinters everywhere. I was so used to it by now that I could dodge her attacks in my sleep.

"The reason you're traveling. We made a bet to see who could get out first, remember? Though in the end, we both left at the same time."

"Hmm… I suppose we did agree to something like that…," she said, as though she had completely forgotten about it until now. "Now, what to do? Like I told you, I don't mind explaining, but…"

"What's this about? …Is it because you need my help with

something? I guess I can lend you a hand… You'll owe me big time, though."

Come morning, both of us would return to our own lives. In some ways, I would be sad to see it end. Being with her had been like reliving my previous life, laughing and joking with my friends. Perhaps if I knew what she was questing for, I could accompany her. For just a little while longer…

"Oh my, feeling lonely are we?" said Tomato-Top, grinning at me. "Poor thing, you're like a lost little kitten…"

"Would you quit it for once? I'm trying to do you a favor," I shot back, but her assessment wasn't entirely off the mark. I felt the heat rise to my face.

Goddammit. Calm down, blood vessels!

I hoped she wouldn't notice, but she was not one to let a person's weakness go unseen.

"Heh-heh-heh. My, your cheeks are so flushed. Did I get it right?"

"Raaaaargh! Stop trying to change the subject! Come on, answer the question!" I yelled. But as the girl slowly rose to her feet and looked up at the sky, a piercing chill ran from my toes to the top of my head.

"…!"

"Come to think of it," she said, "I never did catch your name. Isn't that strange? After we've spent so long together, I still do not know what I should call you."

"…It's Kaito. My name's Kaito," I said, pinned to the spot in terror. It wasn't as though she was behaving strangely. She didn't seem poised to attack or cast a spell. And yet I was terrified of her. Or to be more precise, I felt a sense of unease, as though I shouldn't have been there.

"I see. It's a nice name, Kaito."

There was nothing different about her, yet it felt like I was looking at someone new. I didn't believe my eyes. It was like the past ten days had been nothing but a dream.

Somewhere inside her was a deep, dark void. Not the kind formed of an absence of light, but the kind that swallowed up everything that dared draw near.

"Kaito. I am afraid you cannot accompany me on my travels."

"...Wh-why not? I'm not that useless, you know."

"It isn't about skill, Kaito. You simply haven't ever stood where I have. You would never have so lightly offered to assist if you had."

When she turned to me, she was smiling, but it was hollow. Somehow, I knew from just one look that I could never reach her, no matter how hard I tried. There was an inalienable gulf of loneliness that I just could not cross.

"There's a fire in the pit of my stomach. A sore throughout my entire body. A grief inside my heart that I can never scream away. You don't know that pain, do you, Kaito?"

"..."

Her smile looked like it might give way to tears at any moment. There was sorrow in her eyes, there was pain... But above all else, there was a burning hate that would strip off my flesh if I dared approach.

"Listen well, Kaito. It is for vengeance that I journey. I cannot forgive. Nor can I forget. I must tear my enemy apart with my own hands."

"Vengeance...?" I muttered, as the meaning of the word slowly sunk in.

"Indeed. The urge not just to kill, but to utterly destroy. For my own sake, and no one else's. I must drag them down to the very pits of hell. I must pluck out their eyeballs and flay their skin while they still draw breath. I must grind down their arms from the fingertips in, mince their legs from the toes up. I must sear the flesh of their back on iron rods, make them know pain, suffering, and total humiliation... All I long to hear is their tortured wails as I hold their heart in my hand, and to crush it between my fingers. For that moment, Kaito, I would give anything... Heh-heh-heh... Ah-ha! Ah-ha-ha!"

It was like being hit in the face by a blunt object or being dragged to the bottom of the cold, dark ocean. She laughed. A maddening, intoxicating cackle—her soul set free. And then she refashioned her mask and turned to me with a grin once more.

"Sto—," I began, when I felt the touch of her finger on my lips.

Stop this. Revenge will never bring you happiness. That was what I felt I should say. But those weren't my words, and in this moment, they felt trite and cheap.

But the touch of her finger, cold as it was, felt realer than anything else.

"You know what, Kaito?" she said. "I have enjoyed myself these past ten days. I really have."

As she stood before me, a horrifying crescent spread across her lips. Through the cracks in her mask, I caught glimpses of a dreadful black flame. Something terribly bewitching.

"So do not touch me. Do not even come near. Stay right where you are, for only there will you be able to live out your days with a restful heart."

The girl slowly shook her head. Faced with such direct rebuke, I couldn't even open my mouth to speak. I stood rooted to the spot, frozen in a waking nightmare.

After that, the girl went to sleep, while I simply laid there with my eyes shut. For the entire night until the first light of dawn, I drifted in and out of shallow slumber.

"*Phew!* I suppose that shall be all for breakfast."

"'*That's all?*' You emptied the entire pot."

Tomato-Top was acting as though the previous night had never happened, so I decided to act in kind. Soon, the time would come when we would part, perhaps never to see each other again.

All of a sudden, an awesome presence flooded the area, and a tremendous cry rang out over the forest.

"*Roooaaaaaarrrr!*"

I looked up to see a dragon with crimson scales, and a blond young woman sitting atop its back.

"There you are! Where have you been?!" she shouted down at us. But I was too shocked by what I was seeing to respond.

"A…a Fire Dragon?!"

Dragons. Terrifying creatures that stood atop the monster ecosystem. But while every possible alarm system in my body was on high alert, Tomato-Top stepped forward with a big smile on her face.

"It's okay," she said to me. "Guren! Sister! How great it is to see you again!"

As the creature swooped overhead, the lady riding it dropped down to meet us.

"Don't give me that!" she said, marching toward Tomato-Top in a fit of anger. "Don't you know how much you've made me worry?!"

Her blond hair was tied up, lending her a mature air. But I was more engrossed in what happened next, for in a *poof*, the enormous Fire Dragon changed its form into that of a juvenile dragon pup and rushed over, nearly tackling its master to the floor.

"*Rowr!*"

"Wh-whoa?!"

I was flabbergasted. How could a dragon, that majestic solitary hunter, ever be so friendly with humans?

"Who's a good boy? You are! Yes, you are!"

"*Rowr! ♪*"

The dragon pup licked Tomato-Top's cheek, and she gave a ticklish laugh.

"I don't know what you're looking so pleased about," her sister interjected with all the tone of a scolding parent. "You're going to get a good talking-to later, do you understand?"

"S-Sister! Wait! Allow me to explain! It wasn't completely my fault this time!"

"I've had enough of your excuses. No dinner for you until you've learned your lesson."

"Nooooooo!" Tomato-Top screamed. Then with a deep sigh, she patted the dragon pup on the head. "Well, I suppose it is time for us to go. Come on, Guren."

"Rowr!"

The pup gave a yelp as if in reply, before taking the form of an enormous Fire Dragon once more. The blond girl hoisted herself up into the saddle and called down to her sister.

"Come along, let's go."

Tomato-Top turned to me. "Very well. I suppose I shall see you again, if the fates are kind enough to allow it."

"Hrk!"

My voice caught in my throat. I always knew this time would come, and yet something in my heart was burning. I didn't understand why, but I was still not ready to say good-bye.

"W-wait!"

Before I knew it, I was shouting after her.

"Mm? What is it?" she asked, turning back to me, but there was no reason for me to speak. My mind raced as I tried to figure out how to continue.

"Y-your name! Tell me your name! Are you really going to leave after asking me mine?"

The image popped into my head of her saying *"I—I don't need to give my name to a rude man like you!"* and pouting. This time, however, she reacted differently. After a pause, she addressed me.

"Mrh… I suppose I can tell you that much."

"W-wait!" said her sister. "You can't! That's dangerous!"

"It is fine, Sister. I am never one to leave a debt unpaid. Besides, what harm can a name do?"

After reassuring her sister, she turned to face me, a dignified expression on her face.

"Leticia. My name is Leticia. A super-ultra-mega-pretty name, is it not?" She chuckled. Her smile was the same mischievous smile I had grown accustomed to over the past ten days.

"Well then, Kaito. Be sure to not lose all your hair before our next meeting."

"I keep telling you, I'm not going bald!"

"Heh. Then farewell, you ignorant buffoon."

"Get lost already, you braindead moron!"

After returning to our usual banter, Leticia smiled and mounted the dragon behind her sister. Then it took to the skies in a single wingbeat.

"…Leticia, huh?"

Alone in the forest, I reflected on the past week and a half.

"I-it's not cruelty, and I'm not an animal! I was doing my best, you know! I was trying!"

"Pfft! Imagine making all that fuss only to be so swiftly proven wrong! I couldn't have done it better myself!"

"I do declare, never have I seen a face so undeservedly smug as yours was then. It's going straight into my top five. Have you ever considered giving up the adventurer life and settling down as a comedian?"

Goddammit, fine. I admit it. It had been fun.

It had been fun shouting at her and arguing with her. It was fun complaining about the obnoxious dungeon together. All the surprise, all the relief, all the pranks, all the abuse, all the laughter. I had forgotten that mealtimes could be a source of joy. I had forgotten

that talking to people wasn't supposed to be a chore. And so when she hungrily wolfed down the meals I spent ages making, I'd been happy... Really, truly happy.

"Why...? Why choose vengeance over me? You were plenty happy without it."

I spilled those words into the air, where they faded away to nothing like sea-foam.

"...And that's basically it. That's the story of how I met Leticia."

After that, I'd met back up with the shitheads in my old party and brought them back to where I'd been swallowed up, but the dungeon was nowhere to be found. The entrance was a pitfall, and the exit was a portal. With the hole closed, the dungeon was impossible to find, so we'd had no choice but to throw up our hands in defeat. To be fair, I still wasn't sure if it was even a dungeon at all. There were just too many things about it that weren't quite right.

I proceeded to talk about the other times I'd bumped into Leticia in my travels. The time I found her in some nobleman's house dressed as a maid. The time we teamed up to defeat a horde of monsters. The time we both had to enter an eating competition. And many more stories besides.

"Right, that's all for tonight. It's getting late, and I think I've basically covered everything you didn't see in your visions."

The large quantity of Grateful Boar soup I had made was finally reaching the dregs at the bottom of the pot. I had gone on for longer than I meant to, but once I started talking, the emotions all came flooding back, and I found it difficult to stop.

""..."""

"Come on. Are you going to keep staring at me like that? Say something. You're making me feel awkward."

They had listened to me speak from start to finish without saying a word, but even now, Minnalis and Shuria remained silent. I didn't mean to be like *So what do you think?* but it would've been nice for them to *react* at least. In fact, it was starting to get embarrassing. If after all that, they just said something like *Hey, last night was fun, wasn't it?* I think I'd drop dead on the spot.

"Well, the thing is…," Minnalis began.

Shuria shared an awkward glance with her. "…What do you wish us to say? *Thanks for boasting?*"

"B-boasting? I didn't think I was boasting…," I said. I mean, I guess I was a little proud, but they didn't have to put it like that…

"But there is something I wanted to ask," ventured Minnalis.

"Me too," added Shuria. "It's probably nothing, but I may as well."

Two pairs of eyes, yellow and crimson, turned to face me.

"You've told us everything. We know now that you loved Leticia more than anything else…," Shuria began.

"…So then answer us. Are you sure you don't want to meet up with her again this time?" asked Minnalis.

Their eyes shot right through me, preemptively destroying any lies, bluster, or misdirection I might come up with. I gave a small chuckle.

"Oh, don't worry. I'm not going to lose my mind when I see her. I still love her, it's true, and I treasure her, just as I treasure you two. I wouldn't be able to kill her, even if my life depended on it."

I still wanted to be with her, even now. The ache in my heart attested to that.

"…But I'm determined to not make the same mistake. I've given up clinging to whatever wishful thinking suits me."

The world was not so kind as to grant me whatever I yearned for. I had learned that a long, long time ago. How could I choose the wrong option and pursue a life of happiness now, after I'd confronted these two with that very same choice?

"I will not waver in my vengeance for a second. I would love for nothing more than to have my revenge *and* save her, but I can't. And if Leticia hates me for that, if she tries to kill me for that, then what else can I do? I have to go on living."

If Leticia truly loathed me, if killing me would make her feel better, I would accept death after my vengeance was complete. But I couldn't let that happen just yet... I couldn't allow the demon lord to defeat the hero. And even after I broke free of these hateful days, I could never betray my partners. I had Minnalis and Shuria. I couldn't kick the bucket just because I felt like it.

"So here's my answer. I know I can never be by her side. I always have."

My heart twinged even as I said it. I knew it to be true, but convincing myself to accept it was another thing entirely. Heck, it might not have even been possible. As miserable as it was, I might well be carrying those feelings with me until the day I died.

"I...see," responded Minnalis. "If that's the case, then there's nothing more for me to say. I will continue to assist you to the best of my capacity."

"I think so, too," added Shuria. "You won't be lonely anymore with both of us."

I hadn't meant to let my feelings show, but it seemed they sensed them nonetheless. The two of them leaned in close as if to comfort me, a gentle look on each of their faces. I was only too grateful to have their purehearted goodness at my side.

"I see. Minnalis, Shuria, thank you."

I didn't need friends. I would tread the path of vengeance alone if I must. But solitude brought pain, so I treasured our relationship. Ties without trust. Without mutual interest. So tightly bound that it left no room for suspicion, for betrayal. A bond so deep that every-thing started to blend together.

It's just... I'm happy you care about me, but...watch your girly bits! I've got the melons on one side and the lemons on the other! Please, ladies, I don't know if you don't care or just plain don't know, but...!

I mean, I'm a boy, sure. Part of me enjoys this (and I think you know which part). But that doesn't mean I don't feel ashamed at turn-ing this into a grope-fest in my mind when they're trying to be nice to me. Am I supposed to say something? Should I keep my mouth shut? I know how it's going to go if I point it out. *Get your mind out of the gutter, pervert!* But if I don't say anything when they're trying to cheer me up, they're going to think I'm a silent loner, and that's just as bad!

At this point, I noticed both their faces had gone a little red... Wait, had it been part of their plan to console me all along? But when it came time to do it, they got flustered? Is that it?

Uh-oh... Urge to tease...rising...

I wanted to see how they would panic if I went, *Oh, the two of you look flushed. What's the matter?*

No. I can't. I mustn't. Only utter trash would say something like that at a time like this.

Wait, no, I'm already *garbage. I would only be increasing my level of trash.*

"Uhhh... *Ahem.* Sorry for talking so long. Let's hit the hay for tonight. We've almost reached our next destination."

With that, I stood up and retrieved the expensive sleeping bag I'd acquired in Elmia.

In other words, I backed out of the choice-select screen.

"May I go hunting for a while, Master? I'd like to work off some of that food."

"Ah, I will come with you, too, Minnalis. I am not feeling sleepy yet."

"Um, I guess that's okay, but don't go too far, will you?"

"Understood, Master!"

"Yes, Kaito!"

Minnalis bowed, holding the ends of her skirt, while Shuria gave a flourish of her hand, like a salute.

"Then off we go."

"Lead the way, Minnalis!"

And the two disappeared into the forest.

"...Minnalis is really starting to look like a maid now. Is it just because of the costume...?"

Ever since she changed outfits, Minnalis's maidliness had been growing. Part of that was her appearance, but lately, even her attitude and mannerisms, the way she spoke and her choice of words, were becoming more and more refined. I knew it was because of me somehow, but why did she have to pick that direction to go in...?

I let out a sigh and began talking to distract myself from my guilt.

"I'm sorry, Minnalis, but I can't even think about it until after I've settled things with Leticia."

I'd been around her long enough to know the way she felt about me, but it would be disrespectful of me to answer her while my heart was still split. It was better to go on pretending I didn't notice for now.

"...If Leticia could see me now...I wonder what she'd call me."

I burrowed deep into my sleeping bag, as if attempting to escape my uninvited thoughts. Right now, all I cared about was what came next. Our next destination was a town called Dartras, in the north of the kingdom near the border of the empire. There, I sought the president of the Grond Company, Grond Gordott. He was one of the fiends who'd taken everything away from me. One of the people I longed to kill.

"Just you wait... I'll drag you down to the bowels of the Earth, to where not even a single ray of moonlight can touch."

I'd kill him. Kill him. Kill him.

Torture him, play with him. Crush his confidence, his determination, his dignity. Grind it all to dust. Take away everything he took from me. Have him sink into the fires of hell.

The whirling blackness in the pit of my heart worked its way up through my body and past my lips. "Oh, I just can't wait. Smile while you still can, you smug son of a bitch."

Then I closed my eyes and went to sleep.

" . . . . . . "

" . . . "

We had left Master at the campsite and ventured into the forest.

"I believe this is far enough."

"Indeed. Kaito won't be able to hear us here."

Shuria and I turned to face each other and latched onto each other's hands, all the pent-up emotion we'd been hiding bursting out of us at once.

"Ha! Ha-ha-ha! We did it! We wheedled it out of him!"

"Hooray! Hooray! Now we're one step closer!"

"We finally got him to say that he'll break up with his girlfriend! At last!"

"How great it is to hear it straight from the horse's mouth! That's how we know his will is truly broken!"

Shuria was clearly excited from the frenzied manner in which she spoke. Well, she wasn't alone, and I didn't care who knew it.

"Yes! Like in *Lilies on a Midsummer Night*. Princess Pyral is so headstrong at the beginning, but then she falls apart so easily once she puts her doubts into words!"

That was fiction, of course. I knew reality didn't work like that, but still. It was another step toward our goal.

"And! And! Did you see how he reacted when we pressed ourselves against him?!"

"I did. He was trying so hard to distract himself at first, but then I could see him getting turned on. His heart rate was higher than usual, too."

"That was his sadistic streak, no doubt about it! My radar was going beep, beep, beep!"

"I'm not sure I have something like that, but I noticed it, too. He looked like he wanted to tease us so badly."

It was the same look he got whenever he poked fun at us for slipping up. I'd read a book that said this was called "verbal abuse," but part of me was starting to enjoy it lately. I asked Shuria about it, and she said she'd been enjoying it the whole time. In fact, it was one of the things she wanted to explore further when her relationship with Master reached that stage.

"I love getting a taste of what's to come! ♪" she had said.

As it happened, I had come to learn many new things while comparing my tastes with Shuria's. Her idea of lovemaking included Master punishing and humiliating her, and while I wasn't sure I felt quite the same way, I could agree on the point of wanting Master to exploit me for his own pleasure rather than the other way around. It seemed Shuria understood this to some extent, for she had said, *"Ahhh, you are a soft sub, then. But I also feel the dom influence in your desire to lure him in and trap him with no way out. Perhaps you're a soft switch?"* I didn't really follow.

Meanwhile, my estimation of Shuria, of course, was that she was a "loving but dark sub who wanted awful things done to her."

In any case, we had won one battle, but we couldn't rest on our laurels.

"We must not let this victory distract us from the larger issue," I said.

"Indeed," concurred Shuria. "I could almost feel the love radiating off him as he spoke of her. It was sweet, sickeningly so."

Just thinking back to it put a damper on our celebratory mood. We were tied to Master by a bond of vengeance thicker than blood, and even though he'd told us we were just as important to him as Leticia, I couldn't help but feel jealous. I don't know if Master realized, but it was abundantly clear from the way he talked that he was still head over heels for her. It was like he was looking at something so precious, he couldn't even touch it out of fear he would stain it forever.

"But that is exactly why we have to support him at this trying time. The stronger his love, the harder it will be for him to say his good-byes when the time comes."

If Master was ever to reconcile his desires, then Leticia could not be a part of it. As long as that simple fact remained, he would not let her kill him. He would live with her ire to avoid making her cry. There would be no apology, no making up, no allowing himself to die as penance.

And so we had to take Master back from her. It was for his own good. With us reliably by his side, his poor wounded heart could heal ever so slightly. Our own desires aside, this was all so that he wouldn't have to shoulder that painful burden any longer.

…Well, okay. Maybe not *all* because of that. Perhaps there was a teeny-tiny bit of my own longings in there as well. But that's not important.

"When the time comes for Master to say good-bye to her, that's when he will hurt the most. The wound may never heal. But that is when our battle truly begins," I stated.

"That's right. When he's hurt, we will wrap him up in our warmth and spoil him rotten. And then once he wants us so badly that he can no longer control himself… Ooh-hoo-hoo! Aaah-ha-ha!"

Ahhh, the very thought makes me feel all tingly! I think I'm getting wet...

Master, we cannot sit idly by and watch you get hurt. Just you wait. It will be painful, but we will be there to nurse you back to health.

"Well then," said Shuria, "we must prepare for that day. Let us resume our training!"

"Indeed," I replied. "Master has become less guarded these days. We must keep at it."

"Yes! Let's go! The prize is debauchery!"

Thus began our fevered discussion of how best to please Master.

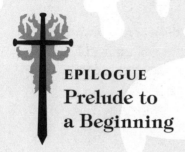

EPILOGUE
Prelude to a Beginning

"Why...? How could you do this?!"

The woman before me pounded her hands on my chest.

It would have been so easy for me to answer her.

It wasn't me.

But what purpose would that serve now? I was tired. Sick of it all. This was just another consequence of my unmitigated foolishness.

"You killed him! And for what? To steal his sword?! Why?! You're the hero! And the children, too! You played with them! They loved you!"

It wasn't me.

"How could you do that to them?! Why?! Why you of all people?!"

All I could come up with were weak excuses.

It wasn't supposed to end like this.

"Give them back! Give them back! Give! Them! Back!"

That's all they were: excuses.

I never wanted this to happen.

But if only I had known what tragedy was about to unfold, I could have stopped it.

That was why...all this was my fault.

Those days had long since passed, yet still, they remained in my heart. They had made me realize this world was something I loved, something I wished to protect.

And now, after everything I've been through, they're all that's holding me back from destroying this world and everyone in it.

"U-urgh…"

Before my eyes was a challenge far greater than anything I could find in the A-rank section of the quest board.

"Come on, Mr. Hero, eat up!" said the boy. As he brought the wriggling *thing* in his hands closer, I recoiled in disgust.

"W-wait just a second! Just a second, Kelly! Come on, let's talk about this!"

From the pail in his hand, the boy took out one of many lime-green grubs around the size of a tangerine and shoved it toward me. I winced at the sight of it flailing its corpulent body between the boy's thumb and forefinger.

Compared with those I'd fought in the dungeon alongside Leticia, most bugs didn't seem so disgusting any more, but fighting them was one thing. *Eating* them was another.

Yes, I knew it was edible. It might have even tasted nice, but as a Japanese person, I simply could not rewire my brain to recognize insects as food. It just wasn't in the cards.

"You were the one who said it's not good to be picky, Mr. Hero!" chided a girl.

"Ugh. Shenfa. That…that's still true… But look, I'm a big, strong hero now, so I'm allowed to be picky, you see?"

"Aww, that's no fair!"

"You're a big meanie, Mr. Hero!"

"I don't care! Adults are allowed to be unfair, and heroes are allowed to reject things they don't like!" I cast my gaze into a far-off direction, frantically trying to deflect their well-placed criticisms and those big, round childish eyes.

"Geez, why do you hate it so much? It's good for you. Plus, it's yummy, too!"

"Yeah, it's sticky and sweet. You'll like it! Come on!"

"Urgh… Can I at least swallow it without chewing?"

""No! Who was it who said to always chew our food?!""

"…That was me…," I admitted.

In Japan, every child was taught to chew before swallowing, but that custom was not followed here. In fact, it was good manners to gulp down your food as quickly as possible, while it was still fresh. I understood the logic, but I still thought it was important to chew, both to aid in digestion and to make sure you got all the nutrients out of the meal.

Although…

I can't help what I can't eat. How can you kids see these living creatures as snacks? And, Kelly, that liquid hanging from your mouth, it's drool, right? Right?

"Oh, Kelly. You've got some of its goo on your mouth there," said Shenfa, and leaning over, she licked the mysterious substance off his lips.

"Wh-whoa? What are you doing?!" shouted the blushing young boy. Shenfa looked puzzled. The two of them couldn't have been older than eight, but Kelly was just starting to get embarrassed when in close proximity to girls.

It was a heartwarming scene, disregarding the bucket of squirming creatures in the boy's pail.

"Look, Kelly, Shenfa... I'm sorry. The frog, I could just about manage, but this... It's just too much."

Apologies to all the boys and girls who were just trying to live life to the fullest, but I just couldn't touch that stuff.

It was then, while I was playing in the orphanage garden with the children, that Metelia called out to me.

"Ah, Kaito. There you are."

"Hmm? Oh, hey, Metelia."

The kids looked up when she arrived, letting out cries of "Hey, it's the priestess lady!" and "Are you coming to pick up Mr. Hero?"

Even on a hot day like today, Metelia was dressed in her usual floor-length robes. That was partially a blessing for me, though, because if I had to see those massive breasts of hers under any less clothing, I think I'd lose my mind. With how benevolent and modest she was, I couldn't believe she was only a year older than Mai and Alicia. Although those two were beautiful in their own right, Metelia was truly a sight for sore eyes. I was only just realizing it now, but the average person here was far prettier than back home.

"I'm afraid so," said Metelia with a warm smile, "but I've brought you something to make up for it. Here, it's freshly baked ricolle pie." She opened the basket in her hand and took out a delicious-smelling pastry.

""Yay!"" cried the children.

"Hold it, you little whelps!" I shouted, slapping away two hands that reached eagerly for the pie. "Make sure you share that with Miss Myun and the other children, you hear?"

""Oww!""

That teacher was particularly fond of sweets, and she did so much work looking after the children that she deserved a break like this once in a while.

"Anyway, nice work, Metelia."

"Nice...work?" she asked, puzzled. "Are we on a job, Kaito?"

"No, it just means you did a good thing."

"Ah, no, not at all. I am simply following the teachings. This is what any decent follower of Lunaris would do." Metelia wore a peaceful smile and clasped her hands in front of her face in prayer. Then she turned to the children and added, "Worry not, children, for I have packed much more than usual, so there will be plenty to go around. I am afraid this shall be the last care package for a while, though."

"..."

I had nothing to add to that. It was as she said. We would be leaving the city tonight. It had taken a bit of time, but our fight with the demons was coming to a head, and the empire and the beast lands were finally mobilizing for all-out war. I had done everything I could here, too. It was time for me to take the fight to the demon lord and end it once and for all.

At this proclamation, though, the kids started complaining again.

"Aww... Why can't you stay here for a bit? We only just met..."

"Yeah, yeah! I want the priestess lady to bring us more sweets, too!"

At that point, Miss Myun, who ran the place, showed up.

"Settle down, children. You mustn't ask the impossible!"

""Miss Myun!""

"The hero has his own work to do," she continued. Then to us, she said, "I apologize for their imprudence."

"Oh, no, not at all," I reassured her. "We've enjoyed our time here as well."

When I thought of an orphanage matron, the image came to mind of a wizened old lady, but Miss Myun was actually quite young. I had heard she used to have a husband who helped her manage the place, but unfortunately, he'd passed away when out hunting monsters to help pay off the orphanage's debts. As luck would have it, her spouse had been in possession of a rather expensive sword, so Miss Myun had been able to sell it to keep the place afloat. Ever since, she'd been taking care of the orphanage all by herself.

"I made some pie, Miss Myun. Would you care to share it with the children?"

"Why, thank you, Metelia. They'll love this. Why don't you come inside, and I'll pour you some tea?"

"Kaito!" came a voice as someone suddenly hugged my legs from behind.

"Whoa, Toria. Stop running into people like that; it's dangerous!" I said.

Toria was the first girl I'd met from the orphanage; I'd saved her from monsters, which was how I had gotten involved with Miss Myun and the kids in the first place. She was the eldest of the girls, and quite mature for her age, and it seemed she had wanted to surprise Miss Myun by picking some herbs from the surrounding forests to sell. When the kids turned eight, they usually began working in town, but Toria had heard about the price the herbs sold for while working at the guild and had decided to go looking for them by herself. If I hadn't happened to have been passing by at the time, she might have been killed. Ever since then, she clung to me more than any of the other children. Whenever she spotted me, she would run right up and give me a big hug.

"No, no! Don't go, hero! Let me come with you!"

"Toria?"

She was dressed in her going-out clothes and wore a small pouch with her things in it.

"I wanna be together! If you're going, then I'm going, too!"

She had black hair and black eyes, an unusual combination around these parts. Perhaps that was why I felt such an affinity with her. Her face looked slightly Japanese as well, and she demanded attention all the time... It reminded me of Mai when she was younger.

"T-Toria… Come on, calm down… I'm not going away right now…"

"Yes, you are! Because once you go home, you're not coming back tomorrow!"

"Come on, Toria," said Miss Myun in an attempt to placate her. "Let go; you mustn't interfere with the hero's duties."

"I don't wanna, I don't wanna!"

"Toria…"

The girl usually did whatever Miss Myun instructed, but now she was clinging to me and sobbing, shaking her head furiously into my back. I tried to treat all the children fairly, but I couldn't help but feel a special fondness for her in particular. I knew I had to be firm with her and tell her off, but when I looked into those round, tear-filled eyes, I lost my nerve.

"…You know you can't come with me. It's dangerous out there."

Out in the wider world, I couldn't predict what could happen. I had grown strong enough in these last two years to handle whatever evil it had in store, but I couldn't always come running to Toria's aid whenever she got in trouble. Above all else, though, I couldn't bring a child onto the battlefield and let them witness the horrors that took place there.

"Waaah…waaah…"

Toria didn't respond, but her grip slackened.

"Please, Toria. If you come with me, who's going to look after the others? They'll be all alone without their big sister."

"…*Hic*… Waaaaaaaaaaaaah!"

Toria seemed to understand my point of view, for she let go of me and instead just stood there bawling in a flood of emotion.

"Come on, don't cry, don't cry… You look so pretty when you smile…"

I tried to calm her down by gently patting her head. Miss Myun had kindly given us some space by corralling Metelia and the other children inside.

"Hic…hic."

We stayed like that for a while until Toria had finally let it all out.

"Oh yeah, I've got something for you."

"…For me?"

"Yeah. I was going to give it to my sister when I got home, but you can have it instead."

It was a pendant I had picked up in the elven forest, a plain wooden carving that was suspended on a string and depicted a bird. I placed it around her neck, and the crystal in place of its eye glimmered in the sun.

"Here you are. See? It looks good on you."

"…Really? Do you think I'm cute?"

"Ha-ha! I don't just think it; I *know* it."

It was a little funny because she reacted just like Mai. I suppose girls that age were all worried about the same things.

"Hee-hee-hee! Then I'm gonna be your mistress, hero!"

"*Pfft!* What?! T-Toria?! Wh-where did you learn that word?!"

The pleasant mood I had worked so hard to achieve immediately came crashing down. I mean, I thought she might say something close to *I'm gonna marry you when I grow up*, but not this!

"Er…it was the lady at the guild information desk. I heard her saying something like '*Who needs a wife when you have a mistress like me?*'"

"…I really didn't need to hear that…"

"Huh?"

I see. I didn't realize that lovely receptionist lady talked like that… Ahhh, the world's a grim place…

"So, um, Mr. Hero."

"Hmm? What?"

"I'm gonna wait for you to come back! Make sure you do, okay?" she said with an expression of pure joy brighter than the sun itself.

"…Yeah, for sure," I replied, giving her a reassuring smile.

"…A dream, huh?"

I awoke and slowly sat up in bed. It was still dark inside the room. It seemed my brain was unearthing old memories now that we had come to Dartras once more. After taking supper at a nearby pub, we had dropped the proprietor a little extra to learn where to find the softest beds in town.

"…"

In this world, I was finally strong. I really thought, without a single doubt, that if I couldn't save everything, I could at least save the things that mattered to me.

That was why I smiled at her back then. I really thought I could save them all.

It was that self-indulgent pride that led to what happened next, and in this cruel world, it might as well have been me who pulled the trigger.

"Still, this sentimentality is getting to be a bother."

Had I always been such a wistful person? Thinking back to Elmia, the same thing had happened my first night there, too, but I didn't think I'd dream of the past *again*. Was this going to happen every time?

"Don't tell me…"

I silently conjured up the Holy Sword of Retribution. Using my Appraise ability, I double-checked its unlock requirements and effect. When I did, I noticed the text had changed somewhat from before. Where previously there had been a blank spot, it now read, *Makes you dream about traumatic moments from your past.*

"How is that supposed to help…?" I muttered with a sigh. There was no way to tell when they would occur, or even which dreams were the product of this effect, and it wasn't like the visions advantaged or disadvantaged me in any way.

"Hurh… What the hell, man…?"

My intrinsic ability, Soul Blade, could be awfully unkind at times. Whenever I gained a new soul blade, I understood its effect more or less immediately. I could also Appraise it for more detail if I wanted to, but that still didn't tell me everything. There were certain hidden abilities it didn't alert me to up front, some of which even Appraise only displayed as a row of question marks. Others, like the one I had just gained, came with no prior indication they existed at all. They only appeared if certain conditions were met, similar to the requirements for unlocking a soul blade in the first place, or else they showed up once the user noticed their effects, as I had just done. All in all, it was a very user-unfriendly experience.

Let's take the Fairy's Blade of Water, for which I had recently reunlocked all the abilities, as an example. Its ability to control fluids was granted upon defeating a specific monster, but it wasn't until I got a strange feeling on the battlefield that I learned of its ability to control the *temperature* of fluids. If I hadn't noticed that, it might have stayed hidden forever.

Well, it was what it was, I guess. It wasn't as if someone designed soul blades specifically to be intuitive, like a game mechanic. I had learned the hard way that this world was far more complicated than it needed to be. Whatever mental model I could construe, reality was always one step ahead of me.

"Mmrh... Master...?"

Lying in the bed next to mine was Minnalis. She slowly sat up, rubbing her eyes.

"Oh, sorry," I whispered. "Did I wake you up?"

The room we'd rented contained three separate beds. I had given up trying to convince the others to let me have my own space, but in return, I stipulated that I at least have my own bed to stretch out in. Leaving aside the bad dreams, the bed itself was exceedingly comfortable. Ahhh, there's nothing better than a nice warm bed all to myself...

Minnalis did a few meager stretches and looked at me with a lazy expression on her face.

"Mm… Mmm… Hwaaah… Master…gimme a kiss…"

She leaned over the short gap between the beds and craned her neck out toward me. She was starting to remind me of the old Minnalis from when I first met her, before she'd gotten obsessed with all this maid nonsense. However, she was only wearing the thin nightgown she slept in. I might get a glimpse of all sorts of bits and pieces if I wasn't careful, and that would be bad. Especially in the morning.

"Sure, whatever," I said, pushing her back. "Just go wash your face."

"Mmm…okay…"

Minnalis got up and put on a cloak before heading outside to the well. It didn't really matter what I agreed to in this state, because there was no way she was awake enough to remember it by the time she came back anyway.

"And, Shuria, I'm not going to step on you, so please get up off the floor."

"Hmph. You're such a meanie, Kaito," she pouted. However, she stayed where she was on the floor beside my bed. There was only one way to get her to do as I asked, so I lowered my voice and said:

"…Get up and wash your face already, you flat-chested mongrel!"

"Y-yes! At once, Kaito!"

Shuria sprung to her feet and disappeared out the door in a flash, looking worryingly thrilled at my frankly abusive words.

"…Ahhh… How did it come to this…?" I moaned, head in my hands.

My head hurt. It throbbed even more when I realized that they seemed to be doing this because of me.

"…God, I just need to stop thinking about it, or I'll get stuck in a loop."

It was not for me to say what other people could or couldn't enjoy. They weren't doing any harm, either, and there were other, more important things to put my brain to work on.

"I guess I should go freshen up, too."

Everything looks different with a clean face. I couldn't laze around forever. I was finally here, in the town where Grond lived.

"Mr. Gordott, sir! I've collected the information you requested. Here's my report."

"I see. Give it here."

An orangish light came in through the window. Sitting in my office, immaculate as it always was, I perused the report my subordinate had brought me. After giving it a once-over, I placed the bundle of papers on my desk.

"I see. So she has finally agreed to relinquish that sword."

I sat down in my large armchair, which creaked under my weight. The brand-new leather perfectly and luxuriously accommodated me.

"Yes, sir. Her husband passed away the other day, so once we threatened to take away the orphanage, she caved immediately. I wish you'd seen the look on that woman's face, sir. It was so damn hot seeing her cry. If it hadn't been for those screeching kids nearby, I'd have taken her right there and then."

"That's quite enough of that. Tell me about the sword."

"Oh, yes. It's right here, sir."

With a soft *clunk*, the subordinate placed upon my desk a sword in a dark-green sheath decorated with light ocher trimmings. The blade was about seventy centimeters long, and the handle looked to be made of raw wood, like tree branches twisted together.

"Ah, so this is the legendary 'Leafstone Blade,' the rank-4 magic item from the A-class dungeon 'Dragonfang Trail.'"

I stood up and withdrew the weapon from its scabbard, revealing the gleaming steel of the blade.

Rank-4 magic items were so scarce that only the very best adventurers, or decently rich noblemen, were able to get their hands on them. I sighed as I held it in my hand.

"What a waste of time. Even if I can shift the liability now, this is going to run our projections into the red."

"Sir?"

"You'll see what I mean, liability."

I clicked my fingers, and into the room ran two more of my subordinates, who pinned the first one in place.

"Wh-what?! What is…? *Guh?!*"

With a punch to the gut, the worm stopped struggling. He simply looked up at me with fear and surprise in his eyes and slumped to his knees.

"Wh…why…?"

"Did you really think you could fool me with this fake blade? You think I don't know what you're up to?"

It was not a dungeon-made sword, that was for certain. Most likely, this worm had gotten it forged by some blacksmith somewhere. I placed it down on the desk and stood up.

"I would venture to say that you were hoping I'd try to sell this counterfeit and embarrass myself in front of my business partner. Then with my influence curtailed, *you'd* show up with the real sword and take my place as president. Isn't that right, you vermin?!"

"Kh…hah!"

Coming around the desk, *I* stomped on the trash beneath my feet.

"How *dare* you defy me?! You rat! You maggot! Because of you…! I'm going to be late…! To my next meeting…! You think your time is worth even a fraction of mine?! Talk to me! Tell me how you're going to repay your debt to me!"

I relentlessly kicked the *thing* that was my subordinate, letting all my anger fall upon him.

"This sword…! Was supposed to be…! A gift for Count Garland! You…! And that bitch of a matron, too! You're all cutting into my bottom line!"

The request had come in from one of my regular Imperial clients about a month ago. He wanted a powerful blade for his son to use in the upcoming festival, and the earlier I could secure the goods, the better, as that would give his son more time to practice with it. I'd get a bonus for a prompt delivery. We could have arranged to procure the goods through normal channels, but that would have been so slow as to ensure we forfeited this bonus.

That was when I learned of the orphanage. It seemed the place used to be run by an ex-adventurer and his wife, but for the last few years, it had been struggling. A couple of weeks ago, that man had lost his life in a terrible accident, and now the orphanage stood on the brink of financial ruin.

So I'd attempted to step in and offered to make the woman's money troubles disappear in return for the sword her late husband left behind. However, she refused. And for what ludicrous reason but that it reminded her of her husband.

"Haah…haah…*phew*…"

After calming down a little, I began to think. Presumably, he wasn't lying when he said he'd gotten that wench to part with the weapon. He surely knew I would discover a lie like that before the deal with Count Garland took place. If the fool was *that* shortsighted, I'd have fired him long ago.

That meant that he had to be keeping the real sword elsewhere.

"Extract the location of the sword from him. You know the drill. Use whatever means you have to."

"Pl…please… No…"

"Silence, mongrel! You steal from me, you pay the price! Take him away!" I roared, and the two men dragged him out of my office.

"Urgh... Now then."

I rang a bell on my desk, and after a few moments, there was a knock at the door.

"Come in," I said.

"You called, sir?" came the gravelly voice as a slender older gentleman in a black tailcoat walked into the room. While his age was clear from the deep wrinkles on his face and his graying yet well-kept hair, his blue-green eyes blazed with a vigor not in keeping with his years.

This man was Fegner Rielt. His family had served the Gordott line for generations. He was a man who swiftly completed any task given to him and was well-suited to a range of activities, both public and private.

"Fegner, take a message to Nonorick. He is to come to my office after suppertime. I have a job for him."

"Understood, sir. I shall take care of it at once."

Then with a bow, Fegner left.

My ambition was to make as much money as possible and spend it on living a life of luxury. Money could become anything. Food, housing, clothes, titles, weapons, pride, prestige, power, human lives...even nations.

It was impossible to find happiness in this world without wealth. To feel truly satisfied, you needed more money than you knew what to do with.

Everything in this world had a price. A price paid in gold. To me, money was no different than a god. It could ensure I had everything I ever wanted.

I would keep on making coin, as much as it took, until I stood at the top of this world, with more than anyone else.

"All right then, that should be enough."

"U...urgh..."

"Ghh..."

In the darkness of the alley, Grond's henchmen lay writhing around in agony. They had left his mansion to find somewhere away from prying eyes, which made it very easy for me to ambush them. I took the dolly they were using to transport their precious cargo and headed for the slums. Eventually, the rattling cartwheels came to a stop outside a building in the heart of the run-down district.

"Up we go."

I lifted the wooden box off the dolly and into the cellar of the dilapidated house.

"We've been waiting for you, Master," came Minnalis's voice.

"We've already finished preparing on our end," added Shuria.

"Yeah, I barely recognize the place."

What used to be a pile of rubble and dust had now ranked up from a "destroyed room" to merely a "messy room."

In its center was a worn-out chair and a few broken pieces of furniture. Minnalis and Shuria were miracle workers, that was for certain.

"Now, it's time for the grand unveiling."

I pried the lid off the crate to reveal a man, bound and gagged.

"Mmm... Gh..."

I tipped him out and undid his gag.

"Wh-who are you...? *Wph?!*"

As the man peered around, trying to figure out where he was, I stuffed a potion down his throat. Before my eyes, any trace of the pummeling he had received at Grond's hands disappeared.

"I—I see. Friends, are you? Thank you... Dammit! That old man... He really gave me a beating."

"..."

"Hey, would you mind undoing the rest of my ropes? They're digging into my wrists."

"Listen, I think you've got the wrong end of the stick here."

"What? *Guph!*"

I launched my foot into the man's jaw.

"Minnalis, Shuria, give me a hand with this."

""Okay!""

"Wh-what?! Gaaagh!"

I pulled the man to his feet before Minnalis and Shuria sat him down in the chair in the center of the room. Its splintered wood and protruding nails gave rise to a series of groans that were as music to my ears. The two girls swiftly tied him to the chair so he couldn't struggle.

"Wh-what is the meaning of this?! I thought you had come to save me! *Guh!*"

"Ha-ha-ha! You must be kidding! Who the hell would come to your rescue? You're disgusting."

I couldn't stand to hear his whining any longer, so I silenced him with a punch to the gut.

"Seriously. What's wrong with you? You think that orphanage is just there for you to leech off of?"

"Urgggggh! Gah!"

I stomped down on the man's bare foot.

"Save you? I'm here to do nothing of the sort. I just need something from you before you're completely broken. Besides…"

"Rrrgh! Aaaargh!"

"…I've already decided you're all going to hell."

Then I picked up a splintered plank off the floor and drove it like a stake through the man's leg.

"GAAAAAAAAAAGH!"

"That's not fair!" whined Shuria. "I wanted to go first!"

"I'll take the other leg, then!" said Minnalis, drawing the sword at her hip and slashing at his toes.

"Hgrhhhh!"

"Heh-heh-heh. For a toad, you have a rather nice voice," said Minnalis, licking her lips with a sadistic smile.

Suddenly, Shuria interrupted our fun. "Aah, geez, you two! He hasn't taken his medicine yet! What if you kill him?!"

We both stopped. ""Ah.""

Whoops, I forgot.

"Really, what am I going to do with you two…?"

"Ahhh, sorry. You're right. We've got to stay cool," I said.

Otherwise, I was no different from them. There was plenty of time, so we didn't have to kill him just yet.

"I must be more careful…," said Minnalis, dejected. "It has simply been a while since I cut loose… Well, no matter. First things first, we shall have you drink this."

At this, Minnalis took out the tonic she had prepared earlier.

"Grh! Guh! Ghh! Ghoh?!"

"Don't worry, this is just a little something to keep you alive and awake. Well, it does turn you into a mummy after four days, but I doubt you're going to last that long anyway! Hee-hee-hee!"

"Aaargh! Grhhhh! Owww! Wh-what the hell is going on?!"

The man fought and struggled against his bindings, rattling the chair against the floor.

"And since you're going to be awake, that of course means you're going to feel everything we do to you," said Shuria, pressing a carving knife into the flesh of the man's upper arm as though she were dicing up meat for supper. "Come on, let me hear some different screams already! ♪"

"Hrg! Grhhh! Raaaargh!"

"Yes, that's good. More screams. More shouts. It's too soon for you to break."

This building had not seen use in over two years, but we liked it just as it was.

"Nobody will hear you die here. We're going to take things nice and slow."

The air in that cellar was sordid and stagnant, but soon, it would be rich in the sound of screams and the smell of fresh blood.

"*Phew.* What lovely weather."

"The sun feels so nice and warm."

The three of us emerged from the cellar into the ruins of the building, through which we could see the clear sky above. Just as I stretched my arms and cracked my back, our three stomachs sounded off in sync.

"Oh my," said Minnalis. "Now that I think about it, I am rather peckish. Let us have supper."

"Yeah," I replied, "but before that, we need a bath. We reek of blood."

"Yes!" Shuria chimed in enthusiastically, and the three of us departed. The only thing left in that cellar was a shriveled-up cadaver, face frozen in a look of utter despair, his body covered in the scars of brutal torture. Torture not for information or persuasion, but for the sole purpose of giving him an agonizing death.

"Now, Grond. You're next. I'll send you to hell myself," I muttered, twisting my lips into a sadistic smile as I savored the thought.

The Hero Laughs While Walking the Path of VENGEANCE a Second Time

NERO KIZUKA

Illustration by SINSORA

"I'll hack them up. Toy with them. And snuff them out."

VOLUME 4 COMING SOON!

HAVE YOU BEEN TURNED ON TO LIGHT NOVELS YET?

86—EIGHTY-SIX, VOL. 1-10

In truth, there is no such thing as a bloodless war. Beyond the fortified walls protecting the eighty-five Republic Sectors lies the "nonexistent" Eighty-Sixth Sector. The young men and women of this forsaken land are branded the Eighty-Six and, stripped of their humanity, pilot "unmanned" weapons into battle...

Manga adaptation available now!

WOLF & PARCHMENT, VOL. 1-6

The young man Col dreams of one day joining the holy clergy and departs on a journey from the bathhouse, Spice and Wolf. Winfiel Kingdom's prince has invited him to help correct the sins of the Church. But as his travels begin, Col discovers in his luggage a young girl with a wolf's ears and tail named Myuri who stowed away for the ride!

Manga adaptation available now!

SOLO LEVELING, VOL. 1-5

E-rank hunter Jinwoo Sung has no money, no talent, and no prospects to speak of—and apparently, no luck, either! When he enters a hidden double dungeon one fateful day, he's abandoned by his party and left to die at the hands of some of the most horrific monsters he's ever encountered.

Comic adaptation available now!